Ecological Methods

D1585195

Hugh Machin .

Ecological Methods

WITH PARTICULAR REFERENCE TO THE STUDY OF INSECT POPULATIONS

T. R. E. SOUTHWOOD D.SC., PH.D.

*Professor of Zoology and Applied Entomology, Imperial College,
University of London*

LONDON

CHAPMAN AND HALL

First published by Methuen & Co. Ltd 1966
Reprinted with minor corrections 1968
Third impression, published by Chapman and Hall Ltd, 1971
Reprinted 1975
© 1966 T. R. E. Southwood
Printed in Great Britain
by Butler & Tanner Ltd
Frome and London
SBN 412 10760 0

Distributed in the U.S.A.
by Halsted Press, a Division
of John Wiley & Sons, Inc.
New York

Contents

v

Contents

Preface

This volume aims to provide a handbook of ecological methods pertinent for the study of animals. Emphasis is placed on those most relevant to work on insects and other non-microscopic invertebrates of terrestrial and aquatic environments, but it is believed that the principles and general techniques will be found of value in studies on vertebrates and marine animals.

The term ecology is now widely used in the field of social, as well as biological, science; whilst the subject of ecology, covering as it does the relationship of the organism to its environment, has many facets. It is, in fact, true to say that the ecologist may have need of recourse to almost all of the methods of the biologist and many of those of the physical scientist: the measurement of the physical factors of the environment may be a particularly important part of an ecologist's work and he will refer to books such as R. B. Platt & J. E. Griffiths' (1964) *Environmental Measurement and Interpretation*.

There are, however, certain methods that are peculiar to the ecologist, those concerning the central themes of his subject, the measurement, description and analysis of both the population and the community. These are *ecological* methods (as opposed to 'methods for ecologists' which would need to cover everything from laboratory workshop practice to information theory); they are the topic of this book.

During the ten years that I have been giving advanced and elementary courses on ecological methods at Imperial College, London, and at various Field Centres, the number and range of techniques available to the ecologist have increased enormously. It has been the comments of past students on the utility of these courses in helping to overcome the difficulties of coping with the scattered and growing literature that have encouraged me to attempt the present compilation. I am grateful to many former students for their criticisms and comments, as I am to the members of classes I was privileged to teach at the University of California, Berkeley, and at the Escuela Nacional de Agricultura, Mexico, whilst writing this book.

Although the general principles of most methods are of wide application, the study of a particular animal in a particular habitat may require certain special modifications. It is clearly impossible to cover all variants and therefore the reader is urged to consult the original papers that appear relevant to his problem. I am grateful to my publishers for agreeing to the publication of the extensive bibliographies, it is hoped that these will provide many leads on specific problems; they are, however, by no means exhaustive.

The present book is designed to be of use to those who teach the practical aspects of animal ecology in schools, training colleges and universities; insects, being numerically the dominant component of the macrofauna of terrestrial and many aquatic habitats, almost invariably come to the forefront of ecological field work. This volume is intended as an aid to all who need to measure and compare populations and communities of animals, not only for the research ecologist, but also for the conservationist and the economic entomologist. Population measurement is as necessary in the assessment of the effects of a pesticide and in the determination of the need for control measures, as it is in intensive ecological studies. It is frequently pointed out that ecological theories have outstripped facts about animal populations and I trust that it is not too presumptuous of me to hope that this collection of methods may encourage more precise studies and more critical analysis of the assembled data so that, in the words of O. W. Richards, we may have 'more light and less heat', in our discussions.

The topics have been arranged on a functional basis, that is, according to the type of information given by a particular method. As a result some techniques are discussed in several places, e.g. radiotracers will be found under marking methods for absolute population estimates (chapter 3), the measurement of predation and dispersal (chapter 9) and the construction of energy budgets (chapter 14). By its very nature ecology cannot be divided into rigid compartments, but frequent cross-references in the text, together with the detailed contents list and index, should enable the reader to find the information he needs. The sequence of chapters parallels, to a large extent, the succession of operations in a piece of intensive research.

It is a pleasure to express my great indebtedness to colleagues who have read and criticized various chapters in draft: Dr N. H. Anderson (ch. 6), Dr R. E. Blackith (ch. 2 & 13), Dr J. P. Dempster (ch. 1, 2 & 3), Mr G. R. Gradwell (ch. 10), Dr C. S. Holling (ch. 12), Mr S. Hubbell (ch. 14), Dr C. B. Huffaker (ch. 2), Dr G. M. Jolly, (section II of ch. 3), Dr C. T. Lewis, (section I of ch. 3), Dr R. F. Morris (ch. 10), Dr O. H. Paris (ch. 9 & 14), Mr L. R. Taylor (ch. 2 & 4), Professor G. C. Varley (ch. 10) and Dr N. Waloff (ch. 1, 2 & 10); frequently these colleagues have also made available unpublished material; they are of course in no way responsible for the views I have expressed or any errors. For access to 'in press' manuscripts, for unpublished data and for advice on specific points I am grateful to: Drs J. R. Anderson, R. Craig and D. J. Cross, Mr R. J. Dalleske, Drs W. Danthanarayana, H. V. Daly, E. A. G. Duffey, P. J. M. Greenslade, M. P. Hassell, P. H. Leslie, J. MacLeod, C. O. Mohr, W. W. Murdoch and F. Sonleitner, Mr W. O. Steel, Drs A. J. Thorsteinson, R. L. Usinger, H. F. van Emden, E. G. White, D. L. Wood and E. C. Young. Ecologists in all parts of the world have greatly helped by sending me reprints of their papers. I have been extremely fortunate too in the assistance I have received in translating; Mrs M. van Emden has generously made extensive translations of works in German, and with other languages I have been helped by Dr F. Baranyovits (Hungarian), Dr T. Bilewicz-Pawinska (Polish), Mr Guro Kuno (Japanese), Dr P. Stys (Czechoslovakian) and Dr N. Waloff (Russian).

Much of the manuscript was prepared whilst I held a visiting professorship in the Department of Entomology and Parasitology of the University of California, Berkeley; I am indebted to the Chairman of that Department, Dr Ray F. Smith, for his interest and the many kindnesses and facilities extended to me and to the Head of my own Department, Professor O. W. Richards, F.R.S., for his support and advice. I wish to thank Mrs M. P. Candey and Mrs C. A. Lunn for assisting me greatly in the tedious tasks of preparing the bibliographies and checking the manuscript. My wife has encouraged me throughout and helped in many ways, including typing the manuscript.

T. R. E. Southwood

London, October 1965

ACKNOWLEDGEMENTS

Grateful acknowledgement is hereby made to authors and publishers of the original material that has been modified to give the figures, tables and formulae used in this book; full citations are given in the appropriate places in the text, together with the relevant entry in the bibliography. Gratitude is expressed to Messrs Butterworths (fig. 95), the Editor of the Journal of Ecology (fig. 94) and the Controller of H.M. Stationery Office (fig. 23) for permission to reproduce the figures indicated, and to Dr F. Winsor and Messrs Simon and Schuster Ltd, for permission to reprint part of *The Theory that Jack Built* that appears on page xviii.

For permission to reproduce re-drawn illustrations, modify published tables or to make short quotations, thanks are due to the Director of the Anti-Locust Research Centre, the Editor of the Annals of Applied Biology, Biological Reviews, Biometrika, Biometrics, Bulletin of Entomological Research, Annals of the Entomological Society of America, Archives Néerlandaises de Zoologie, Canadian Entomologist, Canadian Journal of Zoology, Proceedings of the Ceylon Association for the Advancement of Science, Ecology, Ecological Mongraphs, Entomologist's Monthly Magazine, Entomologia Experimentia et Applicata, Indian Journal of Entomology, Journal of Animal Ecology, Journal of Economic Entomology, Nature, Oikos, Pedobiologia, Statistica Neerlandica and Zeitschrift für Angewandte Entomologie, and to Annual Reviews Inc., Butterworths, Blakiston Co., B. Bishop Museum, Finnish State Agricultural Research Board, Holt, Rinehart & Winston, Reinhold Inc., Royal Entomological Society of London, F. Warne & Co. and Dr R. L. Usinger.

Most population theories, so far as they are not purely inductive, are based on imperfect field data that are not derived from planned population studies in which all the relevant factors were measured simultaneously. . . . When . . . more of such fundamental studies [are] available, we may be able to discuss our theories with more light and less heat.

O. W. RICHARDS, 1961
Annual Review of Entomology p. 147

The ecology of pest populations should be studied to gain understanding of the dynamics of the populations in hope that its mechanisms may be revealed. We hope this will enable us to manipulate the populations and ability to manipulate surely is the aim of all attempts to control animal populations.

D. A. CHANT, 1963
Memoirs of the Entomological
Society of Canada No. 32, p. 33

A cautionary rhyme

This is the Cybernetics and Stuff
That covered Chaotic Confusion and Bluff
That hung on the Turn of a Plausible Phrase
And thickened the Erudite Verbal Haze
Cloaking Constant K
That saved the Summary
Based on the Mummery
Hiding the Flaw
That lay in the Theory Jack built.

F. WINSOR: *The Space Child's Mother Goose*
Simon & Schuster

CHAPTER 1

Introduction to the Study of Animal Populations

Information about animal populations is sought for a variety of purposes; but the *object* of a study will largely determine the methods used and thus this must be clearly defined at the outset. Very broadly studies may be divided into *extensive* and *intensive* (Morris, 1960). Extensive studies are carried out over a large area and are normally concerned with the distribution of insect species or with the relation of insect pest population to crop damage or with the prediction of damage and the application of control measures (e.g. Kaelin & Auer, 1954; Strickland, 1961; Chiang *et al.*, 1961). A particular area will be sampled once or at the most a few times during the season, and emphasis will normally be placed on a particular developmental stage of the insect. Such studies will produce considerable information about the pattern of population level over a large area or in successive years, and it is often possible to relate the level of the population to certain edaphic or climatic factors (Kaelin & Auer, 1954; Chiang *et al.*, 1961).

Intensive studies involve the continual observation of the population of an animal in the same area. Usually information is required on the sizes of the populations of successive developmental stages so that a life-table or budget may be constructed and an attempt made at determining the factors that cause the major fluctuations in population size (key factors) and those that govern or regulate it (Morris, 1960; Richards, 1961; Varley & Gradwell, 1963). It is important to consider at the start the type of analysis (see chapter 10) that will be applied and so ensure that the necessary data is collected in the best manner. Intensive studies may have more limited objectives, such as the determination of the level of parasitism, the amount of dispersal or the overall rate of population change.

The census of populations and the stages at which mortality factors operate are necessary first stages in the estimation of the productivity (chapter 14) of ecosystems. In survey and conservation work, the species make-up of the population and changes in its diversity associated with man's activities are most frequently the features it is desired to measure. Special methods of analysis need to be used (chapter 13), but difficulties usually arise because of the virtual impossibility of extracting the many different species from a habitat with equal efficiency by a single method (e.g. Nef, 1960).

Population estimates can be classified into a number of different types; the

1

most convenient classification is that adopted by Morris (1955), although he used the terms somewhat differently in a later paper (1960).

1. Absolute and related estimates

The animal numbers may be expressed as a density per unit area of the ground of the habitat. Such estimates are given by nearest neighbour and related techniques (chapter 2), marking and recapture (chapter 3), by sampling a known fraction of the habitat (chapter 4–6) and by removal sampling and random walk techniques (chapter 7).

a. Absolute population

The number of animals per unit area (e.g. hectare, acre). It is almost impossible to construct a budget or to study mortality factors without the conversion of population estimates to absolute figures, for not only do insects often move from the plant to the soil at different developmental stages, but the amount of plant material is itself always changing. The importance of obtaining absolute estimates cannot be overemphasized.

b. Population intensity

The number of animals per unit of habitat, e.g. per leaf, per shoot, per plant, per host. Such a measure is often, from the nature of the sampling, the type

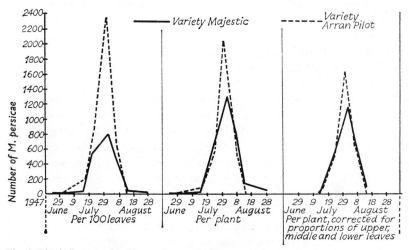

Fig. 1. The influence of habitat unit on relative population levels when these are measured in terms of population intensity; the populations of *Myzus persicae* on different varieties of potato (after Broadbent, 1948).

first obtained (see also p. 107) and when the level of the insect population is being related to plant or host damage it is more meaningful than an estimate in absolute terms. It is also valuable in comparing the densities of natural enemies and their prey. However, the number of habitat units/area should be assessed, for differences in plant density can easily lead to the most intense population being the least dense in absolute terms (Pimentel, 1961). When dealing with different varieties of plants differences in leaf area may account for apparently denser populations, in absolute terms, on certain varieties (Bradley, 1952), and the actual choice of the leaf or of the plant as the unit for expressing population intensity can affect the relative population levels (Broadbent, 1948) (fig. 1). With litter fauna owing to the effects of seasonal leaf fall the intensity measure (on animals/weight of litter) will give a different seasonal picture from an absolute estimate per square metre (Gabbutt, 1958). These examples also underline the importance of absolute estimates where one's interest lies primarily in the animal population.

c. Basic population
In some habitats, especially forests, it is often convenient to have an intermediate unit between that used for measuring intensity and absolute measures of ground area, e.g. 10 sq ft of branch surface (Morris, 1955).

2. Relative estimates
These estimates, in which the population is measured in unknown units, allow only comparisons in space or time; they are especially useful in extensive work, in studies on animal activity or in the investigation of the constitution of a polymorphic population. The methods employed are either the catch per unit effort type or various forms of trapping, the results of which depend on a number of factors besides population (chapter 7). There is no hard and fast line between relative and absolute methods, for absolute methods of sampling are seldom 100% efficient and relative methods can sometimes be corrected in various ways to give density estimates.

3. Population indices
The animals themselves are not counted, but their products (e.g. frass, webs, exuviae, nests) or effects (especially plant damage) are recorded.

Both population indices and relative estimates of population can sometimes be related to absolute population (if this is measured at the same time) by regression analysis, and if such a study has been based on sufficient data subsequent estimates from relative methods or indices can be converted to absolute terms using various correction factors; such an approach is common in fisheries research (e.g. Beverton & Holt, 1957).

The statistical errors of various estimates can usually be calculated and are referred to as the fiducial limits (the estimate (x) being expressed as $x \pm y$, where $y =$ fiducial limits). These are sometimes incorrectly referred to as 'confidence' limits, but the distinction between the two terms is in practice unimportant. The fiducial limits are calculated for a given probability level, normally the 0·05 level, which means that there are 5 chances in 100 that the true estimate lies outside the range given by the fiducial limits (hence the expressions: 5% probability level and 95% fiducial limits). The chances are that the actual true value for the population lies closer to the estimate than at the extremes of the fiducial limits, but these are only chances. However, they can be assessed qualitatively by making another estimate of the population by another method. If this lies close to the first the chances that it is near the true population are much greater than its fiducial limits may indicate, although these chances cannot be expressed in precise statistical terms. Furthermore the use of another method will help to check that a portion of the population is not being missed altogether (see also p. 48). Therefore, whenever possible especially in critical budget work, *estimate the population by more than one method simultaneously* (see Richards & Waloff, 1954).

The level of accuracy that should be aimed at is a difficult problem for the ecologist; Morris (1960) has aptly said that 'we are not likely to learn what precision is required by pessimistic contemplation of individual' fiducial limits. As the amount of time and labour that can be put into any problem is invariably limited it should always be borne in mind that the law of diminishing returns applies as one attempts to reduce the statistical errors of sampling and, in the long run, more knowledge of the ecology of the animal may be gained by studying other areas or making other estimates or even by just taking further samples than by straining for a very high level of accuracy in each operation. Against this must be set the fact that when animals are being extracted from samples the errors will all lie on one side of the true value (i.e. too few will be found). A number of very carefully conducted control samples may allow a correction factor to be applied, but the percentage of animals missed may vary with density; sometimes more are overlooked at the lowest densities (Morris, 1955).

REFERENCES

BEVERTON, R. J. H. and HOLT, S. J., 1957. On the dynamics of exploited fish populations. *Fisheries investigations, ser. 2.* **19,** 533 pp. Min. Agric. Fish. Food Gt Britain, London, H.M.S.O.

BRADLEY, R. H. E., 1952. Methods of recording aphid (Homoptera: Aphididae) populations on potatoes and the distribution of species on the plant. *Canad. Ent.* **84,** 93–102.

BROADBENT, L., 1948. Methods of recording aphid populations for use in research on potato virus diseases. *Ann. appl. Biol.* **35,** 551–66.

CHIANG, H. C., *et al.*, 1961. Populations of european corn borer, *Ostrinia nubilalis* (Hbn.) in field corn, *Zea mays* (L.). *Univ. Missouri Res. Bull.* **776,** 96 pp.

GABBUTT, P. D., 1958. The seasonal abundance of some arthropods collected from oak leaf litter in S.E. Devon. *Proc. X int. Congr. Ent.* **2,** 717.

KAELIN, A. and AUER, C., 1954. Statistische Methoden zur Untersuchung von Insektenpopulationen dargestellt am Beispiel des Grauen Lärchen-Wicklers (*Eucosoma grisea* Hb., *Semasia diniana* Gm.). *Z. angew. Ent.* **36,** 241–83.

MORRIS, R. F., 1955. The development of sampling techniques for forest insect defoliators, with particular reference to the spruce budworm. *Canad. J. Zool.* **33**, 225–94.

MORRIS, R. F., 1960. Sampling insect populations. *A. Rev. Ent.* **5**, 243–64.

NEF, L., 1960. Comparaison de l'efficacité de différentes variantes de l'appareil de Berlese-Tullgren. *Z. angew. Ent.* **46**, 178–99.

PIMENTEL, D., 1961. The influence of plant spatial patterns on insect populations. *Ann. ent. Soc. Amer.* **54**, 61–9.

RICHARDS, O. W., 1961. The theoretical and practical study of natural insect populations. *A. Rev. Ent.* **6**, 147–62.

RICHARDS, O. W. and WALOFF, N., 1954. Studies on the biology and population dynamics of British grasshoppers. *Anti-Locust Bull.* **17**, 1–182.

STRICKLAND, A. H., 1961. Sampling crop pests and their hosts. *A. Rev. Ent.*, **6**, 201–20.

VARLEY, G. C. and GRADWELL, G. R., 1963. The interpretation of insect population changes. *Proc. Ceylon Assoc. Adv. Sci.* **18** (D), 142–56.

SOME USEFUL COMPILATIONS

GOODALL, D. W., 1962. Bibliography of statistical plant sociology. *Excerpta Bot. B.* **4**, 253–322.

MOSBY, H. S. (ed.), 1963. *Wildlife Investigational Techniques* (2nd ed.). Wildlife Society, U.S.A.

NICHOLLS, C. F., 1963. Some entomological equipment. *Res. Inst. Can. Dept. Agric. Belleville, Inf. Bull.* **2**, 85 pp.

PETERSON, A., 1934. *A manual of entomological equipment and methods.* Pt 1. Ann Arbor.

SCHULTZ, V., 1961. An annotated bibliography on the uses of statistics in ecology – a search of 31 periodicals. *U.S. Atom. Energy Comm. Off. tech. Inf. TID* – **3908**, 315 pp.

CHAPTER 2

The Sampling Programme and the Measurement and Description of Dispersion

---

Planning and field work

As it is normally impossible to count all the invertebrates in a habitat, it is necessary to estimate the population by sampling; naturally the estimates should have the highest accuracy commensurate with the amount of work expended, and if this is to be so·a sampling programme which lays down the distribution, size and number of samples will need to be drawn up. There is no universal sampling method and although the statistical principles are given in textbooks such as Cochran (1963), Hansen, Hurwitz & Madow (1953), Stuart (1962) and Yates (1953), 'the sampling of a particular insect population must be resolved about the distribution and life-cycle of the insect involved' (Graham & Stark, 1954). Assuming that the life-cycle is known, preliminary work will be necessary to gain some knowledge of the distribution of the insect and the cost (work involved) of sampling; the worker will also need to be quite clear as to the exact problem he is proposing to investigate (Lamb, 1958; Morris, 1960; Strickland, 1961).

The first decision concerns the universe to be sampled; whether this is to be a single habitat (e.g. field, woodland) or representatives of the habitat type from a wide geographical area will depend on whether an intensive or an extensive study is planned (p. 1), and the second decision must determine the magnitude of population change it is desired to record. Many species of insect pest exhibit ten- or even hundred-fold population changes in a single season (Southwood & Jepson, 1961) and therefore an estimate of population density with a standard error of about 25% of the mean, which will enable a doubling or halving of the population to be detected, is sufficiently accurate for damage assessment and control studies on such species (Church & Strickland, 1954). For life-table studies, more especially on natural populations, a higher level of accuracy will be necessary; the level is frequently set at 10%.

In extensive work the amount of sampling in a particular locality will be limited and therefore a further decision concerns the best stage for sampling (Burrage & Gyrisco, 1954); it may be desirable that this is the stage most closely correlated with the amount of damage, or if the purpose of the survey is to assess the necessity for control the timing should be such that it will give advanced information of an outbreak (Tunstall & Matthews, 1961). Within these limits two other factors need consideration; the stage should preferably be present in the field for a long period, at least sufficiently long to allow the survey to be completed before an appreciable number have developed to a later stage, and the easier the stage is to sample and count the better.

Although the preliminary sampling and the analysis of the assembled data will provide a measure of many of the variables the actual decisions must still, in many cases, be a matter of judgement. Furthermore, as the density changes, so will many of the statistical parameters, and a method that is suitable at a higher density may be found inadequate if the population level drops. Shaw (1955) found that Thomas & Jacob's (1943) recommendation for sampling potato aphids, one upper, middle and lower leaf from each of fifty plants, was unsatisfactory in Scotland, in certain years, because of the lower densities.

Details of the development of sampling programmes for various insects are given by Morris (1955), LeRoux & Reimer (1959), Harcourt (1961*a*, 1964) and Lyons (1964), amongst others, and these papers may be used as models.

Assuming that the study is planned in one field, this should be divided up into a number of plots, say 10–20. The habitat must now be considered from the biological angle and a decision made as to whether it might need further division; if it is woodland the various levels of the tree, upper, middle and lower canopy and probably the tips and bases of the branches, would on *a priori* grounds be considered as potentially different divisions; the aspect of the tree might also be important. In herbage or grassland, if leaves or other small sampling units are being taken, the upper and lower parts of the plants should be treated separately.

It is also of value to take at least two different sized sampling units (Waters & Henson, 1959), one should be towards the smallest possible limit, e.g. a leaf blade or half a leaf, for as a general principle a higher level of reproducibility is obtained (for the same cost) by taking more smaller units than by taking fewer large ones.* Small sampling units may also enable precision to be increased by distinguishing between favourable and unfavourable microhabitats; Condrashoff (1964) found with a leaf miner that the upper and lower leaf surfaces should be considered as separate units. Two examples of any one size sampling unit should be taken within each sampling

---

* The only disadvantage of sampling by small units is the number of zeros that may result at low densities; this truncation may make analysis difficult and has led to the suggestion that larger sized samples should be taken (Pradhan & Menon, 1945; Spiller, 1948, 1952). The decision must be related to the density of the animal, although moderate truncation can be overcome by suitable transformation; in other cases it may be necessary to increase the size of the unit (Andersen, 1965).

plot or subsection. For example for a field crop a preliminary plan could be:

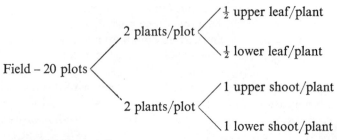

giving a total of 160 samples.

At the same time a record should be kept of the *cost* of each part of the sampling routine; this is normally measured in man hours and will be made up of the time required to select and take the sample and count the animals in it, together with that spent moving from one sampling site to the next.

Statistical aspects

Before the data gathered in the preliminary samples can be analysed some aspects of statistics need to be considered.

1. The normal distribution and transformations

The normal or Gaussian distribution is the term applied to a continuous variable which when frequency is plotted against magnitude gives a symmetrical bell-shaped curve. Although the properties of animals – for example the heights of man – often describe a normal curve, the dispersion pattern of the individuals of a population is seldom, if ever, normal. The dispersion of a field population could approach towards the normal only if the dispersion was random, but the population was so dense or the size of sampling unit so large that considerable numbers were present in each sample. Therefore, in contrast to other distributions described below, the normal distribution is not of interest to ecologists as a means of describing dispersion; its importance arises solely from the fact that for most statistical methods to be applied to a set of data the frequency distribution must be normal and it should possess the associated properties that the variance is independent of the mean and its components additive. Although the analysis of variance is more robust in some respects than the χ^2 (Reimer, 1959), data whose frequency distribution is considerably skewed and with the variance closely related to the mean cannot be analysed without the risk of errors (Beall, 1942).

In order to overcome these problems the data are transformed; that is the actual numbers are replaced by a function whose distribution is such that it normalizes the data or stabilizes the variance. For example, if the square root transformation were applied to 9, 16 and 64 they would become 3, 4 and 8, and it will be observed that this tends to reduce the spread of the larger values, the interval between the second and third observations (16 and 64) is on the first scale nearly 7 times that between the first and second observations; when transformed the interval between the second and third observations is only 4 times that between the first and second. It is thus easy to visualize that a transformation of this type would tend to 'push' the long tail of a skew distribution in, so that the curve becomes more symmetrically bell-shaped. Before proceeding to discuss the correct transformation, the relationship of the mean and variance must be considered further.

a. Taylor's power law

As mentioned above the distribution of individuals in natural populations is such that the variance is not independent of the mean.* Now if the mean and variance of a series of samples are plotted, they tend to increase together (Fracker & Brischle, 1944; Kleczkowski, 1949; Bancroft & Brindley, 1958; Waters & Henson, 1959; Harcourt, 1961b, 1963). This relationship has been shown by Taylor (1961, 1965) to obey a power law. It holds in a continuous series of distributions from regular through random to highly aggregated and is expressed by:

$$s^2 = a\bar{x}^b$$

where a and b are constants, a is largely a sampling factor, while b appears to be a true index of aggregation characteristic of the species. The same relationship between the mean ($\bar{x}$) and the variance (s^2) has been discovered independently by Fracker & Brischle (1944) for quadrat counts of the currant, *Ribes*, and by Hayman & Lowe (1961) for counts of the cabbage aphid, *Brevicoryne brassicae*.

The series of means and variances necessary to calculate a and b may be obtained from several sets of samples from different areas, from sets of samples of different sizes or by combining samples to form different sized sampling units. The mean and the variance are calculated from the raw data by the usual methods or by the use of probability paper (p. 12) for a less exact approach. The values of $\bar{x}$ and s^2 are plotted on a log/log scale (fig. 2) and the value of a read off on the s^2 axis at the value of $\bar{x}=1$. The value of b can then be found from the equation:

$$\log s^2 = \log a + b \log \bar{x}$$

It can be shown that as the variance varies with the mean in this way the appropriate variance stabilizing transformation function, $f(\bar{x})$, is of the form:

$$f(x) = Q \int \bar{x}^{-b/2} d\bar{x}$$

* The mean, $(\bar{x}) = \dfrac{\Sigma x}{N}$ and the estimate of the variance, $s^2 = \dfrac{\Sigma(x^2) - (\Sigma x)^2/N}{N-1}$ where

$x =$ no. of animals/sample; $N =$ total number of samples of that size and $\Sigma =$ sum of . . .

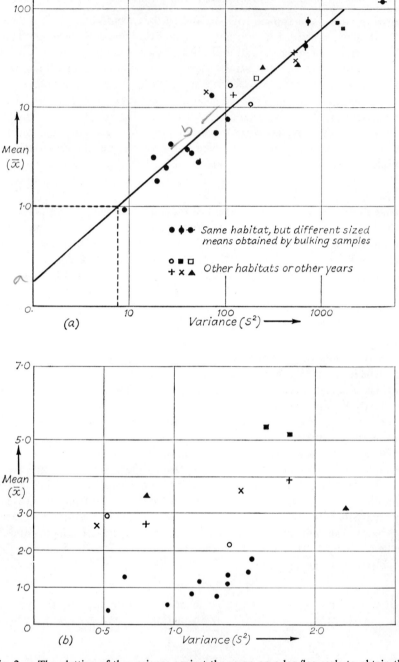

Fig. 2. *a*. The plotting of the variance against the mean on a log/log scale to obtain the constant *a* of Taylor's power law, data from samples of olive scales (*Parlatoria oleae*) per twig. *b*. The same data transformed to $x^{0.4}$ showing the relative independence of the variance from the mean.

Therefore, to transform one finds the value z in the expression:

$$z = x^p$$

where $x=$ the original ('raw') number, $z=$ the transformed value and $p=1-\frac{1}{2}b$.

b. Choosing the transformation

As Taylor's power law holds so widely, the value of b may be found as above and hence that of p. If $p=0$ a logarithmic transformation should be used, $p=0.5$ square roots, $p=-0.5$ reciprocal square roots, -1.0 reciprocals. Healy & Taylor (1962) give tables for $p=0.2$, 0.4, 0.6, 0.8 and for the negative powers.

These are precise transformations, but in practice where sampling and other errors are fairly large it will usually be found adequate to transform the data from a regular population by using squares, that from a slightly contagious one by using square roots and that from distinctly aggregated or contagious populations by using logarithms.

In order to overcome difficulties with zero counts in log transformations a constant (normally one) is generally added to the original count (x); this is expressed as 'log $(x+1)$'. Anscombe (1948) has suggested that a better transformation would be obtained by taking log $(x+k/2)$ where k is the dispersion parameter of the negative binomial (see below). As k is frequently in the region of 2, in many cases this refinement would have little effect. Andersen (1965) has shown that if the mean and k are very small (less than 3 and approaching zero, respectively) then the variance will not be stabilized by $k^{1/2}$ or any of the common transformations, but if independent samples are pooled or the size of the sampling unit increased the data may be satisfactorily transformed.

It is customary to transform percentages to angles (arcsin), but Reimer (1959) has suggested this is only of value when the probability of finding the individual bearing the attribute (i.e. the leaf having a gall) is uniform within each area (for which a % infestation has been calculated), but varies considerably between the different classes (whose various % infestation one wishes to analyse). Even in such cases it is necessary only when a number of the % points lie outside the 20–80 range. When the various percentages are based on grossly unequal numbers of individuals, they will need to be weighted before the analysis of variance can be applied (Reimer, 1959).

The use of transformations can lead to problems when comparing means, which may be based on different transformations, in constructing life-tables. There is therefore justification in such work for not transforming the data unless it seriously violates the conditions necessary for the analysis of variance (LeRoux & Reimer, 1959). There is indeed much to commend the use of the arithmetic mean (i.e. that based on the untransformed data) in population studies (van Emden, Jepson & Southwood, 1961; Lyons, 1964) and if the distribution of the animal is random (see below) the fiducial limits are available in tables (Pearson & Hartley, 1958).

c. *Checking the adequacy of the transformation*

An adequate transformation should eliminate or considerably reduce two attributes of the data that are easily tested for. These are:

(*i*) the skewness of the frequency curve, which is shown on arithmetic probability paper (fig. 3) as well as by plotting the frequencies of different sample sizes:

(*ii*) the dependence of the variance on the mean (instability of the variance) which may be shown graphically (fig. 2).

Thus the value of any transformation in normalizing the data (eliminating skewness) may be crudely tested by the use of probability paper (see below), but as Hayman & Lowe (1961) have pointed out 'as non-normality must be extreme to invalidate the analysis of variance it is better to concentrate on stabilizing the variance of the samples'. A correct transformation for this property will also ensure the third property necessary for the analysis of variance, the additivity of the variance (Bliss & Owen, 1958); indeed all three properties are related and for practical purposes the distinction between transformation for normality and that for stabilizing the variance need not be emphasized. The adequacy of a transformation in stabilizing the variance may be tested for graphically (fig. 2*b*) or by calculating the correlation coefficient for the two terms (Harcourt, 1961*b*, 1965).

Alternatively more precise methods may be used as described by Forsythe & Gyrisco (1961), who used a non-parametric rank correlation coefficient to test for non-normality. When normality had been established the heterogeneity of the variance could be tested for by Hartley's (1950) test and its non-additivity by Tukey's (1949).

2. The use of probability paper

Probability paper is often a valuable time-saving tool in the preliminary stages of statistical analysis. Its use enables the following to be assessed graphically: the normality of the data, the mean and the variance; it also tests the uniformity of the samples, discloses any polymodality and may allow the separation of the components responsible for the polymodality (Harding, 1949). Estimates made from probability paper may not be as accurate as those that are computed because of the difficulty of fitting a line by eye and reading off the graph.

There are two methods of using probability paper; first with a large number of samples, say over 20, they can be grouped in frequency classes and the cumulative frequencies plotted. If for example one had 100 observations on the numbers of galls on a leaf and the smallest was 5 and the largest 85, the vertical scale of the probability would then be marked out from 5 to 85; the smallest sample of which there was only one therefore accounts for 1% of

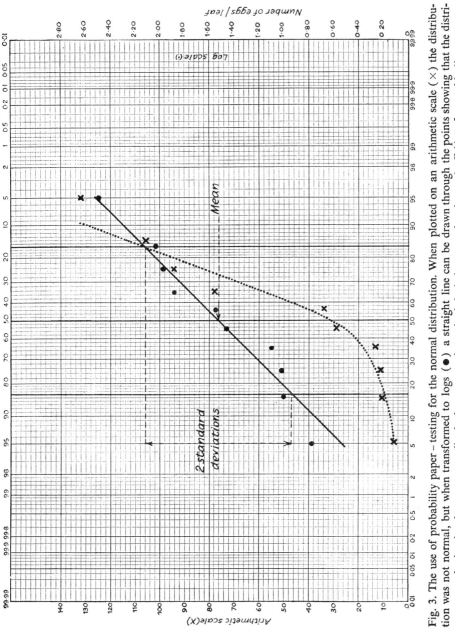

Fig. 3. The use of probability paper – testing for the normal distribution. When plotted on an arithmetic scale (×) the distribution was not normal, but when transformed to logs (●) a straight line can be drawn through the points showing that the distribution has become normalized; the mean and standard deviation may then be read off (data from table 1).

Sampling and Dispersion

the samples and thus a point is inserted on intersection of the 1% and 5 lines. The next smallest number of galls per leaf are 10, 13, 15 (two leaves), then our next points are at 2% and 10, 3% and 13, and 5% and 15 (because 5% of the leaves sampled have 5 or fewer galls). This process is continued until the size of the penultimate sample provides the 99% point and the last sample the 99·99% point.

The second method which is more applicable to the preliminary type of analysis, for which probability paper is useful, is valid for a smaller number of samples. Here the samples are ranked, but *not* grouped, and points corresponding to their size are placed at equal intervals along the frequency scale. The smallest sample is inserted at the % value corresponding to $50/N$ (where N=the number of samples). Subsequent samples are inserted at intervals of $100/N$%. An example is given in table 1 and fig. 3.

Table 1. The numbers of eggs of the white fly, *Aleurotrachelus jelinekii*, per leaf of its host plant, *Viburnum tinus*; data used for fig. 3. (By calculation log mean= 1·528; log standard deviation=0·555; read off fig. 3, line drawn by eye, log mean=1·52, log standard deviation= 0·59)

Leaf No.	% point (for plotting on probability paper)	No. of eggs/leaf (ranked)	Log No. of eggs/leaf
1	5	6	0·77
2	15	10	1·00
3	25	11	1·04
4	35	13	1·11
5	45	29	1·46
6	55	34	1·53
7	65	77	1·88
8	75	94	1·97
9	85	106	2·02
10	95	132	2·50

If a normally distributed set of frequency data are plotted on probability paper they will give a straight line, and the mean will lie at the 50% mark. The standard deviation (s) is found by reading off the values of x at the 15·87% mark (x_1) and at the 84·13% mark (x_2), then

$$s = \frac{x_2 - x_1}{2}$$

However, if the data are not normally distributed they will form a curve (fig. 3). Shallow curves can be made to approximate to the straight line by transforming them in square roots, deeper curves by transformation in logarithms. The transformed values are then plotted on the x axis or logarithmic probability paper may be used (table 1, fig. 3).

If, however, the distribution is not of the same type throughout the field

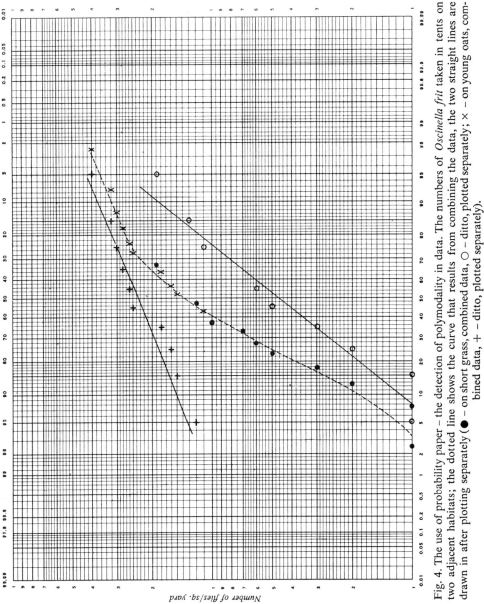

Fig. 4. The use of probability paper – the detection of polymodality in data. The numbers of *Oscinella frit* taken in tents on two adjacent habitats; the dotted line shows the curve that results from combining the data, the two straight lines are drawn in after plotting separately (● – on short grass, combined data, ○ – ditto, plotted separately; × – on young oats, combined data, + – ditto, plotted separately).

(or area sampled) a straight line will not be obtained, the plot will have a kink in it (fig. 4) (Harding, 1949; Cassie, 1954). Such a change in distribution (polymodality) is almost certainly of considerable biological significance, and quite apart from statistical considerations it is important to recognize it at the outset. If it is found, then further preliminary sampling will be necessary to delimit the areas of differing distributions and each must, in subsequent work, be treated as a separate universe.

Besides arithmetic and logarithmic probability paper described above, Poisson and binomial probability papers are available and may be of considerable assistance with certain problems (Mosteller & Tukey, 1949; Ferguson, 1957).

3. Analysis of variance

In any complex situation, e.g. where different parts of the plant have been sampled, it is necessary to carry out an analysis of the variance (see standard statistical textbooks) of the whole data. The amount of the variance due to within-plant and within-plots variation should be compared with that for between plants and between plots.

THE SAMPLING PROGRAMME

The number of samples per habitat unit (e.g. plant)

There are two aspects, firstly whether different regions of the unit need to be sampled separately and secondly the number of samples within each unit or subunit (if these are necessary) that should be taken for maximum efficiency. Although the habitat unit could, for example, be the fleece of a sheep, a bag of grain or a rock in a stream, for convenience the word plant will, in general, be used in its place in the discussion below.

1. Subdivision of the habitat

If the distribution of the population throughout the habitat is biased towards certain subdivisions, but the samples are taken randomly, what LeRoux and Reimer (1959) aptly term *systematic errors* will arise. This can be overcome either by sampling so that the differential number of samples from each subdivision reproduces in the samples the gradient in the habitat, or by regarding each part separately and correcting at the end. The question of the estimation of the area or volume of the plant is discussed in chapter 4. The amount of subdivision of the plant that various workers have found necessary varies greatly. On apple the eggs, larvae and pupae of the tortricid moth, *Archips argyrospilus*, were found for most of the year to be randomly distributed over the tree so that only one level (the lower for ease) needed to be sampled (Paradis & LeRoux, 1962). In contrast on the same trees and in the same years the immature stages of two other moths showed marked differences between levels at all seasons (LeRoux & Reimer, 1959). With the spruce bud-worm (*Choristoneura fumiferana*), Morris (1955) found that there were 'substantial and significant differences from one crown level to another' and that there was a tendency for eggs and larvae to be more abundant at the top levels, but there was no significant difference associated with different sides of the same tree. A similar variation with height was found with the eggs of the larch sawfly (*Pristiphora erichsonii*), although here it was concluded that in view of the cost and mechanical difficulties of stratified sampling at different heights a reasonable index of the population would be obtained by sampling the mid-crown only (Ives, 1955). Studying all the organisms on aspen (*Populus tremuloides*) Henson (1954) found it is necessary to sample at three different levels of the crown and even with field crops height often needs to be considered: Broadbent (1948) recommended that potato aphids be estimated by picking three leaves – lower, middle and upper – from each plant and when estimating the population of the european corn borer (*Ostrinia nubilalis*), Hudon & LeRoux (1961) showed that the lower and the upper halves of the maize stem needed to be considered separately, the former containing the majority of the larvae. The distribution of the eggs of various cabbage-feeding Lepidoptera was found by Hirata (1962) to depend on the age of the plant.

Aspect is sometimes important; in Nova Scotia in the early part of the season the codling moth lays mostly on the south-east of the apple trees, but later this bias disappears (MacLellan, 1962). Aspect has also been found to influence the distribution on citrus of the long-tailed mealy bug, *Pseudococcus adonidum* (Browning, 1959), and of three species of mite, each of which was most prevalent on a different side (Dean, 1959). Variations in the spatial distribution of similar species in the same habitat, which complicates a sampling programme designed to record both, has also been recorded for two potato aphids by Helson (1958). Some insects are distributed without bias on either side of the mid vein of leaves, so that they may be conveniently subsampled, and Nelson, Slen & Banky (1957) record that when estimating populations of sheep keds, the fleece of only one side need be sampled.

Occasionally it may be found that such a large and constant proportion of the population occur on a part of the plant that sampling may be restricted to this: Wilson (1959) showed that in Minnesota 84% of the eggs of the spruce budworm (*Choristoneura fumiferana*) are laid on the tips of the branches and if sampling is confined to these, rather than entire branches, sampling time may be reduced by up to 40%.

The taking of a certain number of samples randomly within a site which is itself selected randomly from within a larger area, e.g. a field, is often referred to as *nested sampling*, and may be on two, three or more levels (Bancroft & Brindley, 1958).

2. The number of samples per subdivision

To determine the optimum number of samples per plant (or part of it) (n), the variance of within-plant samples $(s_s{}^2)$ must be compared with the variance of the between-plant samples $(s_p{}^2)$ and set against the cost of sampling within the same plant (c_s) or of moving to another plant and sampling within it (c_p):

$$n_s = \sqrt{\frac{s_s{}^2}{s_p{}^2} \times \frac{C_p}{C_s}}$$

If the interplant variance $(s_p{}^2)$ is the major source of variance and unless the cost of moving from plant to plant is very high n will be in the order of one or less (which means one in practice). Interplant variance has been found to be much greater than within-plant variance for the spruce sawfly (*Gilpinia hercyniae*) (Prebble, 1943), the lodgepole needle miner (*Recurvaria starki*) (Stark, 1952*b*), the cabbage aphid (*Brevicoryne brassicae*) (Church & Strickland, 1954), the spruce budworm (*Choristoneura fumiferana*) (Morris, 1955), the winter moth (*Operophtera brumata*) (Morris & Reeks, 1954), the diamondback moth (*Plutella maculipennis*) (Harcourt, 1961*a*) and the cabbage butterfly (*Pieris rapae*) (Harcourt, 1962). In most of these examples the within-plant variance was small so that only one sample was taken per plant or per stratum of that plant. With some apple insects the within-tree variance $(s_s{}^2)$ becomes larger, especially at certain seasons, and then as many as seven samples may be taken from a single tree (LeRoux & Reimer, 1959; LeRoux, 1961; Paradis & LeRoux, 1962).

Often a considerable saving in cost without loss of accuracy in the estimation of the population, but with loss of information on the sampling error, may be obtained by taking randomly a number of subsamples which are bulked before sorting and counting. This is especially true where the extraction process is complex as with soil samples; Jepson & Southwood (1958) bulked four random, 3-in. row samples of young oat plants and soil to make a single 1-ft row sample that was then washed and the eggs of the frit fly (*Oscinella frit*) extracted. Such a process gave a mean as accurate as that obtained by washing all the 3-in. samples separately (greater cost). Paradis and LeRoux (1962) sampled the eggs of a tortricid moth, *Archips argyrospilus*, on apple by bulking 25 cluster samples.

The sampling unit, its selection and size

Morris (1955) has laid down six criteria for the sample unit, they are broadly:

(1) It must be such that all units of the universe have an equal chance of selection.

(2) It must have stability (or if not its changes should be easily and continuously measured – as with the number of shoots in a cereal crop).

(3) The *proportion* of the insect population using the sample unit as a habitat must remain constant.

(4) The sampling unit must lend itself to conversion to unit areas.

(5) The sampling unit must be easily delineated in the field.

(6) The sampling unit should be of such a size as to provide a reasonable balance between the variance and the cost.

To compare various sampling units in respect to variance and cost it is generally convenient to keep one or other constant. The same method of sampling must, of course, be used throughout. From preliminary sampling the variances of each of the different units ($s_u{}^2$) can be calculated; these should then be computed to a common basis, which is often conveniently the size of the smallest unit. For example if the smallest unit is 1 ft of row, then the variance of 2 ft row unit will be divided by 2 and those of 4 ft by 4. The costs will similarly be reduced to a common basis (C_u). Then the relative net cost for the same precision for each unit will be proportional to:

$$C_u s_u{}^2$$

where C_u = cost per unit on a common basis and $s_u{}^2$ = variance per unit on a common basis. Alternatively the relative net precision of each will be proportional to: $1/C_u s_u{}^2$. The higher this value, the greater the precision for the same cost.

A full treatment of the methods of selecting the optimum size sampling unit is given in Cochran (1963) and other textbooks, but as population density, and hence variance, is always fluctuating, too much stress should not be placed on a precise determination of optimum size of the sampling unit.

Even with soil animals, where such a procedure might be of most value, Yates & Finney (1942) showed that although 4- and 6-in. diameter cores are equally efficient at low densities, at high densities the comparative efficiency of the 6-in. sample falls off. With insects on plants the nature of the plant usually restricts the possible sample sizes to, for example, half leaf, single leaf, or shoot (see p. 107).

The number of samples

The total number of samples depends on the degree of precision required; which as has already been pointed out is itself affected by the type of study. For many purposes an error of 10% of the mean is a reasonable standard; it has been adopted by Morris (1955), Harcourt (1961a, 1962) and others; this means that at the chosen probability level (usually 19 in 20) the estimated mean has this chosen (i.e. 19 in 20) chance of being within 10% of the true mean.

With continuous data, that is within an ecologically homogeneous habitat the number of samples required (N) is approximately given by:

$$N = \left(\frac{ts}{D\bar{x}}\right)^2$$

where s = standard deviation, D = the required level of accuracy expressed as a decimal (i.e. normally 0·1) and t is a quantity, depending on the number of samples, and is obtained from tables; for more than 10 samples, t approximates to 2 at the 5% level. This may be regarded as comparing the standard deviation of the observations (s) with the standard error acceptable for the contrasts we need to make with the data (D); the larger s is with respect to D the larger the number of samples that are necessary. It will be noted from this equation that in any given situation the value of the standard error will change with the square root of the number of samples; thus a large increase in N is necessary to bring about a small improvement in s.

Where sampling is necessary at two levels, e.g. a number of clusters per tree, the number of units (Nt) that need to be sampled at the higher level, e.g. trees (LeRoux & Reimer, 1959; Harcourt, 1961a) is given by:

$$Nt = \frac{(s_s^2/n_s) + s_p^2}{(\bar{x} \times D)^2}$$

where n_s = the number of samples within the habitat unit (calculated as above), s_s^2 = variance within the habitat unit, s_p^2 variance between the habitat unit (= interplant variance), $\bar{x}$ = mean per sample (calculated from the transformed data and given in this form and D as above.

Rojas (1964) has shown that if the dispersion of the population has been found to be well described by the negative binomial the desired number of samples is given by:

$$N = \frac{1/\bar{x} + 1/k}{D^2}$$

where k = the dispersion parameter of the negative binomial (see below).

Another type of sampling programme concerns the measurement of the frequency of occurrence of a particular organism or event, for example the frequency of occurrence of galls on a leaf or of a certain genotype in the population (Cornfield, 1951, Cochran 1963; Oakland, 1953; Henson, 1954). Before an estimate can be made of the total number of samples required, an approximate value of the probability of occurrence must be obtained. For example, if it is found in a preliminary survey that 25% of the leaves of oak trees bear galls the probability is 0·25. The number of samples (N) is given by:

$$N = \frac{t^2 pq}{D^2}$$

where p = the probability of occurrence (i.e. 0·25 in the above example), $q = 1 - p$; t and D are as above.

If it is found that the leaves (or other units) are distributed differently in the different parts of the habitat, they should be sampled in proportion to the variances. For example, Henson (1954) found from an analysis of variance of the distribution of the leaf-bunches of aspen that the level of the crown from which the leaves had been drawn caused a significant variation and when this variance was portioned into levels the values were: lower 112993, middle

68012, upper 39436. Therefore leaf-bunches were sampled in the ratio of 3 : 2 : 1 from these three levels of the crown.

The pattern of sampling

Once again it is important to consider the object of the programme carefully. If the aim is to obtain estimates of the mean density for use in, for example, life-tables, then it is desirable to minimize variance. But if the dispersion (= distribution = pattern) of the animal is of prime interest then there is no virtue in a small variance.

In order to obtain an unbiased estimate of the population the sampling data should be collected at *random*, that is so that every sampling unit in the universe has an equal chance of selection. In the simplest form – the *unrestricted random* sample – the samples are selected by the use of random numbers from the whole area (universe) being studied (random number tables are in many statistical works, or the last two figures in the columns of numbers in most telephone books provide a substitute). Such a method eliminates any personal choice by the worker whose bias in selecting sampling sites may lead to large errors (Handford, 1956).

However, just because it is absolutely random this method is not very efficient for minimizing the variance, since the majority of the samples may turn out to come from one area of the field. The method of *stratified random* sampling is therefore to be preferred for most ecological work (Yates & Finney, 1942; Healy, 1962); here the area is divided up into a number of equal sized subdivisions or strata and one sample is randomly selected from each strata. Alternatively if the strata are unequal in size the number of units taken in each part is proportional to the size of the part; this is referred to as self-weighting (Wadley, 1952). Such an approach maximizes the accuracy of the estimate of the population, but an exact estimate of sampling error can only be obtained if additional samples are taken from one (or two) strata (Yates & Finney, 1942). The taking of one sample randomly and the other a fixed distance from it has been recommended by Hughes (1962) as a method of mapping aggregations.

When the habitat is stratified biological knowledge can often be used to eliminate strata in which few insects would be found. Such a restricted universe will give a greater level of precision for the calculation of a mean than an unrestricted and completely random sample with a wide variance. Prebble (1943) found with a pine sawfly: satisfactory estimates of the pupae were only obtained if sampling was limited to the areas around the bases of the trees, the variance of completely random sampling throughout the whole forest was too great, as many areas were included that were unsuitable pupation sites (see also Stark & Dahlsten, 1961).

The other approach is the *systematic sample*, taken at a fixed interval in space (or time). In general such data cannot be analysed statistically, but

Milne (1959) has shown that if the *centric systematic area-sample* is analysed as if it were a random sample, the resulting statistics are 'at least as good, if not rather better', than those obtained from random sampling. The centric systematic sample is the one drawn from the exact centre of each area or stratum and its theoretical weakness is that it might coincide with some unsuspected systematic distribution pattern. As Milne points out, the biologist should, and probably would, always watch for any systematic pattern, either disclosing itself as the samples are recorded on the sampling plan or apparent from other knowledge. Such a sampling programme may be carried out more quickly than the random method and so has a distinct advantage from the aspect of cost.

An example of an unbiased systematic method is given by Anscombe (1948). All the units (e.g. leaves) are counted systematically (e.g. from top to bottom and each stem in turn), then every time a certain number (say 50) is reached that unit is sampled and the numbering is commenced again from 1; only one allocation of a random number is needed and that is the number (say somewhere between 1 and 20) allotted to the first unit.

Biologists often use methods for random sampling that are less precise than the use of random numbers, such as throwing a stick or quadrant or the haphazard selection of sites. Such methods are not strictly random; their most serious objection is that they allow the intrusion of a personal bias, quite frequently marginal areas tend to be under sampled.

It may be worthwhile doing an extensive trial comparing a simple haphazard method with a fully randomized or systematic one, especially if the cost of the latter is high when compared with the former. Spiller (1952) found that scale insects on citrus leaves could be satisfactorily sampled by walking round the tree, clockwise and then anticlockwise, with the eyes shut and picking leaves haphazardly. For assessing the level of red bollworm eggs (*Diparopsis castanea*) to determine the application of control measures Tunstall & Matthews (1961) recommended two diagonal traverses across the field counting the eggs at regular intervals.

Bias may intrude due to causes other than personal selection by the worker: grains of wheat that contain the older larvae or pupae of the grain weevil (*Sitophilus granarius*) are lighter than uninfested grains. The most widespread method of sampling is to spread the grains over the bottom of a glass dish and then scoop up samples of a certain volume; as the lighter infected grains tend to be at the top this method can easily overestimate the population of these stages (Howe, 1963). In contrast, for the earlier larval instars before they have appreciably altered the weight of the grain such a simple method gives reliable results (Howe, 1963); it was undoubtedly this difference that led to Krause & Pedersen (1960) stressing the need for samples to contain a relatively high proportion of the same stage if good replication was to be obtained.

The timing of sampling

The seasonal timing of sampling will be determined by the life-cycle of the insect (Morris, 1955). In extensive work when only a single stage is being sampled, it is obviously most important that this operation should coincide with peak numbers (e.g. Edwards, 1962). This can sometimes be determined by phenological considerations (Unterstenhöfer, 1957), but the possibility of a control population in an outdoor cage (Harcourt, 1961a) to act as an indicator should be borne in mind. The faster the development rate, the more critical the timing. With intensive studies that are designed to provide a life-table regular sampling will be needed throughout the season.

It is not always realized that the time of day at which the samples are taken

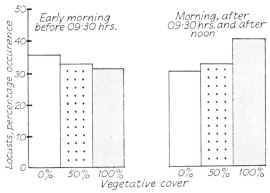

Fig. 5. The variation in the distribution of adults of the Moroccan locust *Dociostaurus maroccanus* at different times of the day; the histograms show the relative numbers on bare ground and areas with moderate and dense vegetation. (After Dempster, 1957.)

may also considerably affect them. The diurnal rhythms of the insects may cause them to move from one part of the habitat to another as Dempster (1957) found with the Moroccan locust (*Dociostaurus maroccanus*) (fig. 5). Many grassland insects move up and down the vegetation not only in response to weather changes, but also at certain times of the day or night (p. 189) and during the day quite a proportion of active insects may be airborne (cf. the observations of Southwood, Jepson & Van Emden (1961) on the numbers of adults of the frit fly (*Oscinella frit*) on oats). The ecologist may find that some of his sampling problems can be overcome, or at least additional information gained, if he works at night or at dusk and dawn, rather than during conventional working hours.

DISPERSION

The dispersion of a population, the description of the pattern of the distribution of the animals in space, is of considerable ecological significance. Not only does it affect the sampling programme (Rojas, 1964) and the method of analysis of the data, but it may be used to give a measure of population size (nearest neighbour and related techniques) and, in its own right, is a description of the condition of the population. Changes in the dispersion pattern should be considered alongside changes in size when interpreting population dynamics. For example, if a mortality factor reduces the clumping of a sessile organism this is an indication that it acts most severely on the highest densities, or if the dispersion of a population becomes more regular then intensification of competition should be suspected.

Mathematical distributions that serve as models

It is necessary to outline some of the mathematical models that have been proposed to describe the distribution of organisms in space; for a fuller treatment reference should be made to Anscombe (1950), Wadley (1950), Brian (1953) and Cassie (1962), to other papers cited in the text and to textbooks, e.g. Bliss & Calhoun (1954).

1. Binomial family
The central place in this family is occupied by the *Poisson series* which describes a *random distribution* (fig. 6). It is important to realize that this does not mean an even or uniform distribution (fig. 6), but that there is an equal probability of an organism occupying any point in space and that the presence

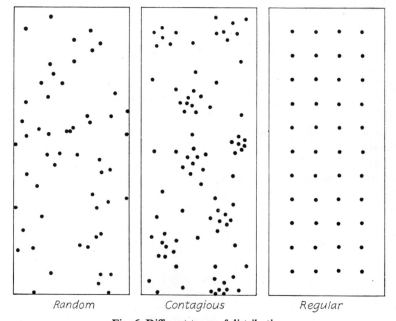

Random   Contagious   Regular

Fig. 6. Different types of distribution.

of one individual does not influence the distribution of another. When plotted, the Poisson series gives a curve which is described completely by one parameter, for the variance (s^2) is equal to the mean ($\bar{x}$). A full discussion of variance and its calculation will be found in most statistical textbooks (e.g. Bailey, 1959; Bliss & Calhoun, 1954; Goulden, 1952), but the observed, variance (s^2) of a distribution may be calculated:

$$s^2 = \frac{\Sigma\,(fx^2) - [(\Sigma fx)^2/N]}{N-1}$$

where Σ = the sum of . . .
  f = frequency of . . .
  x = various values of the number of animal/sample
  N = number of samples

The probability (p) of finding a certain number (x) of animals in a sample from a population with a given mean ($\bar{x}$) and a Poisson distribution is given by:

$$p_x = e^{-\bar{x}}\,\frac{\bar{x}^x}{x!}$$

where e = base of natural (Napierian) logarithms, so that $e^{-\bar{x}}$ may be found by using a table of these logs 'backwards'. The goodness of fit of a set of data to the Poisson distribution may be tested by a χ^2 on the observed and expected values or by the index of dispersion (p. 36).

Occasionally it may be found that the variance is less than the mean; this implies a more regular (or uniform or even) distribution than is described by a Poisson series (fig. 6).

Most commonly in ecological studies the variance will be found to be larger than the mean, that is, the distribution is contagious* (fig. 6), the population is clumped or aggregated. Many contagious insect populations that have been studied can adequately be expressed by the *negative binomial distribution* (Bliss & Owen, 1958; Rojas, 1964; Lyons, 1964; Harcourt, 1965; Ibarra *et al.*, 1965). This distribution is described by two parameters, the mean and the exponent k, which is a measure of the amount of clumping and is often referred to as the dispersion parameter.

Generally values of k are in the region of 2; as they become larger the distribution approaches and is eventually identical with that of the Poisson, whilst fractional values of k lead into the logarithmic series. The value of k is

---

* The term 'contagious' is a mathematical one coined in connection with work on epidemiology and has certain implications that to some extent make its use in ecology inappropriate (Waters & Henson, 1959). An alternative is the term 'over-dispersion' first introduced into ecology by Romell (1930), with its opposite – for more uniform spacing – 'under-dispersion'; unfortunately, however, the use of these terms has been reversed by some ecologists, therefore the terms used here are contagious and regular, which are also those commonly used in plant ecology (Greig-Smith, 1964).

not a constant for a population, but often increases with the mean (Anscombe, 1949; Bliss & Owen, 1958; Waters & Henson, 1959 (see p. 34).

The truncated Poisson may be of value where the distribution is non-random, but the data are too limited to allow the fitting of the negative binomial (Finney & Varley, 1955).

a. Calculating k of the negative binomial
The value of k may be computed by several methods (Anscombe, 1949, 1950; Bliss & Fisher, 1953; Debauche, 1962; Legay, 1963). Three are presented here, two approximate and one (No. 3) more accurate. Another method is described by Katti and Gurland (1962).

$$(1) \qquad k = \frac{\bar{x}^2}{s^2 - \bar{x}}$$

The variance is calculated by the formula given above. The efficiency of this

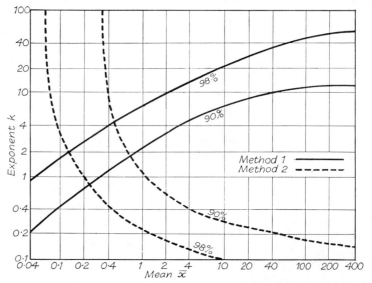

Fig. 7. Large sample efficiencies of the estimation of k of the negative binomial distribution by methods 1 and 2 (redrawn from Anscombe, 1950).

estimate in relation to various values of k and $\bar{x}$ can be seen in fig. 7, from which it is clear that unless the mean is low it is not reliable for use with populations that show a moderate degree of clumping (i.e. a k of 3 or less). This virtually limits its use to *low density populations*.

$$(2) \qquad \log \left(\frac{N}{n_0}\right) = k \log \left(1 + \frac{\bar{x}}{k}\right)$$

where N = total number of samples, n_0 = number of samples containing no animals and others as before.

The easiest way to find the unknown 'k' is by the method of trial and error (iterative solution); that is, various values of k are substituted into the equations until the two sides are equal. A reasonable value of k to start with is 2.

It will be seen from fig. 7 that this method is efficient for most populations with very small means, but for large ones only where there is extensive clumping. This can be expressed another way by saying that about one-third of the samples must be blank (empty) if the mean is below 10; with larger means more blank samples must have been found for the method to be reasonably efficient.

$$(3) \qquad N \ln \left(1 + \frac{\bar{x}}{k} \right) = \sum \left(\frac{Ax}{k+x} \right)$$

where $\ln = $ Napierian logs, $Ax = $ the sum of all frequencies of sampling units containing more than x individuals (e.g. $A_6 = \Sigma f_7 + f_8 + f_9$).

The two sides of this equation must again be made to balance by iteration (trial and error); correctly it is solved by maximum likelihood. As a first step the value of k should be obtained from one of the approximate methods above. If the left-hand side of the equation is found to be too large, then the approximate estimate of k is too large; conversely if the right-hand side is the larger the estimate of k is too low. When two estimates of k have been tried and have given slight excesses in the left- and right-hand sides respectively, a final k can be found by proportion, but this solution should be checked back in the equation. Shenton & Wallington (1962) have shown that even this maximum likelihood estimator of k will have a bias if the mean is small and k large.

b. Testing the fit of the negative binomial
When the value of k has been found the agreement between the negative binomial series as a model and the actual distribution can be tested in three ways.

The expected frequencies of each value may be calculated and these compared by a χ^2 with the actual values (Bliss & Fisher, 1953). The expected values are given by:

$$p_x = \frac{\Gamma(k+x)}{x! \Gamma(k)} \times \left(\frac{\bar{x}}{\bar{x}+k} \right)^x \times \left(\frac{k}{k+\bar{x}} \right)^{-k}$$

where $p_x = $ the probability of a sample containing x animals and the values of $x!$ and $\Gamma(k)$ can be found from tables of factorials and of log gamma functions respectively. χ^2 has three fewer degrees of freedom than the number of comparisons that are made between expected and actual frequencies; those with small expectations are pooled.

Such a comparison between actual and expected frequencies may be distorted by irregularities due to chance; there are two alternative tests based on the difference between the actual and expected moments (mean, variance or skewness) compared with their standard errors (Anscombe, 1950; Bliss & Fisher 1953). Which of these tests is most efficient will depend on the sizes of $\bar{x}$ and k. Evans (1953) has shown that with small means ($\bar{x}$), unless k is large, the most efficient test is that based on the second moment (variance); for other values of $\bar{x}$ and k the test based on the third moment (skewness) should be used. The actual dividing line between the two tests (E–E) is given in fig. 8.

The test based on the second moment involves the calculation of the

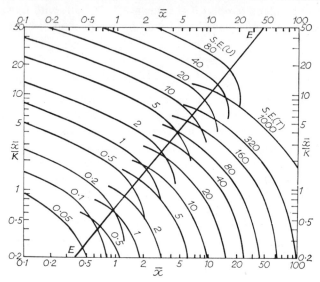

Fig. 8. Testing the fit of the negative binomial distribution – the standard errors of T and U for $N=100$. For other values of N multiply the standard error by $10/\sqrt{N}$. The line E–E represents the contour along which the efficiencies of the methods are equal, the use of the second moment test is preferable in the area to the left of the line and of the third moment test in the area to the right (after Evans, 1953).

statistic U which is the difference between the actual variance and the expected variance given by:

$$U = s^2 - \left(\bar{x} + \frac{\bar{x}^2}{k}\right)$$

the value of k being derived by the second method above. If U is significantly less than its standard error, (S.E. (U)), most conveniently calculated from fig. 8 (the exact formula is given by Evans, 1953), then the negative binomial may be taken as a satisfactory model.

The third moment test involves the calculation of T, the difference between the actual third moment (skewness) of the data and its value predicted from the first two moments (mean and variance) of the same sample:

$$T = \left(\frac{\Sigma fx^3 - 3\bar{x}\,\Sigma fx^2 + 2\bar{x}^2\,\Sigma fx}{N}\right) - s^2\left(\frac{2s^2}{\bar{x}} - 1\right)$$

This should be compared with its standard error (the square root of its large variance) and if the negative binomial is a satisfactory model, T will be significantly smaller than the S.E. The standard error (S.E. (T)) may be approximately read off from fig. 8 or calculated:

$$\text{S.E. } (T) = \sqrt{\frac{2\bar{x}(k+1)\frac{\bar{x}^2}{k^2}\left(1+\frac{\bar{x}}{k}\right)^2\left[2\left(3+5\frac{\bar{x}}{k}\right)+3k\left(1-\frac{\bar{x}}{k}\right)\right]}{N}}$$

where the symbols are as above and the value of k derived by method 3 above. A large positive value of U or T means that the actual distribution is more skew than that described by the negative binomial, a large negative value that the actual distribution is less skew.

c. Calculating a common k

Samples may be taken from various fields or other units and each will have a separate k. The comparison of these and the calculation of a common k (if there is one) will be of value in transforming the data for the analysis of variance (p. 16) and for sequential sampling (p. 43). The simplest method is

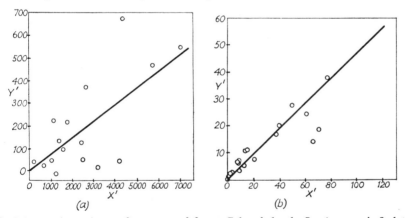

Fig. 9. Regression estimate of a common k for: *a*. Colorado beetle, *Leptinotarsa*, in 8 plots within each of 16 blocks, *b*. wireworms (Col. Elateridae) in 175 sampling units in each of 24 irrigated fields (after Bliss & Owen, 1958).

the moment or regression method (Bliss & Owen, 1958; Bliss, 1958). Two statistics are calculated for each unit

$$x^1 = \bar{x}^2 - \left(\frac{s^2}{N}\right)$$

$$y^1 = s^2 - \bar{x}$$

where $\bar{x}=$ the mean, $s^2=$ variance and $N=$ number of individual counts on which $\bar{x}$ is based. When y^1 is plotted against x^1 (fig. 9) (including occasional negative or zero values of y^1) the regression line of y^1 on x^1 passes through the origins and has the slope $1/k$. An approximate estimate of the common k (k_c) is given by

$$\frac{1}{k_c} = \frac{\Sigma \, y^1}{\Sigma \, x^1}$$

It may be apparent from the plotting of y^1 on x^1 that a few points lie completely outside the main trend, and therefore although their exclusion will mean that the resultant k is not common to the whole series of samples, it is doubtful if the k_c derived by including them would really be meaningful.

A further graphical test of the homogeneity of the samples is obtained by plotting $(1/k)(=y^1/x^1)$ against the mean $(\bar{x})$ for each sub-area or group of samples. If there is neither trend nor clustering (fig. 10a) we may regard the

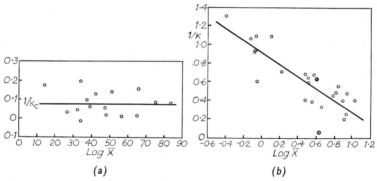

Fig. 10. The relation of $1/k$ to the mean for: a. Colorado beetle, b. wireworms based on the same data as fig. 9 (after Bliss & Owen, 1958).

fitting of a common k as justified, but if a trend (fig. 10b) or clustering occurs it is doubtful if the calculation of a common k is justified.

Fairly rough estimates of k_c are usually adequate, but in critical cases a weighted estimate of k_c should be obtained and whether or not this lies within the sampling error can be tested by the computation of χ^2. The method is given by Bliss (1958) and Bliss & Owen (1958). The latter authors describe another method of calculating a common k especially suitable for field experiments arranged in restricted designs (e.g. randomized blocks).

2. Logarithmic and other contagious models

A number of other mathematical models have been developed to describe various non-random distributions, and several of these may have more than one mode. Anscombe (1950) and Evans (1953) have reviewed these and they include the Thomas, Neyman's types A, B and C and the Polya-Aeppli. The Thomas (1949) type is based on the assumption of randomly distributed colonies whose individual populations are values plus one, from a Poisson series. Neyman's (1939) distributions are similar and are intended to describe conditions found soon after insect larvae hatched from egg batches; the modes are equally spaced. Skellam (1958) has shown that Neyman's type A is particularly applicable where the organisms occur in compact clusters, but that it can be used as an approximation in certain conditions when the clustering is less compact. The Polya-Aeppli distribution describes the situation when an initial wave of simultaneous invaders have settled and produced clusters of offspring; it may have one or two modes.

As mentioned above, the logarithmic model describes situations for which the negative binomial would give a very small value of k. The logarithmic series (Fisher, Corbet & Williams, 1943), which is derived from the negative binomial with k tending to zero and with the zero readings neglected, and the *discrete* and *truncated* (and censored) *log normal* distributions (Preston, 1948; Grundy, 1952) have been found of most value in the description of the relationship between numbers of species and numbers of individuals and are discussed later (p. 332). Also they have been found to give a reasonable description of the distribution of the individuals of some insects (e.g. the citrus scale insect, *Aonidiella ornatum* (Spiller, 1952), eggs of the larch sawfly, *Pristiphora erichsonii* (Ives, 1955)).

Working with plankton, with large mean values, Cassie (1962) suggested that the action of a series of environmental factors led to the population being distributed in a succession of Poisson series, the means of the series being themselves distributed according to the log normal model. He called this the *Poisson log normal*; it differs from the negative binomial mainly in the left-hand flank, as ordinarily plotted, where it allows for fewer zero values.

3. Implications of the distribution models and of changes in the type of distribution

Neyman's distributions are based on precise models, and as Upholt & Craig (1940) found, if the biological assumptions underlying the distribution are not fulfilled it will not adequately describe the disperson of the population. It is perhaps for this reason that Neyman's distributions have been used relatively little by entomologists, most preferring the other distributions that can be derived from a number of different hypotheses. The negative binomial can arise in at least five different ways (Anscombe, 1950; Waters & Henson, 1959):

(1) Inverse binomial sampling: if a proportion of individuals in a population possess a certain character, the number of samples, in excess of k, that have to be taken to obtain k individuals with this character will have a negative binomial distribution with exponent k.

(2) Heterogeneous Poisson sampling: if the mean of a Poisson varies randomly from occasion to occasion, under certain conditions a negative binomial results. A biological example of this is the observation of Itô *et al.* (1962) that a series of counts of a gall-wasp on chestnut trees were distributed as a Poisson for each single tree, but when the counts from all trees were combined they were described by a negative binomial.

(3) Compounding of Poisson and logarithmic distributions: if a number of

colonies are distributed as a Poisson, but the number of individuals per colony follows a logarithmic distribution, the resulting distribution per unit area (i.e. independent of colonies) will be a negative binomial. Counts of bacteria have been shown to satisfy this model (Quenouille, 1949).

(4) Constant birth–death–immigration rates, the former two expressed per individual and the immigration rate per unit of time, will lead to a population whose size will form a negative binomial series.

(5) True contagion: where the presence of one individual in a unit increases the chance that another will occur there also.

The logarithmic series (Fisher, Corbet & Williams, 1943) can also be derived from several modes of population growth (Kendall, 1948; Shinozaki & Urata, 1953).

It is clear, therefore, that from mathematical considerations alone it is unsound to attempt to analyse the details of the biological processes involved in generating a distribution from the mathematical model it can be shown to fit or, more often, approximately fit (Waters, 1959). Nevertheless, the models do measure the extent of clumping and this, and the changes in it, provide important evidence about the population. The uses and interpretation of the parameters will be discussed later (p. 34), here changes in the actual type of distribution will be discussed.

The main distinction lies between regular, random and contagious distributions, with the respective implications that the animals compete (or at least tend to keep apart), have no effect on each other, or are aggregated or clumped.

The first difficulty is that the sampling method chosen by the experimenter may effect the apparent distribution (Waters & Henson, 1959), as is shown by the example from the work of Itô *et al.* (1962) quoted above and that of Shibuya & Ouchi (1955), who found that the distribution of the gall-midge, *Asphondylia*, on soya bean was contagious if the plant was taken as the sampling unit, but random if the numbers per pod were considered. The contagion appeared to be due to there being more eggs on those plants with more pods. The effect of the size of the sampling unit on the apparent distribution has also been demonstrated for chafer beetle larvae (Burrage & Gyrisco, 1954) and grasshopper egg pods (Putnam & Shklov, 1956). Careful testing of the size and pattern of sampling as suggested above will help to discover such an artifact. If, however, the contagion is real it may arise from patchiness of the habitat, including differential predation (Waters, 1959) or from the behaviour of the animals themselves, or a combination of both. The behaviour leading to aggregation in the absence of special attractive areas in the habitat, may be of two types; inter-individual attraction or the laying of eggs (or young) in groups (Cole, 1946).

The dispersion of the initial insect invaders of a crop is often random; this randomness may be real or an artifact due to the low density relative to the sample size (see below). The distribution of aphids in a field during the initial phase of infestation is random, becoming contagious as each aphid reproduces

(Sylvester & Cox, 1961; Shiyomi & Nakamura, 1964). The egg masses of many insects are randomly distributed (e.g. Chiang & Hodson, 1959) and the individual eggs and young larvae are clumped; however, the dispersion of the larvae may become random, or approach it, in later instars. Such changes in distribution with the age of the population have been observed in wireworms (Salt & Hollick, 1946), the rice stem borer (*Chilo simplex*) (Kono, 1953), a chafer beetle, *Amphimallon majalis* (Burrage & Gyrisco, 1954), the cabbage butterfly (*Pieris rapae*) (Itô, Gotoh & Miyashita, 1960), the diamond-back moth (*Plutella maculipennis*) (Harcourt, 1961*a*) and others. It is tempting to infer from such changes that either mortality or emigration or both are density-dependent; however, as Morisita (1962) has shown, this conclusion may not be justified with non-sedentary animals, and such changes could result from the alteration of the size of the area occupied by the colony relative to that of the sample or from the decrease in population density (see below). In contrast, the tendency to aggregate may be such that density-dependent mortality is masked, as in the pear lace-bug (*Stephanitis nashi*), where even after the bugs have been artificially removed so as to produce a random distribution, it returns to non-randomness in a few days (Takeda & Hukusima, 1961).

Changes in the density of the insect often lead to changes, or at least apparent changes, in the distribution. When the population is very sparse the chances of individuals occurring in any sampling unit is so low that their distribution is effectively random. The random distribution of low populations and the contagious distributions of higher ones have often been observed; for example, with wireworms (Finney, 1941), grasshopper egg pods (Davis & Wadley, 1949), a ladybird beetle, *Epilachna 28-maculata* (Iwao, 1956), the cabbage butterfly (*Pieris rapae*) (Harcourt, 1961*b*) and the pea aphid (*Acyrthosiphon pisum*) (Forsythe & Gyrisco, 1963). However, with the Nantucket pine tip moth (*Rhyacionia frustrana*), as the population density increases still further the distribution tends towards the Poisson again, i.e. the k value becomes high (Waters, 1959). Populations of several other forest insects (Waters, 1959) and of the periodical cicadas (Dybas & Davis, 1962) also show a tendency to become more random at higher densities (p. 24). Indeed one can envisage that at even higher densities the distribution would pass beyond the Poisson and become regular.

In different habitats the type of distribution may change, as Yoshihara (1953) found with populations of the winkle, *Tectarius granularis* (Mollusca) on rough and smooth rocks, although it is difficult to separate this habitat effect from associated changes in density.

Within the same habitat different species will usually show different dispersion patterns as has been found with leaf hoppers (Homoptera: Auchenorrhyncha) on rice plants (Kuno, 1963). These differences can arise from several biological causes: one species may aggregate more than another in the same habitat because it disperses less or because it reproduces more or because only certain parts of the habitat are suitable for it. A discussion of the various factors that might be responsible for the negative binomial distribution of the gall-midge *Mikiola fagi* on beech is given by Legay (1963).

Biological interpretation of dispersion parameters and 'nearest neighbour'
techniques for population estimation

1. 'k' of the negative binomial – an index of aggregation in the population
If the negative binomial (p. 27) can be fitted to the data the value of k gives a measure of dispersion; the smaller the value of k the greater the extent of aggregation, whereas a large value (over about 8) indicates that the distribution is approaching a Poisson, i.e. is virtually random. Unfortunately the value of k is often influenced by the size of the sampling unit (Cole, 1946; Morris, 1954; Waters & Henson, 1959; Harcourt, 1961a) and therefore comparisons can only be made using the same sized unit. But within this restriction it does provide a useful measure of the degree of aggregation of the particular population, varying with the habitat and the developmental stage (Hairston, 1959; Waters, 1959; Harcourt, 1961a; Dybas & Davis, 1962). Examples of these variations are given in table 2. As Waters (1959) has pointed out, the degree of aggregation of a population, which k expresses, could well affect the influence of predators and parasites.

The aggregation recognized by the negative binomial may be due either to active aggregation by the insects or to some heterogeneity of the environment at large (microclimate, soil, plant, natural enemies (p. 247)). Dr R. E. Blackith has suggested (see also in Richards & Waloff, 1961) that if mean size of a clump is calculated using Arbous & Kerrich's (1951) formula and this is found to be *less than 2* then the 'aggregation' would seem to be due to some environmental effect and not to an active process. Aggregations of 2 or more insects could be caused by either factor. The mean number of individuals in the aggregation is calculated by:

$$\lambda = \frac{\bar{x}}{2k} \nu$$

where $\bar{x}$=the mean, ν is a function with a χ^2 distribution with $2k$ degrees of freedom and λ=the number of individuals in the aggregation for the probability level allocated to ν. To find the mean size of the 'aggregate' the value at the 0·5 probability level is used. $2k$ degrees of freedom will usually be fractional but an adequate χ^2 can be calculated by reference to graphs or by proportionality.

To take two examples from table 2d, the eggs and pupae of *Pieris rapae* –

Eggs: $$\lambda_m = \frac{9 \cdot 5}{3 \cdot 1 \times 2} \times 5 \cdot 55 = 8 \cdot 5$$

Pupae: $$\lambda_m = \frac{1 \cdot 7}{2 \cdot 3 \times 2} \times 3 \cdot 54 = 1 \cdot 3$$

Table 2. The variation of k of the negative binomial with some factors. *a*, *b* & *c* with sampling unit. *d* with developmental stage and change in density. *a. Eriophyes* leaf galls on *Populus tremuloides*. *b.* Nantucket pine tip moth, *Rhyacionia frustrana* (from Waters & Henson, 1959); *c* & *d* cabbage white butterfly, *Pieris rapae* (from Harcourt, 1961*b*)

Sampling unit	Mean number per unit	k
a. Single leaf	0·21±0·01	0·0611±0·0013
1 leaf-bunch	0·88±0·04	0·883 ±0·0024
2 leaf-bunches	1·65±0·08	0·1150±0·0035
5 leaf-bunches	3·78±0·26	0·1740±0·0064
Branch	14·23±1·68	0·2000±0·0119
b. Tip of shoot	0·49±0·03	0·449±0·021
Branch whorl	2·36±0·36	0·214±0·035
Tree	13·13±4·21	0·253±0·074

Sampling unit	k for 1st instar larvae	k for 4th instar larvae
c. Quadrant of cabbage	1·38	1·96
Half cabbage	2·28	4·24
Whole cabbage	2·32	4·28

Stage	Mean density	k
d. Egg	9·5	3·1
1st instar	5·6	2·8
2nd instar	4·4	2·8
3rd instar	4·0	4·6
4th instar	3·6	5·1
5th instar	2·6	7·8
Pupa	1·7	2·3

From this it can be concluded that the 'clumping' of the eggs could be due to a behavioural cause – in this instance the females tending to lay a number of eggs in proximity to one another or to the heterogeneity of the environment – only certain areas being suitable for oviposition, but 'clumping' of the pupae is due to environmental causes.

The values of the k and the mean for $\lambda = 2$ are plotted in fig. 11, from which it can be ascertained for a particular population whose k and mean are known whether the mean 'aggregation' size is above or below 2. 'Aggregations' of less than 2 in sedentary animals could be due to behavioural causes if the majority of the population had been killed between settling and sampling.

2. '*b*' of Taylor's power law – an index of aggregation for the species
The parameter '*b*' of Taylor's power law (p. 9) is a measure of the aggregation characteristic of, and constant for, the species; it is therefore of value in

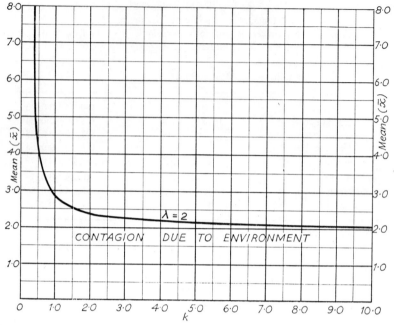

Fig. 11. The cause of contagion in the data – the plot of the 'mean aggregation' (λ) of two individuals for various values of the mean and k of the negative binomial. Populations whose value for the mean plotted against k lie below the line may be considered to exhibit contagion because of some environmental factor; in those populations whose value lies above the line contagion could be due either to an active behavioural process or to the environment.

interspecific comparisons (e.g. Healey, 1964). It would seem that the amount of scatter of the points around the line (fig. 2) which can be approximately estimated as the variance around the appropriate regression line (p. 9) is a measure of the effect of habitat variation on the extent of aggregation.

3. Index of dispersion – the departure of the distribution from randomness
This measure is often referred to as the coefficient of dispersion.

The extent to which the distribution satisfies a Poisson model can be tested by a χ^2.

$$\chi^2 = \frac{s^2(N-1)}{\bar{x}}$$

where s^2=variance, N=number of samples and $\bar{x}$=mean. Now if the distribution is in fact Poisson the χ^2 value calculated above will *not* lie outside the limits (normally taken as 0·95 and 0·05) of χ^2 for $N-1$ in tables.* If the χ^2 value does conform with the Poisson expectation it will be found that the index of dispersion=$\chi^2 \div (N-1)$ will approximate to unity; a value of zero

* For values of N larger than those given in tables, χ^2 may be calculated (see p. 77).

for the index would imply that the animals were regularly distributed and a value significantly greater than one (as tested by χ^2 above) implies aggregation.

As Naylor (1959) has pointed out, the indices may be added if they are from the same sized samples. Examples of the use of this index are in Salt & Hollick's (1946) studies on wireworms, Naylor's (1959) on *Tribolium*, Nielsen's (1963) on *Culicoides* and Milne's (1964) on the chafer beetle, *Phyllopertha*. In contagious populations the value of this index is influenced by the size of the sampling unit (i.e. by the size of the mean), as well as by the density. Greig-Smith (1964) discusses this and other indices in detail.

4. Morisita's indices of dispersion – measures of dispersion pattern

These indices have the great advantage that they are relatively independent of the type of distribution, the number of samples and of the size of the mean. Morisita's (1959, 1962, 1964) first index is given by the formula:

$$I_\delta = N \frac{\sum_{i=1}^{N} n_i(n_i - 1)}{\sum x(\sum x - 1)} = N \frac{\Sigma x^2 - \Sigma x}{(\Sigma x)^2 - \Sigma x}$$

where N=total samples, n_i=nos. in the ith sample and Σx=the sum of the numbers of individuals found in all the samples. When the distribution is Poisson (random) this index will give a value of unity; when the distribution is contagious (e.g. negative binomial) the index will be greater than one and when the distribution is regular (e.g. binomial) less than one. The exact mathematical relations between the index and the parameters of these distributions are discussed by Morisita (1962). The significance of the departure from a random distribution shown by the index may be tested by comparing F_0 calculated:

$$F_0 = \frac{I_\delta(\Sigma x - 1) + N - \Sigma x}{N - 1}$$

with the value of F (variance ratio) in tables, the appropriate value being that for F where $N_1 = N - 1$ and $N_2 = \infty$.

A further index has been devised by Morisita (1962) for the comparison of the distribution of events (or individuals) within periods (or sub-areas) of an event (or area). He uses it for comparing the probability of traps catching voles during the first three and subsequent days of trapping programme; but it could also be used to compare the distribution of, say, mites on leaves on different parts of a tree. It is related to the I_δ index and has the same relation to randomness, contagiousness and regular distributions (unity, greater than unity and less than unity respectively.) Unlike the I_δ index it does allow the direct comparison (from within the same universe) of populations with different numbers of samples; it is given by

$$I_b = I_\delta \frac{G - 1/N}{G - 1}$$

where $G=$ the number of groups, periods or sub-areas (e.g. days), $N=$ the total number of samples in the whole series; I_δ is calculated separately for each group.

5. Breder's equations – a measure of the cohesion of aggregations

Working on fish schools Breder (1954) found that the distance between individuals varied only slightly, and such uniform or regular distribution is indeed characteristic of the distribution of 'crowded' individuals (p. 25). With such schools or social swarms, when the individuals are their normal distance (d) apart the attractive force (a) between individuals can be said to equal the repulsive force (r), so that c, a measure of the cohesion in the equation

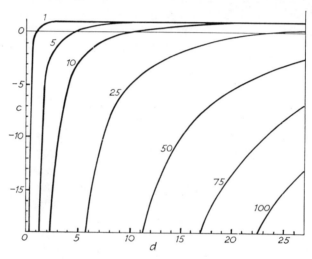

Fig. 12. Breder's curves for the cohesion of aggregations. The mean normal distance between individuals as a decimal fraction of the animal total length gives the value of d for $c=0$, the appropriate curve for r ($=r_1 r_2$) may then be read off (after Breder, 1954).

$c=(a-r)/d^2$, is zero. Negative values of c will show 'overcrowding', there will be a tendency for the individuals to move apart; positive values that normal aggregation has not been obtained – these will approach $+1$ asymptotically if the attractive force is taken as 1. If r_1 and r_2 are the repulsive forces of two animals on each other, then the equation becomes:

$$c = \frac{1-r_1 r_2}{d^2}$$

or
$$r_1 r_2 = d_s^2$$

where $d_s=$ the mean normal distance between individuals in the aggregation, because by definition $c=0$ under these conditions.

The mean distance between individuals in a moving school may be measured from photographs and so the value for r found. It is then possible to plot c

against d for a series of values (see fig. 12). The angle at which the curves cross the 0 value is of interest: the steeper the line the tighter the aggregation, angles of intersection of 40°–50° being characteristic of fish that keep apart by a distance considerably less than their own length; smaller angles indicate looser aggregations, both spatially and probably, Breder suggests, in their tendency to split up. The values of r given in fig. 12 represent $\sqrt{r_1 . r_2}$.

Some insects, such as locusts and army worms, form swarms many of the characters of which would seem to parallel fish schools, and therefore the equations developed by Breder might well be used for comparisons with these insects. From Breder's equations it would seem that the smaller the mean distance, in terms of their total lengths, between individuals the more stable the aggregation.

6. Deevey's coefficient of crowding

This measure was used by Deevey (1947) to express the extent of crowding in barnacle populations, where the individuals actually impinge on one another as they grow and is given by:

$$C_c = 2\pi r^2 N^2$$

where r = the radius of the fully grown animal and N = the density of the animal per unit area. The units of r and N must of course be comparable (e.g. cm and sq cm) and then C_c will define the number of contacts per unit area. This coefficient could be used with any sedentary, approximately circular animal or with plant galls on leaves; when a realistic value can be given to r, for example the radius of a circular home range (p. 261), it could also be used with mobile forms.

7. Nearest neighbour and related techniques – measures of population size or of the departure from randomness of the distribution

There are basically two separate approaches: one may either select an individual at random and measure the distance between it and its nearest neighbour (true nearest neighbour techniques) or one may select a point and measure the distance between this point and the nearest or nth nearest individuals (sometimes referred to as closest individual techniques). From each of these, conclusions may either be drawn about the departure of the distribution from random, if the population density is known from some other method, or alternatively, if one can assume the distribution to be random, its density can be estimated (Morisita, 1954).

These techniques are most easily used with stationary, discrete, easily mapped organisms, e.g. trees, and have been used extensively by botanists (Greig-Smith, 1964). With animals, their mobility and the risk that one will fail to find the nearest neighbour limit their application (Turner, 1960). However, such methods have been applied to studies on grasshoppers (Blackith, 1958) and frogs (Turner, 1960) and, with more success, to studies of fairly conspicuous and relatively stationary animals (e.g. snails; Keuls, Over & de Wit, 1963) or of well-marked colonies (e.g. ant mounds; Waloff & Blackith, 1962; Blackith *et al.*, 1963). Nearest neighbour and related techniques could also be used with other relatively sedentary animals such as barnacles, limpets (*Patella*), scale insects, tube-building animals and gall formers (especially on leaves). The use of photography in mapping natural distributions of snails has been described by Heywood & Edwards (1961), and this could provide a valuable aid to the application of these techniques, not only to fairly sedentary organisms, but also where the substratum is suitable, to far more mobile forms. The various dolichopodid and other flies on mud are an example of a community that might be studied in this way. There are, furthermore, a few other techniques, such as the 'squashing' or 'imprinting' method for estimating mite numbers on leaves (p. 113), or the deadheart method for estimating stem borers (p. 233) that do, or could easily, provide maps of the distribution of the individuals to which nearest neighbour or closest individual methods could be applied. Henson (1961) has used a combination of photography and nearest neighbour methods to study the aggregations of a scolytid beetle in the laboratory.

a. Nearest neighbour methods

In this method a point is selected at random, and then one searches around in tight concentric rings until an animal is found; the searching is then continued until the nearest neighbour is found and the distance between these two animals is measured. There are basically two expressions; the simplest is due to Clark & Evans (1954):

$$m = \frac{1}{4\bar{r}^2}$$

where m = density per unit area; $\bar{r}$ = mean distance between nearest neighbours. As has been pointed out by Blackith (1958), this formula is based on the mean r squared, whereas Craig's (1953) formula is based more correctly on the sum of r squared; the latter formula is, however, less easy to use and describes the density in a quarter segment. Turner (1960) has concluded that for randomly distributed populations Clark & Evans's formula is fairly satisfactory.

The importance of a number of population estimates by different methods has been emphasized elsewhere (p. 4) and therefore in fairly homogeneous habitats (e.g. field crops), unless the species obviously aggregates, these methods would provide a useful 'order of magnitude check' on other estimates obtained by marking and recapture or by sampling methods, and like marking and recapture they are independent of sample size.

If, however, the density has been measured by one of these other methods, the departure of the distribution from randomness will be given by the value of the numerator in the expressions (Clark & Evans, 1954; Waloff & Blackith, 1962).

$$\bar{r}^2 = \frac{1\cdot154}{m} \qquad \text{Uniform, hexagonal spacing-competition}$$

$$\bar{r}^2 = \frac{0\cdot2500}{m} \qquad \text{Random}$$

where $\bar{r}$ = mean distance between nearest neighbours, m = number of individuals per unit area.

Smaller values of the numerator will indicate aggregation or clumping due to environmental or behavioural factors. These estimates should be based on large samples and, of course, the density and distance units of measurement must be the same.

The use of the second, third, . . . nth nearest neighbours, discussed by Morisita (1954) and Thompson (1956), not only enables more accurate density determinations to be made, but also the dispersion pattern to be detected over a larger area. However, as Waloff & Blackith (1962) have pointed out, competition effects detectable between nearest neighbours may be masked at greater distances because of heterogeneity of the habitat. Thompson shows that the statistic:

$$2\pi m \frac{\Sigma \, r_n^{\,2}}{N}$$

where N = number of observations, m = density and r = distance, is distributed as a χ^2 with $2N$ degrees of freedom. This value may be calculated and compared with the expected value under the hypothesis of randomness (the χ^2 value for $2N$ is found from tables). A probability of χ^2 greater than $0\cdot95$ indicates significant regularity, the distances being greater than they would be on a purely random arrangement, whilst a probability of less than $0\cdot05$ indicates significant contagion (clumping).

A simpler but – according to Thompson – less reliable comparison is given by the proportionality constants in the equation:

$$\bar{r}_n^{\,2} = \frac{p}{m}$$

where p = proportionality constant and other symbols as above. For a random distribution for $n=1$ (i.e. the nearest neighbour) as indicated above $p=0\cdot25$; for $n=2$, $p=0\cdot87$; for $n=3$, $p=0\cdot97$; for $n=4$, $p=1\cdot05$.

b. Closest individual or distance method

In this method a point is selected at random and the distance between this and the nth nearest individual measured. Cottam & Curtis (1956) and Cottam, Curtis & Catana (1957) have compared this method with the nearest neighbour and other approaches in botanical studies and they concluded that it was the least reliable.

The method has also been derived, apparently independently, by Keuls, Over & de Wit (1963) and used for population estimations of the snail *Limnaea* (=*Galba*) *truncatula*. It depends on the population being randomly distributed, although if the discontinuities are small, the errors that are made will tend to cancel each other out. The basic equation is:

$$m = \frac{n-1}{\pi} \times \frac{1}{a_n{}^2}$$

where n=the rank of the individual in distance from the randomly selected point, e.g. for the nearest neighbour $n=1$, for the second nearest 2 . . .; a=the distance between the randomly selected point and the individual and other symbols are as above. The values of $(n-1)/\pi$ for a series of values of n are given in table 3; clearly, therefore, in order to estimate population density the reciprocal of the square of the distance of the nth animal from the random point $(1/\bar{a}^2)$ need only be multiplied by the factor in the middle column of this table. The 95% fiducial limits and the coefficient of variation are also given.

Table 3. Multiplication factors for estimating the density of a population by the distance method with 95% fiducial limits and the coefficient of variance of the estimate of density (after Keuls *et al.*, 1963)

| | Multiply $1/\bar{a}^2$ for nth nearest animal from point by value in table for: | | | |
| | 95% lower limit | Estimate of density | 95% upper limit | Coefficient of variation |
n				
1	0·016	—	0·95	—
2	0·113	0·32	1·51	—
3	0·26	0·64	2·01	1·00
4	0·44	0·95	2·47	0·71
5	0·63	1·27	2·91	0·58
6	0·83	1·59	3·35	0·50
7	1·05	1·91	3·77	0·45
8	1·27	2·23	4·19	0·41
9	1·50	2·55	4·60	0·38
10	1·73	2·86	5·00	0·35

In the original paper values of n up to 100 are given, these are not reproduced here as the labour of assessing even the 10th nearest animal is considerable. However, the fiducial limits become narrower with higher values and the third to fifth nearest individuals are probably the most practical. The nearest animal cannot be used for it is without the estimator $(n-1)/\pi$ in the equation for density, neither can the second nearest, as an unbiased estimate of the variance is not available.

Keuls *et al.* suggest that the method could be applied to very mobile animals by recording the nearest individual at s moments (perhaps photo-graphically, p. 40) when the formula becomes:

$$m = \frac{sn-1}{\pi} \times \frac{1}{\underset{1 \to s}{\Sigma a_n^2}}$$

that is one simply adds up, say, four measurements of the nearest animal and regards the sum as the measurement of the fourth nearest.

SEQUENTIAL SAMPLING

In this type of sampling the total number of samples taken is variable and depends on whether or not the results so far obtained give a definite answer to the question posed about the frequency of occurrence of an event (i.e. abundance of an insect). It is of particular value for the assessment of pest density in relation to control measures, when these are applied only if the pest density has reached a certain level. Extensive preliminary work is necessary to establish the type of distribution (the relation of the mean and the variance) and the density levels that are permissible and those that we associated with extensive damage. From such data it would be possible to lay down a fixed number of samples that would enable one to be sure in all instances what was the population level; however, this would frequently lead to unnecessary sampling and a sequential plan usually allows one to stop sampling as soon as adequate data has been gathered. For example, to take extremes, if 80 insects per shoot, or more, caused severe damage and no insects were found in the first 5 samples, common sense would tempt one not to continue for the additional, say 15, samples. Sequential sampling gives an exact measure (based on the known variance) so that with extremely high and extremely low populations very few samples need be taken and the expenditure of time and effort (cost) is minimal.

As the distribution of most insect species can be fitted to the negative binomial (p. 25), formulae will be given only for this type of distribution; of course the principles are the same with other distributions. The method is described by Wald (1948), Goulden (1952) and Waters (1955). Stark (1952b) has applied a sequential plan to normalized data for a needle miner (Lepidoptera).

The first decision must be to fix the insect population levels related to the infestation classes; we wish to distinguish between the hypothesis (H_1) that there are e.g. 200 or more egg masses per branch, sufficient to cause heavy damage, and the hypothesis (H_0) that there are e.g. 100 or fewer egg masses per branch, insufficient to cause damage.

The second decision concerns the level of probability of incorrect assessment one is prepared to tolerate; there are two types of error:

α = the probability of accepting H_1 when H_0 is the true situation
β = the probability of accepting H_0 when H_1 is the true situation

Let us say that the same level is accepted for both, 1 false assessment in 20, i.e. a probability level of 0·05 for α and β.

For an animal whose distribution corresponds to the negative binomial the following values need to be calculated; the common k having been found already (p. 26) and the means being fixed as above (Oakland, 1950; Morris, 1954):

	Infestation level	
	H_0	H_1
Mean $= kp$	kp_0 (e.g. 100)	kp_1 (e.g. 200)
$p = kp/k$	p_0	p_1
$q = 1+p$	q_0	q_1
Variance $= kpq$	kp_0q_0	kp_1q_1

The next aim is to plot the two lines (fig. 13) that mark the 'acceptance' and 'rejection' areas (these terms have come from quality control work where sequential sampling was originally developed).

The formulae for the lines are:

$$d_0 = \theta n + h_0$$
$$d_1 = \theta n + h_1$$

where d=cumulative number of insects, n=number of trees sampled, θ=the slope of the lines given by

$$\theta = k\frac{\log (q_1/q_0)}{\log (p_1q_0/p_0q_1)}$$

and h_0 and h_1 the intercepts given by

$$h_0 = \frac{\log [\beta/(1-\alpha)]}{\log (p_1q_0/p_0q_1)}$$
$$h_1 = \frac{\log [(1-\beta)/\alpha]}{\log (p_1q_0/p_0q_1)}$$

Once these calculations are made a graph similar to fig. 13 can be drawn up, and it will be clear that occasionally (especially when the true population lies between the population levels chosen, i.e. 100 and 200 in this example) the cumulative total continues to lie in the uncertain zone and therefore an arbitrary upper limit must be set to the number of samples taken. This limit (x) will be decided on considerations of cost, and normally it will be laid down that if after x samples the result still lies in the uncertain zone treatment will be applied.

It is possible to draw up operating characteristic curves and average sample number curves which give a measure of the probability of accepting the two hypotheses and the average number of samples necessary, respectively, at different population levels (Oakland, 1950; Morris, 1954).

The actual field work may be carried out based on the graph, or a sequential

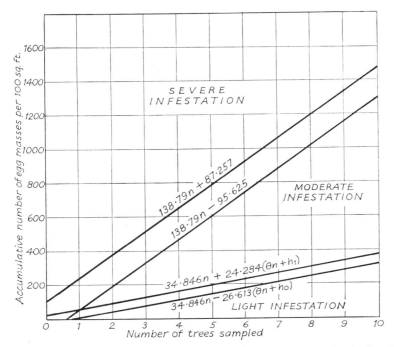

Fig. 13. A sequential sampling chart with two sets of acceptance and rejection lines (after Morris, 1954).

table may be prepared from it. This gives the uncertainty band for various numbers of samples; e.g. (after Morris, 1954):

Sample tree	Moderate vs severe infestation uncertainty band (cumulative total of insects)
1	42–225
2	183–366
3	323–506
4	460–643
5	599–782
6	738–921
etc.	

It is often considered desirable to set up three classes: severe, moderate and light, and then two pairs of lines are calculated.

A general account of the utility of sequential sampling plans for forest insects is given by Ives (1954) and, in addition to the papers already referred to, plans have been developed for the winter moth (*Operophtera brumata*) (Reeks, 1956), the forest tent caterpillar (*Malacosoma disstria*) (Connola, Waters & Smith, 1957), the larch sawfly (*Pristiphora erichsonii*) (Ives & Prentice, 1958), the red-pine sawfly (*Neodiprion nanulus*) (Connola, Waters & Nason, 1959), the coffee shield bug, *Antestiopis* (Rennison, 1962), lodgepole needle miner (*Evagora milleri*) (Stevens & Stark, 1962), the aphid, *Myzus persicae* (Sylvester & Cox, 1961) and others. It must, however, be remembered that these plans are based on particular sampling methods in a certain area with a given developmental stage and, as has been shown (p. 35), the value of k and hence the validity of the plan may alter if any of these are changed.

SAMPLING A FAUNA

Emphasis has been placed on the problems involved in sampling the population of a single species and these are formidable enough. But with faunal surveys the problem of ensuring the detection of an adequate proportion of the species present must be considered. When sampling vegetation, Gleason (1922) pointed out as the area sampled increased the numbers of hitherto unrecorded species added decreased, a concept referred to as the species-area curve, and one that has been often used and disputed in plant ecology (Goodall, 1952; Evans, Clark & Brand, 1955; Greig-Smith, 1964; Watt, 1964). The logarithmic series and log normal distributions (p. 31) express the same basic assumptions another way.

One approach to this problem is therefore to take a number of preliminary samples and calculate the index of diversity based on the log series (p. 337). If one can make an estimate of the total number of individuals in the fauna then the theoretical total number of species present can be arrived at from the index of diversity, and the total number of individuals that should be collected to find $y\%$ of the species present can be determined. The value of y will, of course, depend on the aim of the study. Unfortunately, as pointed out later (chapter 13), this approach has a number of practical and theoretical limitations. The practical ones stem from the mosaic nature of most habitats (Hairston, 1964), and therefore, unless sampling is by a light trap or similar device that is independent of microhabitats, more new species are added by further samples than would be expected. The theoretical problems arise from the discovery that the log normal distribution provides a better description of the phenomenon than the simpler logarithmic series (see p. 334 for a further discussion). An approach which makes no assumptions about the type of distribution is given by Good & Toulmin (1956).

Sometimes the mosaic nature of the habitat can be utilized to facilitate the planning of an optimal sampling programme. This is especially true where the effects of pollution are being studied in streams, but might be extended to other situations where a factor is acting simultaneously over a wide range of special habitats within a major habitat or community type, for example the effect of aerial spraying on the fauna of a mixed woodland. If a fixed number of samples of the fauna are taken – say from three different zones of a stream: riffles, pools and marginal areas – it will be found that the first few samples will provide a more complete picture of the total observed fauna in one zone than in the other (Gaufin, Harris & Walter, 1956). In other words because of the different diversities and microdistributions of the fauna in the different zones, and also possibly because of the differing efficiencies of the collecting methods under these conditions, the rates of accumulation of new species vary from zone to zone. A zone in which a high percentage of the total species taken in a large number of samples (*n*) were recorded in the first few samples, can have a smaller number of samples drawn from it than a zone in which the rate of accumulation is less rapid.

A method of calculating the average number of new species contributed by the *K*th successive sample (when *K* can equal any number from 1 upwards) has been devised by Gaufin, Harris & Walter (1956), who also provide a table of the coefficients necessary for up to a total of ten samples. Their formula is:

$$S_K = \frac{1}{S} \sum_{i=1}^{n-K+1} a_i K S_i$$

where S_K = the number of new species added by the *K*th sample, *n* = the total number of samples taken in the preliminary survey, S = the total number of species taken in the *n* samples, S_i = the number of different species appearing in *i* out of *n* samples and $a_i K$ are coefficients by which successive values of S_i are multiplied in calculating the summation item. By summing a series of values of S_K (for *K* = 1 to a predetermined number *K'*) it is possible to compute the average number of species found in *K'* samples. A method of calculating the standard errors of such estimates has been developed by Harris (1957).

BIOLOGICAL AND OTHER QUALITATIVE ASPECTS OF SAMPLING

Hitherto stress has been laid on the statistical aspects of sampling; however, there are certain biological problems that are of cardinal importance. The ecologist should always remember that the computation of fiducial limits of estimates only tells him the consistency of the samples he has collected, and the statistical techniques cannot be blamed if these have been consistently excluding a major part of the population. This is indeed the most serious biological problem in all sampling work, namely to ensure that there is not a part of the population with a behavioural pattern or habitat preference such that it is never sampled (Macleod, 1958).

Less dangerous because the phenomenon will be recorded, although it may well be misinterpreted, is the tendency for the behaviour of the animal to

E M—C

change and affect its sampling properties. The reactions of the fly *Meromyza* to weather conditions (Hughes, 1955) and of the larvae of different species of corixid water-bug to light (Teyrovský, 1956) lead to errors when net sampling is carried out under different conditions (p. 189). In many, perhaps almost all, insects the behaviour alters with age, and this may lead to a confusion between a change in behaviour and death. For example older females of the mirid grass bug, *Leptopterna dolobrata*, spend more time on the base of the grass shoots and less on the tops than do males. If a marking and recapture experiment is carried out and the bugs collected by sweeping, the females will appear to be much shorter-lived than the males. But this is because as they age, the females enter the sampling zone less frequently; they are actually longer-lived than the males.

The variations in the distribution of the insect may well be linked with some character of the environment or its host plant, and it is important to distinguish this variation from sampling variance otherwise the fiducial limits of the estimates may become so wide that no conclusions can be drawn (cf. Prebble, 1943), that is systematic errors will arise (p. 16). When population trend is eliminated, approximately 50% of the variance of the counts of populations of the sugar cane froghopper (*Aeneolamia varia*), on sugar cane stools could be accounted for in terms of the size of the stools (Fewkes, 1961); hence more 'accurate' estimates would be obtained by taking stool size into consideration and adjusting population estimates, or by allowing for it in the analysis. This is particularly important when comparisons of froghopper numbers are being made between insecticide-treated fields; the fields are of different ages and hence with stools of different sizes. Many other examples could be given of environmental factors influencing distribution; they are commonly microclimatic in nature, e.g. soil moisture affects the distribution of the cocoons of a sawfly (Ives, 1955). Even when the environment appears uniform distribution may be systematically non-random; for examples the most dense populations of the beetle, *Tribolium*, in flour are always adjacent to the walls of the container (Cox & Smith, 1957). Covariance analyses are often helpful in such situations.

In most habitats a random sample can be selected by numbering the habitat on a grid system and using a table of random numbers; an acceptable approximation is to move a certain number of units determined by a random number along one side of a plot and then turn at right angles and move a second number of units into the plot. Such a method can be used for soil samples, crops and herbage, aquatic samples and, with some modifications, with trees (p. 16).

The studies of Howe (1963) on stored grain insects illustrate some of the problems of random sampling. The bag of grain may be selected randomly or the suction probe (p. 122) may be inserted at a random point (the depth of sampling is usually an important biological component of the variability and hence each depth band tends to be sampled separately). The quantity of grain obtained in this way is often more than can conveniently be examined for insects, and thus a subsample must be taken. Howe (1963) has compared four ways of subsampling grain and he has shown that two mechanical separators, a machine devised for the separation of fine granular fuels (Anon, 1955) and the standard apparatus for splitting grain samples for grading, and one hand method gave reliable randomized subsamples. The hand method consisted of pouring the grain over the spherical bottom of a short-necked flask upturned in a glass dish; the grain becomes more or less evenly distributed round the dish and samples of a fixed volume are scooped up radially, the dish being turned through a random angle between each scoop. Although this method was found reliable by Howe, it does depend, as he stresses, on the personal skill and avoidance of bias by the operator.

REFERENCES

ANDERSEN, F. S., 1965. The negative binomial distribution and the sampling of insect populations. *Proc. XII int. Congr. Ent.* 395.

ANON., 1955. British Instrument Industries' exhibition. *Engineering* **180** (22 July 1955). Particle sampling p. 116.

ANSCOMBE, F. J., 1948. On estimating the population of aphids in a potato field. *Ann. appl. Biol.* **35**, 567–71.

ANSCOMBE, F. J., 1949. The statistical analysis of insect counts based on the negative binomial distribution. *Biometrics* **5**, 165–73.

ANSCOMBE, F. J., 1950. Sampling theory of the negative binomial and logarithmic series distributions. *Biometrika* **37**, 358–82.

ARBOUS, A. G. and KERRICH, J. E., 1951. Accident statistics and the concept of accident-proneness. *Biometrics* **7**, 340–432.

BAILEY, N. T. J., 1959. *Statistical methods in biology.* London, 200 pp.

BANCROFT, T. A. and BRINDLEY, T. A., 1958. Methods for estimation of size of corn borer populations. *Proc. X int. Congr. Ent.* **2**, 1003–14.

BEALL, G., 1942. The transformation of data from entomological field experiments so that the analysis of variance becomes applicable. *Biometrika* **32**, 243–362.

BLACKITH, R. E., 1958. Nearest-neighbour distance measurements for the estimation of animal populations. *Ecology* **39**, 147–50.

BLACKITH, R. E., SIDDORN, J. W., WALOFF, N. and EMDEN, H. F. VAN, 1963. Mound nests of the yellow ant, *Lasius flavus* L., on water-logged pasture in Devonshire. *Ent. mon. Mag.* **99**, 48–9.

BLISS, C. I., 1958. The analysis of insect counts as negative binomial distributions. *Proc. X int. Congr. Ent.* **2**, 1015–32.

BLISS, C. I. and CALHOUN, D. W., 1954. *An outline of biometry.* New Haven.

BLISS, C. I. and FISHER, R. A., 1953. Fitting the negative binomial distribution to biological data and note on the efficient fitting of the negative binomial. *Biometrics* **9**, 176–200.

BLISS, C. I. and OWEN, A. R. G., 1958. Negative binomial distributions with a common k. *Biometrika* **45**, 37–58.

BREDER, C. M., 1954. Equations descriptive of fish schools and other animal aggregations. *Ecology* **35**, 361–70.

BRIAN, M. V., 1953. Species frequencies in random samples from animal populations. *J. anim. Ecol.* **22**, 57–64.

BROADBENT, L., 1948. Methods of recording aphid populations for use in research on potato virus diseases. *Ann. appl. Biol.* **35**, 551–66.

BROWNING, T. O., 1959. The long-tailed mealybug, *Pseudococcus adonidum* L. in South Australia. *Aust. J. Agric. Res.* **10**, 322–37.

BURRAGE, R. H. and GYRISCO, G. G., 1954. Estimates of populations and sampling variance of European chafer larvae from samples taken during the first, second and third instar. *J. econ. Ent.* **47**, 811–17.

CASSIE, R. M., 1954. Some uses of probability paper in the analysis of size frequency distributions. *Aust. J. Mar. Freshw. Res.* **5**, 513–22.

CASSIE, R. M., 1962. Frequency distribution models in the ecology of plankton and other organisms. *J. anim. Ecol.* **31**, 65–92.

CHIANG, H. C. and HODSON, A. C., 1959. Distribution of the first-generation egg masses of the European corn borer in corn fields. *J. econ. Ent.* **52**, 295–9.

CHURCH, B. M. and STRICKLAND, A. H., 1954. Sampling cabbage aphid populations on brussels sprouts. *Plant Path.* **3**, 76–80.

CLARK, P. J. and EVANS, F. C., 1954. Distance to nearest neighbor as a measure of spatial relationships in populations. *Ecology* **35**, 445–53.

COCHRAN, W. G., 1963. *Sampling techniques.* 2nd ed. New York, 413 pp.

COLE, L. C., 1946. A theory for analyzing contagiously distributed populations. *Ecology* **27**, 329–41.

CONDRASHOFF, S. F., 1964. Bionomics of the aspen leaf miner, *Phyllocnistis populiella* Cham. (Lepidoptera: Gracillariidae). *Canad. Ent.* **96**, 857–74.

CONNOLA, D. P., WATERS, W. E. and NASON, E. R., 1959. A sequential sampling plan for Red-pine sawfly *Neodiprion nanulus* Schedl. J. econ. Ent. **52**, 600–2.

CONNOLA, D. P., WATERS, W. E. and SMITH, W. E., 1957. The development and application of a sequential sampling plan for forest tent caterpillar in New York. *Bull. N.Y. St. Mus. Sci. Serv.* **366**, 22 pp.

CORNFIELD, J., 1951. The determination of sample size. *Amer. J. Pub. Health* **41**, 654–61.

COTTAM, G. and CURTIS, J. T., 1956. The use of distance measures in phytosociological sampling. *Ecology* **37**, 451–60.

COTTAM, G., CURTIS, J. T. and CATANA, A. J., 1957. Some sampling characteristics of a series of aggregated populations. *Ecology* **38**, 610–22.

COX, D. R. and SMITH, W. L., 1957. On the distribution of *Tribolium confusum* in a container. *Biometrika* **44**, 328–35.

CRAIG, C. C., 1953. On a method of estimating biological populations in the field. *Biometrika* **40**, 216–18.

DAVIS, E. G. and WADLEY, F. M., 1949. Grasshopper egg-pod distribution in the northern Great Plains and its relation to egg-survey methods. *U.S.D.A. Circ.* **816**, 16 pp.

DEAN, H. A., 1959. Quadrant distribution of mites on leaves of texas grapefruit. *J. econ. Ent.* **52**, 725–7.

DEBAUCHE, H. R., 1962. The structural analysis of animal communities of the soil. *In* Murphy, P. W. (ed.), *Progress in soil zoology*, 10–25.

DEEVEY, E. S., 1947. Life tables for natural populations of animals. *Quart. Rev. Biol.* **22**, 283–314.

DEMPSTER, J. P., 1957. The population dynamics of the Moroccan locust (*Dociostaurus maroccanus* Thunberg.) in Cyprus. *Anti-locust Bull.* **27**, 60 pp.

DYBAS, H. S. and DAVIS, D. D., 1962. A population census of seventeen-year periodical cicadas (Homoptera: Cicadidae: *Magicicada*). *Ecology* **43**, 432–44.

EDWARDS, R. L., 1962. The importance of timing in adult grasshopper surveys. *J. econ. Ent.* **55**, 263–4.

EMDEN, H. F. VAN., JEPSON, W. F. and SOUTHWOOD, T. R. E., 1961. The occurrence of a partial fourth generation of *Oscinella frit* L. (Diptera: Chloropidae) in southern England. *Ent. exp. appl.* **4**, 220–5.

EVANS, D. A., 1953. Experimental evidence concerning contagious distributions in ecology. *Biometrika* **40**, 186–211.

EVANS, F. C., CLARK, P. J. and BRAND, R. H., 1955. Estimation of the number of species present in a given area. *Ecology* **36**, 342–3.

FERGUSON, J. H. A., 1957. Some applications of binomial probability paper in genetic analyses. *Euphytica* **5**, 329–38.

FEWKES, D. W., 1961. Stool size as a factor in the sampling of sugarcane froghopper nymph populations. *J. econ. Ent.* **54**, 771–2.

FINNEY, D. J., 1941. Wireworm populations and their affect on crops. *Ann. appl. Biol.* **28**, 282–95.

FINNEY, D. J. and VARLEY, G. C., 1955. An example of the truncated Poisson distribution. *Biometrics* **11**, 387–94.

FISHER, R. A., CORBET, A. S. and WILLIAMS, C. B., 1943. The relation between the number of species and the number of individuals in a random sample of an animal population. *J. anim. Ecol.* **12**, 42–58.

FORSYTHE, H. Y. and GYRISCO, G. G., 1961. Determining the appropriate transformation of data from insect control experiments for use in the analysis of variance. *J. econ. Ent.* **54**, 859–61.

FORSYTHE, H. Y. and GYRISCO, G. G., 1963. The spatial pattern of the pea aphid in alfalfa fields. *J. econ. Ent.*, **56**, 104–7.

FRACKER, S. B. and BRISCHLE, H. A., 1944. Measuring the local distribution of *Ribes*. *Ecology* **25**, 283–303.

GAUFIN, A. R., HARRIS, E. K. and WALTER, H. J., 1956. A statistical evaluation of stream bottom sampling data obtained from three standard samples. *Ecology* **37**, 643–8.

GLEASON, H. A., 1922. On the relation between species and area. *Ecology* **3**, 158–62.

GOOD, I. J. and TOULMIN, G. H., 1956. The number of new species, and the increase in population coverage, when a sample is increased. *Biometrika* **43**, 45–63.

GOODALL, D. W., 1952. Quantitative aspects of plant distribution. *Biol. Rev.* **27**, 194–245.

GOULDEN, C. H., 1952. *Methods of statistical analysis* (2nd ed.). New York, 467 pp.

GRAHAM, K. and STARK, R. W., 1954. Insect population sampling. *Proc. ent. Soc. B.C.* **51**, 15–20.

GREIG-SMITH, P., 1964. *Quantitative plant ecology* (2nd ed.). London, 256 pp.

GRUNDY, P. M., 1952. The fitting of grouped truncated and grouped censored normal distributions. *Biometrika* **39**, 252–9.

HAIRSTON, N. G., 1959. Species abundance and community organisation. *Ecology.* **40**, 404–16.

HAIRSTON, N. G., 1964. Studies on the organization of animal communities. *J. anim. Ecol.* **33** (suppl.), 227–39.

HANDFORD, R. H., 1956. Grasshopper population sampling. *Proc. ent. Soc. B.C.* (1955) **52**, 3–7.

HANSEN, M. H., HURWITZ, W. N. and MADOW, W. G., 1953. *Sample survey methods and theory.* Vol. 1, New York.

HARCOURT, D. G., 1961a. Design of a sampling plan for studies on the population dynamics of the diamond back moth, *Plutella maculipennis* (Curt.) (Lepidoptera: Plutellidae). *Canad. Ent.* **93**, 820–31.

HARCOURT, D. G., 1961b. Spatial pattern of the imported cabbageworm, *Pieris rapae* (L.) (Lepidoptera: Pieridae), on cultivated Cruciferae. *Canad. Ent.* **93**, 945–52.

HARCOURT, D. G., 1962. Design of a sampling plan for studies on the population dynamics of the imported cabbageworm, *Pieris rapae* (L.) (Lepidoptera: Pieridae). *Canad. Ent.* **94**, (8), 849–59.

HARCOURT, D. G., 1963. Population dynamics of *Leptinotarsa decemlineata* (Say) in Eastern Ontario. I. Spatial pattern and transformation of field counts. *Canad. Ent.* **95**, 813–20.

HARCOURT, D. G., 1964. Population dynamics of *Leptinotarsa decemlineata* (Say) in Eastern Ontario. II. Population and mortality estimation during six age intervals. *Canad. Ent.* **96,** 1190–8.

HARCOURT, D. G., 1965. Spatial pattern of the cabbage looper, *Trichoplusia ni*, on Crucifers. *Ann. ent. Soc. Amer.* **58,** 89–94.

HARDING, J. P., 1949. The use of probability paper for the graphical analysis of polymodal frequency distributions. *J. mar. biol. Soc.* **28,** 141–53.

HARRIS, E. K., 1957. Further results in the statistical analysis of stream sampling. *Ecology* **38,** 463–8.

HARTLEY, H. O., 1950. The maximum F-ratio as a short-cut test for heterogeneity of variance. *Biometrika* **37,** 308–12.

HAYMAN, B. I. and LOWE, A. D., 1961. The transformation of counts of the cabbage aphid (*Brevicoryne brassicae* (L.)). *N.Z. J. Sci.* **4,** 271–8.

HEALEY, V., 1964. The density and distribution of two species of *Aptinothrips* (Thysanoptera) in the grass of a woodland. *Entomologist* **97,** 258–63.

HEALY, M. J. R., 1962. Some basic statistical techniques in soil zoology. *In* Murphy, P. W. (ed.), *Progress in soil zoology*: 3–9.

HEALY, M. J. R. and TAYLOR, L. R., 1962. Tables for power-law transformations. *Biometrika* **49,** 557–9.

HELSON, G. A. H., 1958. Aphid populations: Ecology and methods of sampling aphids *Myzus persicae* (Sulz.) and *Aulacorthum solani* (Kltb.). *N.Z. Entomologist* **2,** 20–3.

HENSON, W. R., 1954. A sampling system for Poplar insects. *Canad. J. Zool.* **32,** 421–433.

HENSON, W. R., 1961. Laboratory studies on the adult behaviour of *Conopthorus coniperda* (Schwarz) (Coleoptera: Scolytidae). II. Thigmotropic aggregation. *Ann. ent. Soc. Amer.* **54,** 810–19.

HEYWOOD, J. and EDWARDS, R. W., 1961. Some aspects of the ecology of *Potamopyrgus jenkinsi* Smith. *J. anim. Ecol.* **31,** 239–50.

HIRATA, S., 1962. Comparative studies on the population dynamics of important Lepidopterous pests on cabbage. 2. On the habits of oviposition of *Pieris rapae crucivora*, *Plusia nigrisigna* and *Manestra* (*Barathra*) *brassicae* on cabbage plants. *Jap. J. appl. Ent. Zool.* **6,** 200–7.

HOWE, R. W., 1963. The random sampling of cultures of grain weevils. *Bull. ent. Res.* **54,** 135–46.

HUDON, M. and LEROUX, E. J., 1961. Variation between samples of immature stages, and of mortalities from some factors, of the european corn borer, *Ostrinia nubilalis* (Hübner) (Lepidoptera: Pyralidae) on sweet corn in Quebec. *Canad. Ent.* **93,** 867–88.

HUGHES, R. D., 1955. The influence of the prevailing weather on the numbers of *Meromyza variegata* Meigen (Diptera, Chloropidae) caught with a sweepnet. *J. anim. Ecol.* **24,** 324–35.

HUGHES, R. D., 1962. The study of aggregated populations. *In* Murphy, P. W. (ed.), *Progress in soil zoology*, 51–5.

IBARRA, E. L., WALLWORK, J. A. and RODRIGUEZ, J. G., 1965. Ecological studies of mites found in sheep and cattle pastures. 1. Distribution patterns of Oribatid mites. *Ann. ent. Soc. Amer.* **58,** 153–9.

ITÔ, Y., GOTOH, A. and MIYASHITA, K., 1960. On the spatial distribution of *Pieris rapae crucivora* population. *Jap. J. appl. Ent. Zool.* **4,** 141–5.

ITÔ, Y., NAKAMURA, M., KONDO, M., MIYASHITA, K. and NAKAMURA, K., 1962. Population dynamics of the chestnut gall-wasp, *Dryocosmus kuriphilus* Yasumatsu (Hymenoptera: Cynipidae). II. Distribution of individuals in bud of chestnut tree. *Res. Popul. Ecol.* **4,** 35–46.

IVES, W. G. H., 1954. Sequential sampling of insect populations. *Forestry Chron.* **30,** 287–291.

IVES, W. G. H., 1955. Effect of moisture on the selection of cocooning sites by the larch sawfly, *Pristiphora erichsonii* (Hartig). *Canad. Ent.* **87**, 301–11.

IVES, W. G. H. and PRENTICE, R.M., 1958. A sequential sampling technique for surveys of the larch sawfly. *Canad. Ent.* **90**, 331–8.

IWAO, S., 1956. The relation between the distribution pattern and the population density of the large twenty-eight-spotted lady beetle, *Epilachna 28-maculata* Motschulsky, in egg-plant field. Pattern of the spatial distribution of insect 6. *Jap. J. Ecol.* **5**, 130–5.

JEPSON, W. F. and SOUTHWOOD, T. R. E., 1958. Population studies on *Oscinella frit* L. *Ann. appl. Biol.* **46**, 465–74.

KATTI, S. K. and GURLAND, J., 1962. Efficiency of certain methods of estimation for the negative binomial and the Neyman type A distributions. *Biometrika* **49**, 215–26.

KENDALL, D. G., 1948. On some modes of population growth leading to R. A. Fisher's logarithmic series distribution. *Biometrika* **35**, 6–15.

KEULS, M., OVER, H. J. and DE WIT, C. T., 1963. The distance method for estimating densities. *Statistica Neerlandica* **17**, 71–91.

KLECZKOWSKI, A., 1949. The transformation of local lesion counts for statistical analysis. *Ann. appl. Biol.* **36**, 139–52.

KONO, T., 1953. Basic unit of population observed in the distribution of the rice-stem borer, *Chilo simplex*, in a paddy field. *Res. Popul. Ecol.* **2**, 95–105.

KRAUSE, G. F. and PEDERSEN, J. R., 1960. Estimating immature populations of rice weevils in wheat by using subsamples. *J. econ. Ent.* **53**, 215–16.

KUNO, E., 1963. A comparative analysis on the distribution of nymphal populations of some leaf- and planthoppers on rice plant. *Res. Popul. Ecol.* **5**, 31–43.

LAMB, K. P., 1958. Aphid sampling. *N.Z. Entomologist* **2**, 6–11.

LEGAY, J. M., 1963. A propos de la répartition de la cecidomyie du Hêtre, *Mikiola fagi*. Un exemple de distribution binomiale négative. *Ann. Epiphyt. C* **14**, 49–56.

LEROUX, E. J., 1961. Variations between samples of fruit, and of fruit damage mainly from insect pests, on apple in Quebec. *Canad. Ent.* **93**, 680–94.

LEROUX, E. J. and REIMER, C., 1959. Variation between samples of immature stages and of mortalities from some factors, of the Eye-spotted Bud Moth, *Spilonota ocellana* (D. & S.) (Lepidoptera: Olethreutidae), and the Pistol Casebearer, *Coleophora serratella* (L.) (Lepidoptera: Coleophoridae), on apple in Quebec. *Canad. Ent.* **91**, 428–49.

LYONS, L. A., 1964. The spatial distribution of two pine sawflies and methods of sampling for the study of population dynamics. *Canad. Ent.* **96**, 1373–407.

MACLELLAN, C. R., 1962. Mortality of codling moth eggs and young larvae in an integrated control orchard. *Canad. Ent.* **94**, 655–66.

MACLEOD, J., 1958. The estimation of numbers of mobile insects from low incidence recapture data. *Trans. R. ent. Soc. Lond.* **110**, 363–92.

MILNE, A., 1959. The centric systematic area-sample treated as a random sample. *Biometrics* **15**, 270–97.

MILNE, A., 1964. Biology and ecology of the garden chafer, *Phyllopertha horticola* (L.). IX. Spatial distribution. *Bull. ent. Res.* **54**, 761–95.

MORISITA, M., 1954. Estimation of population density by spacing method. *Mem. Fac. Sci. Kyushu Univ. E* **1**, 187–97.

MORISITA, M., 1959. Measuring of the dispersion of individuals and analysis of the distributional patterns. *Mem. Fac. Sci. Kyushu Univ. E (Biol.)* **2**, 215–35.

MORISITA, M., 1962. I_δ-index, a measure of dispersion of individuals. *Res. Popul. Ecol.* **4**, 1–7.

MORISITA, M., 1964. Application of I_δ-index to sampling techniques. *Res. Popul. Ecol.* **6**, 43–53.

MORRIS, R. F., 1954. A sequential sampling technique for spruce budworm egg surveys. *Canad. J. Zool.* **32**, 302–13.

MORRIS, R. F., 1955. The development of sampling techniques for forest insect defoliators, with particular reference to the spruce budworm. *Canad. J. Zool.* **33**, 225–94.

MORRIS, R. F., 1960. Sampling insect populations. *A. Rev. Ent.* **5**, 243–64.

MORRIS, R. F. and REEKS, W. A., 1954. A larval population technique for the winter moth, *Operophtera brumata* (Linn.) (Lepidoptera: Geometridae). *Canad. Ent.* **86**, 433–8.

MOSTELLER, F. and TUKEY, J. W., 1949. The uses and usefulness of binomial probability paper. *J. Amer. Stats. Assoc.* **44**, 174–212.

NAYLOR, A. F., 1959. An experimental analysis of dispersal in the flour beetle, *Tribolium confusum. Ecology* **40**, 453–65.

NELSON, W. A., SLEN, S. B. and BANKY, E. C., 1957. Evaluation of methods of estimating populations of the sheep ked, *Melophagus ovinus* (L.) (Diptera: Hippoboscidae), on mature ewes and young Lambs. *Canad. J. Anim. Sci.* **37**, 8–13.

NEYMAN, J., 1939. On a new class of 'contagious' distributions, applicable in entomology and bacteriology. *Ann. Math. Stat.* **10**, 35–57.

NIELSEN, B. OVERGAARD, 1963. The biting midges of Lyngby Aamose (Culicoides: Ceratopogonidae). *Natura Jutlandica* **10**, 46 pp.

OAKLAND, G. B., 1950. An application of sequential analysis to whitefish sampling. *Biometrics* **6**, 59–67.

OAKLAND, G. B., 1953. Determining sample size. *Canad. Ent.* **85**, 108–13.

PARADIS, R. O. and LEROUX, E. J., 1962. A sampling technique for population and mortality factors of the fruit-tree leaf roller, *Archips argyrospilus* (Wlk.) (Lepidoptera: Tortricidae), on apple in Quebec. *Canad. Ent.* **94**, 561–73.

PEARSON, E. S. and HARTLEY, H. O., 1958. *Biometrika tables for statisticians.* Vol. 1. Cambridge, 240 pp.

PRADHAN, S. and MENON, R., 1945. Insect population studies. I. Distribution and sampling of spotted bollworm of cotton. *Proc. Nat. Inst. Sci. India* **6** (2), 61–73.

PREBBLE, M. L., 1943. Sampling methods in population studies of the European spruce sawfly, *Gilpinia hercyniae* (Hartig.), in Eastern Canada. *Trans. Roy. Soc. Canada* III, V, **37**, 93–126.

PRESTON, F. W., 1948. The commonness, and rarity, of species. *Ecology* **29**, 254–83.

PUTNAM, L. G. and SHKLOV, N., 1956. Observations on the distribution of grasshopper egg-pods in Western Canadian stubble fields. *Canad. Ent.* **88**, 110–17.

QUENOUILLE, M. H., 1949. A relation between the logarithmic, Poisson, and negative binomial series. *Biometrics* **5**, 162–4.

REEKS, W. A., 1956. Sequential sampling of the winter moth, *Operophtera brumata* (Linn.). *Canad. Ent.* **88**, 241–6.

REIMER, C., 1959. Statistical analysis of percentages based on unequal numbers, with examples from entomological research. *Canad. Ent.* **91**, 88–92.

RENNISON, B. D., 1962. A method of sampling *Antestiopsis* in arabsia coffee in chemical control schemes. *E. Afr. agric. For. J.* **27**, 197–200.

RICHARDS, O. W. and WALOFF, N., 1961. A study of a natural population of *Phytodecta olivacea* (Forster) (Coleoptera, Chrysomeloidea). *Phil. Trans. B.* **244**, 205–57.

ROJAS, B. A., 1964. La binomial negativa y la estimación de intensidad de plagas en el suelo. *Fitotecnia Latinamer.* **1** (1), 27–36.

ROMELL, L. G., 1930. Comments on Raunkiaer's and similar methods of vegetation analysis and the 'law of frequency'. *Ecology* **11**, 589–96.

SALT, G. and HOLLICK, F. S., 1946. Studies of wireworm populations. II. Spatial distribution. *J. exp. Biol.* **23**, 1–46.

SHAW, M. W., 1955. Preliminary studies on potato aphids in north and north-east Scotland. *Ann. appl. Biol.* **43**, 37–50.

SHENTON, L. R. and WALLINGTON, P. A., 1962. The bias of moment estimators with an application to the negative binomial distribution. *Biometrika* **49**, 193–204.

SHIBUYA, M. and OUCHI, Y., 1955. Pattern of spatial distribution of soy bean pod gall midge in a soy bean field. *Ôyô-Kontya* **11**, 91–7.

SHINOZAKI, K. and URATA, N., 1953. Apparent abundance of different species and heterogeneity. *Res. Popul. Ecol.* **2**, 8–21.

SHIYOMI, M. and NAKAMURA, K., 1964. Experimental studies on the distribution of the aphid counts. *Res. Popul. Ecol.* **6**, 79–87.

SKELLAM, J. G., 1952. Studies in statistical ecology. I. Spatial pattern. *Biometrika* **39**, 346–62.

SKELLAM, J. G., 1958. On the derivation and applicability of Neyman's type A distribution. *Biometrika* **45**, 32–6.

SOUTHWOOD, T. R. E. and JEPSON, W. F., 1961. The frit fly – a denizen of grassland and a pest of oats. *Ann. appl. Biol.* **49**, 556.

SOUTHWOOD, T. R. E., JEPSON, W. F. and EMDEN, H. F. VAN, 1961. Studies on the behaviour of *Oscinella frit* L. (Diptera) adults of the panicle generation. *Ent. exp. appl.* **4**, 196–210.

SPILLER, D., 1948. Truncated log-normal and root-normal frequency distributions of insect populations. *Nature Lond.* **162**, 530.

SPILLER, D., 1952. Truncated log-normal distribution of red scale (*Aonidiella aurantii* Mask.) on citrus leaves. *N.Z. J. Sci. Tech.* (*B*) **33**, 483–7.

STARK, R. W., 1952*a*. Analysis of a population sampling method for the lodgepole needle miner in Canadian Rocky Mountain Parks. *Canad. Ent.* **84**, 316–21.

STARK, R. W., 1952*b*. Sequential sampling of the lodgepole needle miner. *Forestry Chron.* **28**, 57–60.

STARK, R. W. and DAHLSTEN, D. L., 1961. Distribution of cocoons of a *Neodiprion* sawfly under open-grown conditions. *Canad. Ent.* **93**, 443–50.

STEVENS, R. E. and STARK, R. W., 1962. Sequential sampling for the lodgepole needle miner, *Evagora milleri. J. econ. Ent.* **55**, 491–4.

STRICKLAND, A. H., 1961. Sampling crop pests and their hosts. *A. Rev. Ent.* **6**, 201–20.

STUART, A., 1962. *Basic ideas of scientific sampling.* London, 99 pp.

SYLVESTER, E. S. and COX, E. L., 1961. Sequential plans for sampling aphids on sugar beets in Kern County, California. *J. econ. Ent.* **54**, 1080–5.

TAKEDA, S. and HUKUSIMA, S., 1961. Spatial distribution of the pear lace bugs, *Stephanitis naski* Esaki at Takeya (Hemiptera: Tingitidae) in an apple tree and an attempt for estimating their populations. *Res. Bull. Fac. Agric., Gifu Univ.* **14**, 68–77.

TAYLOR, L. R., 1961. Aggregation, variance and the mean. *Nature, Lond.* **189**, 732–5.

TAYLOR, L. R., 1965. A natural law for the spatial disposition of insects. *Proc. XII int. Congr. Ent.* 396–7.

TEYROVSKÝ, V., 1956. Fotopathie larey kleštánek (Corixinae). *Acta Univ. agric. silv. Brunn.* **2**, 147–77.

THOMAS, I. and JACOB, F. H., 1943. Ecology of potato aphids in north Wales. *Ann. appl. Biol.* **30**, 97–101.

THOMAS, M., 1949. A generalization of Poisson's binomial limit for use in ecology. *Biometrika* **36**, 18–25.

THOMPSON, H. R., 1956. Distribution of distance to *n*th neighbour in a population of randomly distributed individuals. *Ecology* **37**, 391–4.

TUKEY, J. W., 1949. One degree of freedom for non-additivity. *Biometrics* **5**, 232–42.

TUNSTALL, J. P. and MATTHEWS, G. A., 1961. Cotton insect control recommendations for 1961-2 in the Federation of Rhodesia and Nyasaland. *Rhodesia Agric. J.* **58** (5), 289–99.

TURNER, F. B., 1960. Size and dispersion of a Louisiana population of the cricket frog, *Acris gryllus. Ecology* **41**, 258–68.

UNTERSTENHÖFER, G., 1957. The basic principles of plant protection field tests. *Höfchen-Briefe* **10** (4) (English ed.), 173–236.

UPHOLT, W. M. and CRAIG, R., 1940. A note on the frequency distribution of black scale insects. *J. econ. Ent.* **33** (1), 113–14.

WADLEY, F. M., 1950. Notes on the form of distribution of insect and plant populations. *Ann. ent. Soc. Amer.* **43**, 581–6.

WADLEY, F. M., 1952. Elementary sampling principles in entomology. *U.S.D.A. Pl. Quar. Bur. Ent. E.T.* **302**, 17 pp.

WALD, A., 1948. *Sequential sampling*. New York.

WALOFF, N. and BLACKITH, R. E., 1962. The growth and distribution of the mounds of *Lasius flavus* (Fabricius) (Hym.: Formicidae) in Silwood Park, Berkshire. *J. anim. Ecol.* **31**, 421–37.

WATERS, W. E., 1955. Sequential sampling in forest insect surveys. *For. Sci.* **1**, 68–79.

WATERS, W. E., 1959. A quantitative measure of aggregation in insects. *J. econ. Ent.* **52**, 1180–4.

WATERS, W. E. and HENSON, W. R., 1959. Some sampling attributes of the negative binomial distribution with special reference to forest insects. *For. Sci.* **5** (4), 397–412.

WATT, A. S., 1964. The community and the individual. *J. Ecol.* **52** (suppl.), 203–11.

WILSON, L. F., 1959. Branch 'tip' sampling for determining abundance of spruce budworm egg masses. *J. econ. Ent.* **52**, 618–21.

YATES, F., 1953. *Sampling methods for censuses and surveys*. London.

YATES, F. and FINNEY, D. J., 1942. Statistical problems in field sampling for wireworms. *Ann. appl. Biol.* **29**, 156–67.

YOSHIHARA, T., 1953. On the distribution of *Tectarius granularis*. *Res. Popul. Ecol.* **2**, 112–22.

CHAPTER 3

Absolute Population Estimates
using Marking Techniques

Studying plaice and waterfowl populations respectively, Petersen and Lincoln independently developed a marking method from which the total population may be estimated (Le Cren, 1965). This was based on the principle that if a proportion of the population was marked in some way, returned to the original population and then, after complete mixing, a second sample was taken, the number of marked individuals in the second sample would have the same ratio to the total numbers in the second sample as the total of marked individuals originally released would have to the total population. As the first three quantities were known the latter could easily be calculated. This method has been extensively developed and provides the major alternative absolute method to those based on the count of animals within a fixed unit of the habitat; it has the advantage that its accuracy does not depend on an assessment of the number of sampling units in the habitat and, as has already been stressed (chapter 1), it is a wise practice to use more than one method simultaneously. There are also certain other methods of estimating a population that depend on the presence of marked individuals, but use a different principle to the Lincoln Index.

A basic prerequisite to the use of these methods of population estimation is a technique for marking the animals so that they can be released unharmed and unaffected into the wild and recognized again on recapture. Such techniques may also be used in studies on behaviour, e.g. dispersal, longevity and growth; but for convenience all aspects of marking insects and other invertebrates will be discussed here.

METHODS OF MARKING ANIMALS

A fundamental requirement of any marking technique is that it shall not affect the longevity or behaviour of the animals. An attempt should always be made to confirm that this is true in the particular case under investigation because, for example, although the pigments used in most markers may be non-toxic, the solvents are often toxic. This may be checked in the laboratory by keeping samples of living marked and unmarked individuals and comparing longevity (e.g. Pal, 1947) or in the field by comparing the longevity of individuals bearing differing numbers of marks (e.g. Richards & Waloff, 1954; Dobson &

Morris, 1961). Newly emerged insects may be more sensitive to the toxic substances used in markers than older insects (Jackson, 1948; Dobson, Stephenson & Lofty, 1958) and the attachment of labels to their wings, which has no effect on old insects, may cause distortion due to interference with the blood circulation (Waloff, 1963).

It should also be borne in mind that the presence of conspicuous marks may well destroy an animal's natural camouflage and make it more liable or, as Hartley (1954) observed with marked snails, less liable to predation. This effect is difficult to assess; it can to some extent be avoided by marking in inconspicuous places or by the use of fluorescent powders (Pal, 1947), dyes in powder form (Quarterman, Mathis & Kilpatrick, 1954), phenolphthalein solution (Peffly & Labrecque, 1956) or radioactive tracers whose presence is only detectable by the use of a special technique after recapture. The effect on predation of a conspicuous, but convenient, marking method could be measured by marking further individuals with one of these invisible methods and comparing longevity.

Another aspect of the conspicuous mark is that, where the animals are sampled by a method that relies on the sight of the collector, then the marked individuals may tend to be collected more than unmarked ones (Edwards, 1958).

A third problem concerns the durability of the mark; some paints, particularly cellulose lacquers, may flake off leaving the animal apparently unmarked; student's oil paints and powdered dyes may wash off; some fluorescent powders may lose this property on exposure to sunlight (Polivka, 1949) and a radioactive isotope could decay and/or be excreted by the animal. Immature animals will lose marks on their cuticle when they moult. Laboratory tests of durability are not always reliable; Blinn (1963) found that cellulose lacquers would remain on the shells of land snails for two years in the laboratory, but they only lasted about one in the field, and the rate at which a radioactive isotope is lost may depend upon the animal's diet (p. 69) and other factors (p. 362).

The handling and release of marked individuals may also affect their subsequent life expectancy and behaviour; these problems are discussed below.

The amount of effort that can be put into a marking programme (i.e. its cost) will be related to the percentage of recoveries that can be expected; a high cost per individual marked will be justified where the recovery rate is high.

Group marking methods

These methods enable a large number of animals to be marked in the same way and are perfectly adequate for most capture–recapture population estimations and in dispersal studies. Almost all the methods are capable of one or two variants so that two or three groups may be marked differently, and thus the distinction made by Dobson (1962) between group methods and common marking methods in which all individuals are marked in the same way is not followed. Marking methods have recently been reviewed by Dobson (1962) and by Gangwere, Chavin & Evans (1964), who give further references.

1. Paints and solutions of dyes

a. Materials

Artist's oil paint is perhaps the most extensively used marking material; it can, of course, be obtained in a variety of colours and has been used successfully for marking moths (Collins & Potts, 1932), tsetse flies (Scott, 1931; Jackson, 1933*b*), bed bugs (Mellanby, 1939), locusts and grasshoppers (Richards, 1953; Richards & Waloff, 1954), mirids (Muir, 1958), flies (Cragg & Hobart, 1955; Dobson, Stephenson & Lofty, 1958), beetles (Mitchell, 1963) and others. However, Davey (1956) found them toxic to certain locusts, although this may have been the effect of the dilutant and they are, of course, slow drying. Artist's poster paints have been used to mark mosquitoes (Gillies, 1961).

Nitrocellulose lacquers or paints (e.g. model aircraft dope) are quick drying and have been used by a number of workers; on snails, where they were applied to a small area on the underside of the shell, from which the periostracum had been scraped (Sheppard, 1951), and on grasshoppers (Richard & Waloff, 1954; Clark, 1962), although the first-named authors found them less satisfactory than artist's oil paints. They have also been applied to ants (Holt, 1955), lace bugs (Southwood & Scudder, 1956), dragonflies (Corbet, 1952; Pajunen, 1962), mites (Hunter, 1960), tipulid flies (Freeman, 1964) and carabid beetles (Greenslade, 1964). Fluorescent lacquer enamels (e.g. 'Glo-craft' or 'Dayglo') or fluorescent pigments with gum arabic glue plus a trace of detergent have been used to mark tsetse flies (Jewell, 1956, 1958; McDonald, 1960), chafer beetles (Evans & Gyrisco, 1960) and lepidopterous caterpillars (Wood, 1963). Animals marked in these ways may be spotted after dark in the field at distances of up to 25–30 ft (8–10 m) by the use of a beam of ultraviolet light; such a beam may be produced by a battery-powered lamp (McDonald, 1960).

Reflecting paints may also be used to mark animals for detection at night and have the advantage that they can be seen with a small (12-V) hand torch for up to 30 ft (10 m); Rennison, Lumsden & Webb (1958) used this method with tsetse flies and found that a mixture of the minute glass beads in a thin varnish of shellac or in a gum solution with a trace of detergent was preferable to the commercial aerosol form of the paint (e.g. Codit, 7211, reflecting paint). Aluminium paint was found to adhere well to scraped areas of the elytra of carabid beetles (Murdoch, 1963).

Aniline dyes dissolved in a mixture of alcohol and shellac or in alcohol alone have been used, respectively, to mark cucumber beetles, *Diabrotica* (Dudley & Searles, 1923) and gypsy moths, *Lymantria* (Collins & Potts, 1932).

Solutions of various stains in alcohol, such as eosin, orange G and Congo red, have been used to mark adult Lepidoptera (Meder, 1926; Yetter & Steiner, 1932; Leeuwen, 1940; Nielsen, 1961) and of fluorescent dyes, principally rhodamine B, to mark mosquitoes (Chang, 1946) and *Drosophila* (Wave, Henneberry & Mason, 1963). Working on house flies Peffly & Labrecque (1956) used a 6% solution of phenolphthalein in acetone; the marked flies were identified on recapture by placing them in 1% sodium hydroxide solution, whereupon they became purple. Fales *et al.* (1964) used waterproof inks to mark face flies.

b. Application

When the paints or solutions are in their most concentrated form they are most conveniently applied by the use of an entomological pin, a sharpened match-stick, a single hair, or even a fine dry grass stem (Jackson, 1933*b*; Mellanby, 1939; Corbet, 1952; Muir, 1958; Hunter, 1960). With quick-drying cellulose lacquer it may be necessary to dilute them slightly with acetone or another solvent; if this is not done a fine skin may form over the droplet on the pin and it will not adhere firmly to the animal. With artist's oil paints, dyes in solution or diluted lacquers a camel-hair brush may be used (Dudley & Searles, 1923; Wood, 1963), although generally this method has no advantage over the use of a pin and frequently leads to the application of too large a mark. If the mark covers any of the sense organs or joints the specimen will have to be discarded. Freeman (1964) found a fine syringe was suitable for applying cellulose lacquers to tipulid flies.

The paints or solutions may be further diluted with acetone, dilute alcohol or other solvents and sprayed on. This may be done with a hand atomizer (e.g. a nasal spray) while the insects are contained in a small wire cage (Dudley & Searles, 1923; Leeuwen, 1940; Davey & O'Rourke, 1951; Evans & Gyrisco, 1960); mortality during marking by this method can be reduced if, immediately after spraying, the insects are quickly dried in the draught from an electric fan (Yetter & Steiner, 1932; Leeuwen, 1940). This technique has been extended to field marking of locusts (Davey, 1956) and butterflies (Nielsen, 1961) by the use of a spray gun and an oil can (e.g. 'Plews Oiler') respectively; it was found that individuals could be marked at a distance of 15 feet (5 m) or more. Davey showed that for the same cost (labour and time) nearly ten times as many locusts could be marked by this method than by that involving the capture and handling of each individual, and Davey & O'Rourke (1951) found that handling itself could have fatal effects on tabanid flies, *Chrysops*.

2. Dyes and fluorescent substances in powder form

Hairy insects may be marked by dusting them with various dyes in powder form; this is most easily done by applying the dusts from a powder dispenser or by producing a dust storm in a cage with a jet of air. An apparatus that could be used for this purpose is described by Dunn & Mechalas (1963). Only a very small quantity of powder is necessary.

Non-fluorescent dyes that have been found useful are the rotor and waxoline group. The marked insects are recognized by laying them on a piece of white filter paper and dropping acetone on to them, when a coloured spot or ring forms beneath those that have been marked. As the testing involves the killing of insects this method is not suitable for extensive recapture work, and laboratory tests showed that with blowflies the mark may only last for one week and seldom for more than two (MacLeod & Donnelly, 1957). However, dyes of two different colours may be applied to the same insect and distinguished in the spotting. This method has been used for calypterate flies by Schoof & Mail (1953), Quarterman, Mathis & Kilpatrick (1954) and Mac-Leod & Donnelly (1957) and for the frit fly (*Oscinella frit*) (Southwood & Jepson, unpublished) and various mirids (J. P. Dempster, unpublished). It is possible that under certain circumstances it could be used for marking large aggregated populations in the field.

Fluorescent substances (e.g. zinc sulphide powders, 'Helecon'), whose presence is detected by placing the animals under an UV lamp, have also been used extensively for marking (Zukel, 1945; Pal, 1947; Polivka, 1949; Taft & Agee, 1962). Lists of the various materials that may be used are given by Staniland (1959) and Bailey, Eliason & Iltis (1962). They may be applied directly, but better adhesion can be obtained by mixing one part of the dye with six parts of gum arabic, adding water until a paste is formed, then drying the paste and pulverizing it in a mortar. This powder is applied to the insects which are then placed in a high humidity; the gum arabic particles absorb sufficient moisture to make them adhere to the insect. This method has been used for marking mosquitoes by Reeves, Brookman & Hammon (1948). The movements of foraging bees have been studied by marking them with a fluorescent powder as they leave the hive; this is conveniently done by forcing them to walk between two strips of velveteen liberally dusted with the marker (Smith & Townsend, 1951). Bees have also been marked when visiting flowers by dusting these with a mixture of the fluorescent powder and a carrier such as talc or lycopodium dust. The bees leave a trail of powder, which can be detected after dark with an UV lamp, on the other flowers they have visited (Musgrave, 1949, 1950; Smith, 1958; Johansson, 1959). Fluorescein and rhodamine B have been found useful in this work; all the bees leaving the hive are marked and the marks last for weeks (Smith & Townsend, 1951). The possibility that unmarked individuals may bear a few particles that will fluoresce under UV light should be remembered when using these markers. Wild caught mosquitoes have been found with fluorescent blue, purple, green, white, yellow and orange spots (Reeves *et al.*, 1948), therefore the use of rhodamine B, which fluoresces red, was recommended.

An ingenious self-marking method for newly emerged calypterate flies has been devised by Norris (1957). The principle is that the soil which contains the fly puparia is covered with a mixture of fine sand and fluorescent dust and as the flies emerge a small quantity of the dust adheres to the ptilinum; and when after emergence the ptilinum is retracted the dust becomes lodged in the ptilinal suture, therefore on examination of the faces of such marked flies in UV light this suture will be seen to shine vividly. Although developed for laboratory marking this method might be extended to the field. The only fluorescent powders that Norris found satisfactory were 'Lumogen' L Yellow Orange, 'Lumogen' L Light Yellow and 'Lumogen' L White (manufactured by Badische Anilin und Sodafabrik A.G., Germany). MacLeod & Donnelly (1957) also obtained satisfactory results using commercial anthracene ground up with fine silver sand, but the present author has been unable to repeat this.

3. Labels
Bands and rings are used extensively in work on birds and mammals (Cottam, 1956; Taber, 1956), but the small size of most insects usually precludes these convenient methods. Butterflies and locusts have, however, been marked by attaching small labels with a word or a code written in waterproof black ink to part of their wings; in the Lepidoptera the area should first be denuded of scales. Earlier workers used paper or cellophane stuck on with an adhesive, such as 'Durofix', but recently 'Sellotape' has been found satisfactory (Fletcher, 1936; Williams *et al.*, 1942; Urquart, 1958; Wojtusiak, 1958; Roer, 1959, 1962; Waloff, 1963). Klock, Pimentel & Stenburg (1953) devised a machine that glued lengths of coloured thread to anaesthetized flies. It is possible that large-bodied insects might be tagged internally using the methods of fishery workers (Lindroth, 1953).

4. Mutilation
This method is also more widely used with vertebrates, especially fish, amphibians and reptiles (Ricker, 1956; Woodbury, 1956), than with the smaller insects, for a mark in order to be easily visible may be proportionally so large as to affect the insect's behaviour. Lepidoptera have been marked by clipping their wings (Querci, 1936), carabid beetles by damaging their elytra in various ways: incising the edges (Grüm, 1959), punching or burning small holes (Skuhravý, 1957; Schjøtz-Christensen, 1961) or by scraping away the surface of the elytra between certain striae (Murdoch, 1963); the latter method can be used with large chrysomelids (Southwood, unpublished). Crabs have been marked by cutting some of the teeth on the carapace (Edwards, 1958) and orthopteroids by notching the pronotum and amputating tegmina (Gangwere *et al.*, 1964).

5. Marking internally by injection
If the tissues of the animal can be marked in some way this has the great advantage with an arthropod that the mark is not lost during moulting. It has been found possible to mark crayfish by injecting a small amount of 'Bates

numbering machine ink' into the venter of the abdomen; the black, blue and red inks were found to be non-poisonous (Slack, 1955; Black, 1963). This method might be applied to other large arthropods that have an area of almost transparent cuticle. Attempts have been made to mark adult mosquitoes by feeding the larvae with dyes; these have mostly been unsatisfactory, often leading to high mortalities (Weathersbee & Hasell, 1938; Chang, 1946; Reeves *et al.*, 1948; Bailey *et al.*, 1962).

6. Marking by feeding with dyes

In laboratory studies insects are sometimes fed on a food containing a dye so that the faeces (frass) or vomit become marked (e.g. Arevad & Mourier, 1963). This approach can be extended into the field, by exposing white papers in the resting sites (Bailey *et al.*, 1962), but to detect the dye the animals often have to be crushed. South (1965) marked slugs by feeding them on agar jelly containing 0·2% neutral red; the digestive gland became deeply stained and the colour was easily visible through the foot. Various mosquitoes have been marked by feeding them on a 0·01% solution of rhodamine B in a sugar solution (Reeves *et al.*, 1948); the same dye has also been used to stain the gut of *Drosophila* (Wave *et al.*, 1963). House flies have been marked with thiorescin (Shura-Bura & Grageau, 1956) and fluorescein (Zaidenov, 1960). In some cases only a small proportion of the insects could be induced to feed on the solution and, in general, the application of the dust externally has been found more satisfactory. Bloodsucking Diptera have been marked by allowing them to feed on a cow which had had 200 ml of an aqueous solution, containing 4 g of trypan blue, intravenously administered over 20 minutes. The dyestuff can be detected by a paper chromatographic technique, in which the gut contents of the fly is mixed with 0·1 N sodium hydroxide solution and applied to a narrow strip of Whatman No. 1 chromatographic filter paper, which is developed in 0·1 N sodium hydroxide solution; the trypan blue remains at the origin, other marks due to the gut contents move away (Knight & Southon, 1963). Haematophagous animals may also be marked with specific agglutinins (Cunningham, Harley & Grainge, 1963).

7. Genes, mutant and normal

Dispersal may be studied by the use of mutant genes (Peer, 1957) or when various genotypes are clearly distinct, by their different proportions in adjacent colonies (e.g. Sheppard, 1951; Richards & Waloff, 1954; Goodhart, 1962); however, it should be remembered that selection may operate differentially in the different colonies, perhaps on young stages before the genotype becomes identifiable. Different sexes and age classes also provide naturally marked groups.

8. Radioactive isotopes

It is impossible to provide a full bibliography for this comparatively new, but extensively used, method; one is however given by Anon. (1963) and many papers are listed in reviews by Jenkins & Hassett (1950), Lindquist (1952), Hinton (1954), Pendleton (1956), Dahms (1957) and Jenkins (1963), and recent Russian work by Anon. (1961) and by Andreev (1963).

The radioactive isotopes of elements are unstable and they disintegrate emitting radiations and forming other, usually non-radioactive, isotopes; the rate of disintegration is characteristic for each isotope and is described in terms of its half-life. Of the three types of radiation entitled, alpha, beta and gamma, the isotopes used in ecological work produce only the two last named. Beta particles have less power of penetration than gamma rays; however, the actual energies (expressed as MeV = million electron volts) of the radiations differ for the different isotopes. Radioactivity is measured in units of curies (1 curie = 3.7×10^{10} disintegrations/second) and the actual mass of chemical element constituting one curie will vary depending on the half-life of the iso- tope. The specific activity of any material or solution gives the relationship of the amount of radio-isotope to the total element content and is expressed in terms such as c/g. In biological work smaller units are usually required and these are: millicurie (mc) = 10^{-3}c and microcurie (μc) = 10^{-6}c. Further basic information on isotopes may be found in textbooks, e.g. Comar (1955), Fran- cis, Mulligan & Wormall (1959), Faires & Parks (1958), O'Brien & Wolfe (1964), or in tables, e.g. Hollander, Perlman & Seaborg (1953). Table 4 gives the characters of the principal isotopes used in entomological work. The use of isotopes in ecology is by no means confined to marking; they may also be used in studies on predation and energy flow (see chapters 9 and 14). Great care should be exercised in all work with radioactive isotopes and precautions taken not to contaminate the environment (and the operators!).

Table 4. Some characters of the principal isotopes used in ecological research
(* used as labels)

Isotope	Symbol	Half-life (approximate)	Radiations and energies (MeV) Beta (maximum)	Gamma
Carbon-14	C	5760 years	0·16	
*Cobalt-60	Co	5·27 years	0·31	1·2
*Zinc-65	Zn	245 days	0·33	1·1
*Gold-195	Au	185 days		0·1
Calcium-45	Ca	165 days	0·25	
*Tantalum-182	Ta	115 days	0·51	range, max. 1·2
Sulphur-35	S	87 days	0·17	
*Scandium-46	Sc	84 days	0·36	0·89
Strontium-89	Sr	55 days	1·50	
Iron-59	Fe	45 days	0·46	1·2
Phosphorus-32	P	14·2 days	1·71	
Iodine-131	I	8 days	0·61	0·36

There are basically two methods of marking animals with isotopes, although the dividing line is not sharp. The isotopes may be used as a label outside the animal or alternatively they may be fed to the animal and incorporated in its tissues. Which method and which isotope will depend on the precise nature of the work. If it is desired to trace the animal's movements, in the soil or in wood, or to locate it from a distance, then it is the penetrating gamma radiations that will have to be detected.

If the object is to mark part of the population in a way that can be recognized after the animal has been recaptured, then a wider range of isotopes are available, including those of carbon, calcium, phosphorus and sulphur, which, if fed to the animal, are readily incorporated into its tissues. This marking method is preferable to the use of radioactive labels and, indeed, to many other marking methods in that animals can be tagged with the minimum amount of manipulation and the mark is invisible to predators. It is also almost unique (see above) as the mark will not be shed when the insect moults; this character gives the method great potential for the estimation of population size and mortality in immature stages (Cook & Kettlewell, 1960). It is necessary, however, to choose an isotope (e.g. sulphur) with a reasonably long half-life (unless the insect's life-cycle is very short) and to carry out laboratory tests on the extent to which the radioactive isotope atoms are excreted by the animal and replaced by normal ones (see below and p. 361).

Two situations where the incorporation of the isotope into the animal is not possible or desirable as a marking method are where populations of social insects are being estimated (Odum & Pontin; 1961) and where the stage that is to be marked is non-feeding or a specialized feeder and for some reason (e.g. length of life-cycle in relation to half-life of the isotope) it is not practical to activate an earlier stage.

a. Labels

Radioactive cobalt (Co^{60}) and tantalum (Ta^{182}) are the most convenient sources of gamma radiation for labelling. If cobalt wire is used it needs to be protected from corrosion by gold plating (Fredericksen & Lilly, 1955); alternatively if in the form of the nitrate it can be made up with a water-resistant resin glue (e.g. 'Bond Fast') at a strength of about 1·6 mc/ml and applied to the surface of the insect (Sullivan, 1953; Green, Baldwin & Sullivan, 1957). Minute labels (about 0·05 mm × 0·16 × 0·23–0·46 mm) of metallic tantalum have been used to mark coccinellid larvae and pentatomoid bugs, being attached by seccotine glue or cellulose paint (Banks, 1955; Banks, Brown & Dezfulian, 1961). The initial specific activity of the tantalum labels used by Banks *et al.* on the bugs was about 8μc; with the much smaller young coccinellid larva, labels with an average activity of 7·5 μc produced marked adverse effects and those used in the field work had a lower specific activity (1·3 μc). Workers using cobalt have applied labels with much higher specific activities, and Sullivan (1961) has shown that if this is greater than 50 μc the survival of the weevil, *Pissodes strobi*, is affected; this does not, however, become apparent for several months. But I am doubtful of the validity of the implied claim of some workers that, if the dosage is just small enough for the mortality to be negligible, then the animals' behaviour is normal. The problem of tagging and maximum total radiation dose is discussed fully by Griffin (1952); for the ecologist it is a good principle to use the minimum radiation dose consistent with detection.

Submerging the animals in a solution containing the radioactive isotope is another method that may be classified as labelling, although it is possible that a small amount of the isotope could become incorporated in the tissues. This method was first developed by Roth & Hoffman (1952), who marked house flies, wasps, leafhoppers, grasshoppers and coleoptera by dipping them for one minute into a solution containing P^{32} at the concentration of 5 μc/ml together with a wetting agent. The marker did not penetrate the body of the animal, yet it could be removed only by prolonged washing. Large numbers of insects may be marked quickly by this technique and it has frequently been used; some examples are:

Animal	Isotope	Strength of solution applied	Authors
Boll weevil, *Anthonomus*	Co^{60}	0·5 μc/ml	Babers *et al.*, 1954
Bug, *Eurygaster*	Co^{60}	12 mc/ml	Rakitin, 1963
Pine weevil, *Pissodes*	Sc^{46}	*c.* 7·5 mc/ml	Godwin *et al.*, 1957
Ant, *Lasius*	P^{32}	*c.* 1 μc/ml	Odum & Pontin, 1961
Tick, *Amblyomma*	P^{32}	10 μc/ml	Knapp *et al.*, 1956

The strengths of the solutions applied varied greatly; it is possible that in some instances activity levels well above the minimum necessary were used. Roth & Hoffman found that the isotopes on their insects could be detected for about eighteen days and Godwin *et al.* could recognize their marked weevils for five months; the difference largely stemming from the half-lives of the isotopes. The marking can conveniently be done in a covered funnel, with a constricted neck or straining plate to prevent the insects being washed out (Davis & Nagel, 1956; Knapp *et al.*, 1956). More delicate animals cannot be marked by this method and because of the 'violence' involved it is doubtful if it should be used even with robust species where an alternative technique is available.

A few instances are recorded of marking insects by spraying them with radioactive isotopes; this is, however, extremely hazardous for the operator and cannot be recommended.

b. Incorporation in tissues

Some of the advantages of this method have been alluded to above. The natural food of either the larva or the adult may be made radioactive or, more conveniently, the animal is offered a sugar solution containing the isotope – a large number of species of animal will take up fluid from such solutions. The actual distribution of the isotope in the body will depend on the distribution of the appropriate element and not on the method of feeding (cf. Hoffman, Lindquist & Butts, 1951).

Plants may be made radioactive in a variety of ways (Sudia & Linck, 1963; Wiegert & Lindeborg, 1964); one of the simplest is to grow them in a culture solution containing an isotope. All the parts of a large coniferous tree, including the pollen, may be tagged by introducing P^{32} into the branches and trunk (Graham, 1957). Examples of phytophagous insects that have been marked through their host plant are turnip fly with P^{32} (Oughton, 1951), plum weevil with P^{32} and Sr^{89} (Rings & Layne, 1953), mealy bugs with P^{32} (Cornwell, 1955, 1956), lepidopterous larvae with S^{35} (Cook & Kettlewell, 1960), a pentatomoid, *Eurygaster*, with P^{32} (Quraishi, 1963a and b) and a mirid, *Orthotylus*, with P^{32} (Lewis and Waloff, 1964). The specific activity of the solution depends on the method of detection it is planned to use (see below), on the isotope, on the animal and on the plant. For example, with P^{32} Cornwell (1956) used 15–43 μc/ml where the marked mealy bugs were detected by a Geiger counter, and Lewis & Waloff (1964) 5 μc/ml where the marked mirid bugs were detected by autoradiography. Hubbell *et al.* (1965) found that the quantity of radio-isotope assimilated from a food source would vary under different conditions (see p. 362).

Bloodsucking animals may be marked through their hosts (normally the isotope is injected interperitoneally into the host); this method has been used for example for mosquitoes marked with P^{32} (Yates, Gjullin & Lindquist, 1951), ticks marked with C^{14} (Babenko, 1960), fleas with P^{32} and Sr^{89} (Shura-Bura & Kharlamov *in* Anon., 1961) and blackflies with P^{32} (Bennett, 1963).

Aquatic larvae and the resulting adults become marked if reared in solutions containing isotopes (e.g. the experiments with mosquitoes and blackflies by Bugher & Taylor, 1949; Fredeen *et al.*, 1953; Gillies, 1961; Shemanchuk, Spinks & Fredeen, 1953). The effects of various specific activity levels in the rearing solutions have been investigated by Abdel-Malek (1961), who found with *Culex* that above 1·0 μc/ml of P^{32} the rate of development was affected, and by Baldwin *et al.* (1955) and James (1961), who have used solutions with strengths of 0·1 μc/ml or less. The addition of isotope to arctic pools in which mosquitoes were breeding is recorded by Jenkins (1949), but in most habitats the contamination resulting from such a method would be quite unacceptable.

The incorporation of an isotope in an artificial food, bait or 'drinking water' is a technique that has been widely used (Jensen & Fay, 1951; Radeleff *et al.*, 1952; Schoof *et al.*, 1952; Macleod & Donnelly, 1957; Baldwin *et al.*, 1958; Barnes, 1959; Dow, 1959; Khudadov, 1959a; Shura-Bura *et al.*, 1962;

Eddy *et al.*, 1962; Pelekassis *et al.*, 1962; Fay *et al.*, 1963; Orphanidis *et al.*, 1963).

A convenient method for the mass marking of large numbers of small delicate insects has recently been developed by Lewis & Waloff (1964) for the mirid, *Orthotylus*, and has been used extensively with small Diptera, *Oscinella* and *Drosophila* (Southwood, unpublished); it would seem to be of very wide application. The basic principle is that the insects drink an isotope containing sugar solution which is presented to them on a piece of saturated lens paper in a polystyrene Petri dish (fig. 14). This has three metal studs (rivets) stuck to the base for legs, and holes are made in the upper and lower portions with a hot metal tube. A plastic stopper fits into the top hole and the lower one is covered with gauze (stuck on with acetone or a similar solvent).

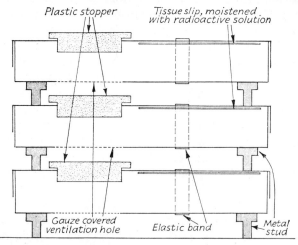

Fig. 14. Stacked polystyrene dishes modified for the presentation of radioactive solutions to small insects (after Lewis & Waloff, 1964).

Most small insects soon die in the laboratory from desiccation and, as marking takes about 24 hours, the dishes are stacked under bell-jars whose atmosphere is kept humid by a tube of an appropriate glycerine solution with a filter-paper wick (Johnson, 1940); 10% solution was used in this work giving 98% R.H.

The procedure is as follows: the lens tissue paper slip is placed on the lid and moistened with the radioactive solution (about 0·2 ml) which should also contain the appropriate quantity (i.e. 10% in the work mentioned above) of glycerine; the paper will then adhere to the lid by surface tension. The two halves of the dish should then be put together and held by an elastic band. A known number of insects (50–100) can then be tipped straight from a specimen tube in which they have been collected into the dish through the hole in the lid and the plastic stopper inserted. The dishes are then stacked under a bell-jar; after about a day they may be taken into the field at an appropriate time (see below) and released by removing the lids.

When working with very low concentrations of an isotope a significant proportion of the ions will become adsorbed on to the fibres of the lens tissue paper and become unavailable to the insects (Lewis & Waloff, 1964). This can be overcome by raising the concentration of non-radioactive ions, i.e. of the 'carrier', normally an orthophosphate or sulphate, so that the final concentration of this salt in the solutions applied to the dishes was not less than 0·1%. This is conveniently done by diluting the stock isotope solution with an omnibus, 5% sugar, 0·1% carrier and 10% glycerine solution. The specific activity of the P^{32} solution used by Lewis & Waloff (1964) was 0·5 μc/ml. Because of the low energy of S^{35} radiations higher concentrations of this isotope must be used; Lewis & Waloff found a specific activity of 20 μc/ml adequate.

c. Detection

There are two simple methods of detection adequate for mark and recapture studies: by a Geiger–Müller tube and by autoradiography. The former is indicated if the animal is to be traced in the field (e.g. Godfrey, 1954); the latter demands that the animals be recaptured and killed, but has the advantage that very low levels of radioactivity can be used for marking so one can discount the possibility that, although the animal may appear normal, its behaviour is affected by the radiations.

The most convenient autoradiographic method for small insects is to stick them between two strips of 'Sellotape'* (Gillies, 1958); these should be labelled. They may, if necessary, be examined under the microscope and retained for permanent reference. However, in the first place the strips must be applied to the surface of an X-ray film (e.g.'Kodirex', 'Ilfrex'); the exposure time will vary with specific activity of the insects and the speed of the film; it is usually between 2 and 10 days. The matching of the Sellotape strip to the subsequent print, and hence the recognition of the actual insects that were marked, will be facilitated if the exact position of the strip during exposure is recorded on the film by, for example, pin scratches marking the outline of the corners or by the use of a radioactive ink on the strip. Gardiner (1963) gives the following formula for such an ink: 1 mc promethium-147 (half-life 2·6 years) in 0·25 ml N hydrochloric acid, diluted with 1·5 ml water and add N ammonia solution until solution neutral to phenol red; add drop by drop mixing continuously to 56 ml 'Mandarin' indian ink (Windsor & Newton Ltd). Autoradiographic methods have been used by Gillies (1958, 1961), Khudadov (1959b), Abdel-Malek & Abdel-Wahab (1961a) and Lewis & Waloff (1964) and are discussed in general by Fitzgerald (1958).

The length of time a radioactively marked animal remains detectable will depend on the initial dose and on the effective half-life; the latter is the

* A transparent adhesive tape – 'Scotch tape' is similar.

resultant of the half-life of the isotope and the rate of replacement of the isotope atoms in the tissues by inactive ones, i.e. on the biological half-life. Jensen & Fay (1951) found with various calypterate flies marked with P^{32} that the rate of replacement was much faster when they were fed on a diet rich in phosphorus (milk) than if on one poor in this element (honey solution). If maintained on sugar after feeding on solutions containing 25–400 $\mu c/ml$ P^{32}, eye gnats, *Hippelates*, remained detectable by a Geiger counter for just over fifteen days (Dow, 1959); Jensen & Fay's results were similar. Autoradiography, of course, will detect lower levels, and Gillies (1961) records that *Anopheles* marked with P^{32} as larvae were readily detectable eight weeks after emerging as adults. In two acridids (*Schistocerca* and *Anacridium*) it was two weeks before P^{32} was accumulated in the brain and the gonads, but the rate of disappearance from the gut was very different in the two species (Abdel-Malek & Abdel-Wahab, 1961*b*). McAllan & Neilson (1965) found that, even after a six-day exposure to feeding pads containing Sr^{89}, different individuals took up different amounts of the isotope; therefore the detection time was determined by the individuals that ingested and assimilated the least quantity of isotope. Although any particular insect should be tested, present evidence would suggest that P^{32} will remain detectable for at least two to three weeks (Anon., 1961; Bennett, 1963) and S^{35} considerably longer (Kettlewell, 1952; Cook & Kettlewell, 1960), the half-life of the isotope being the most important factor.

d. *Autoradiographic discrimination between P^{32} and S^{35} marked insects*
Owing to the different energies of these two isotopes the images they produce on X-ray film are distinct; those due to S^{35} give a clear silhouette of the marked insect; those due to P^{32} are stronger but the shape of the insect is indistinct. However, when these isotopes have been used as two different marks it would be unwise to rely on the different form of the image. The short half-life of P^{32} can be used to identify it; if the test strip containing the insects was exposed to film twice, at about a fourteen-day interval, the P^{32} images could be much weaker on the second than on the first film – those from S^{35} would

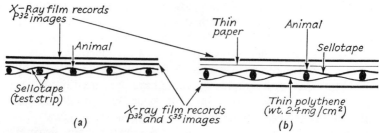

Fig. 15. Double exposure autoradiographic methods of discriminating between animals marked with P^{32} and S^{35} – diagrammatic sections of arrangement of test strip and films in cassette: *a*. method of Gillies (1958); *b*. method of Lewis & Waloff (1964).

alter but little. It is, however, possible to distinguish the two isotopes simultaneously; Duncombe (1959) has pointed out that if X-ray film, coated with emulsion on both sides, is used an image due to S^{35} will appear only on the side nearest the source due to the weak penetration of the S^{35} radiation. In practice this is not easy to see and two other ingenious methods, based on the same principle (the difference in MeV of the radiations), have been described by Gillies (1958) and Lewis & Waloff (1964) and are illustrated diagrammatically in fig. 15.

Individual marking methods

If each individual can be separately marked additional information can be obtained on longevity and dispersal and, if they can be aged and sexed initially, survival can be related to these and other characters. Birth- and death-rates may be more easily calculated and the excessive handling of animals, recaptured more than once, with its attendant problems, may be avoided (Dobson & Morris, 1961). It may also, for example, be possible by weighing individual females to assess the rate of oviposition in the field (Richards & Waloff, 1954), and it provides a method for assessing the randomness of recapture. The extent to which the higher cost, in terms of effort, of marking animals individually is justified will depend on the percentage of the marked individuals that are recovered; high recovery rates justify elaborate marking programmes; with low recovery rates individual marking is seldom justified.

If small labels can be attached to the insects' wings (see above) there is no problem in marking each individual, and Nielsen (1961) records that in the laboratory he marked butterflies individually on the wing with a rubber stamp. With most insects, however, individual marks have to be obtained by a combination of spots in various positions and the use of various colours. The actual pattern will depend on the size and shape of the insect, the number of colours available and the number of individual marks required. Patterns have been devised for dragonflies (Borror, 1934), bed bugs (Mellanby, 1939), tsetse flies (Jackson, 1953), bees (von Frisch, 1950), grasshoppers (Richards & Waloff, 1954), snails (Blinn, 1963) and craneflies (Freeman, 1964). The system of Richards & Waloff is logical and versatile, enabling up to 999 individuals to be marked with continuous numbering (fig. 16). On the right of the thorax is a spot that represents the unit, on the left one that represents the tens, the head spot the hundreds; 1–5 and 10–50 are white spots, 6–0 and 60–00 are red; ten different colours are used for the head mark. With this system the addition of a single further mark would allow another 10,000 individuals to be numbered. The number of spots can be reduced by increasing the number of colours used, as Richards & Waloff did with the hundred mark; however, the practical problem of switching rapidly between more than three colours is serious, and thus although it is feasible to use many colours for the hundred and thousand marks where a colour change will be an infrequent event, it is not desirable to use ten different colours for the unit spot. It also facilitates rapid reading of the code if the same colours and corresponding positions represent the same figures in units and tens. With an insect smaller than a

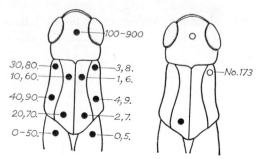

Fig. 16. A system for marking grasshoppers individually: *a.* the pattern; *b.* a marked individual (see text for further explanation) (after Richards & Waloff, 1954).

grasshopper the number of spots on each side of the thorax may be reduced to three, using three colours (e.g. 1–3 white, 4–6 red, 7–9 yellow), but under such a system zeros cannot be represented and nos. 10, 20, 30 ... will bear only one spot (on the left). This is rather unsatisfactory, as with all individual marking systems involving various combinations of spots it is important to remember that an individual spot may be lost and that if the individuals bear different numbers of spots no. 121 can change to no. 21, for example. It is therefore often wise to follow the policy of Michener *et al.* (1955) and ensure that all the

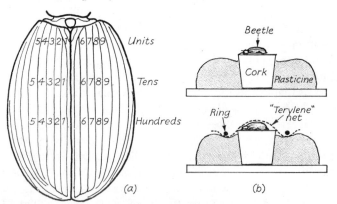

Fig. 17. *a*, A system for marking carabid beetles individually by scraping certain positions on the elytra, applied to *Agonum fuliginosum*. *b*. A device for holding a hard-bodied animal whilst it is marked (modified from Murdoch, 1963).

individuals bear the same number of marks by allocating a colour to zero in the units, tens and hundreds position, as in Richards & Waloff's (1954) method.

If the body is unsuitable for spotting the legs may be marked, but the removal of such marks by the animals during cleaning movements is a real risk. Kuenzler (1958) was able to number lycosid spiders by marking their legs with white enamel paint and Corbet (1956) hippoboscid flies by marking both the body and the legs.

By allocating a code of numbers to the teeth on a crab's carapace it is possible to number up to about forty individuals (depending, of course, on the age and species of crab) by cutting off one or more teeth (Edwards, 1958). In the same way by numbering the interstrial spaces of a carabid, a patch in any one of which could be scraped, approximately 999 individuals could be numbered (Murdoch, 1963) (fig. 17*a*). Gangwere *et al.* (1964) developed a method of individually marking orthopteroids by notching the pronotal margin and amputatinge th tegmina.

Handling techniques

If the animals are to be marked by spraying or dusting this can be done whilst they are still active, either in the field or in small cages (see above); but for marking with paints, especially precise spotting, and for most methods of labelling and mutilation, it is necessary for the animal to be still. Often it can be held between the fingers; where this is impossible the animal must be held by some other method, anaesthetized or chilled.

The animals may be held still under a net or with a hair. One end of the hair is fixed (e.g. in seccotine) and the other has a piece of Plasticine on it; the animal is placed underneath and the hair may be tightened under a stereoscopic microscope by pressure on the Plasticine (Banks, 1955). More robust insects may be held immobile on top of a cork by a piece of Terylene net which is kept taut by a ring (of about 2 in. diameter, but of course depending on the size of the animal); the ring is pushed down into the surrounding Plasticine (fig. 17*b*) and the animal can be marked through the holes of the net (Murdoch, 1963). The device may be placed under a microscope.

Insects can also be held by suction (Hewlett, 1954); Muir (1958) found that a mirid bug was conveniently held by the weak suction of a pipette, formed from the ground-down point of a coarse hypodermic needle, connected to a water pump. The picking up of the bugs by this weak suction was facilitated by coating the inside of the glass dish, in which they were held, by an unsintered dispersion of 'Fluon' GP1, polytetrafluoroethylene (PTFE), which presented an almost frictionless surface (Muir, 1958; Radinovsky & Krantz, 1962).

If none of these methods can be used or if the insects are so active that they cannot even be handled and counted they may have to be immobilized. Chilling at a temperature between 1 and 5°C is probably the best method and may be done in a lagged tank surrounded by an ice–water mixture (MacLeod & Donnelly, 1957). Alternatively an anaesthetic may be employed: carbon dioxide is often used and is easily produced from 'dry ice' (Dalmat, 1950; Roth & Hoffman, 1952; Fredericksen & Lilly, 1955; Green, Baldwin & Sullivan, 1957; Caldwell, 1956). The last mentioned author gives the following table of recovery times of house flies from carbon dioxide anaesthesia at 21°C (70°F):

Exposure time	Recovery time
Up to 5 min	1–2 min
5–30 min	3–5 min
30–60 min	5–10 min

Other anaesthetics are ether, chloroform, nitrogen and nitrous oxide. It has, however, been shown by several workers (Ribbands, 1950; Simpson, 1954) that anaesthesia may prematurely age honey-bees, and Dalmat (1950) found that female blackflies (Simulidae) laid more eggs than normal after being subjected to carbon dioxide; therefore, the use of anaesthetics should, wherever possible, be avoided in ecological studies.

Release

The release of the animals after marking is an operation that is seldom considered. A few methods (e.g Davey, 1956) allow the animals to be marked without capture, others for it to be marked in the field and immediately released again (Jackson, 1933b; Richards, 1953). However, frequently after a period of incarceration, handling and disturbance, the animals are released into the field and it should not be surprising if they show a high level of activity immediately after release; indeed Greenslade (1964) recorded with individually marked ground beetles that there was far greater movement on the day after release than subsequently. Two approaches can be used to minimize this effect.

If the animal has a marked periodicity of movement (i.e. is strictly diurnal or nocturnal) then it should be released during its inactive period; for example I released radioactively tagged individuals of the frit fly (*Oscinella frit*) at dusk (its period of activity is from dawn to late afternoon) (Southwood, 1965). Animals that are active at most times of the day may be restrained from flying immediately after release by covering them with small cages (Evans & Gyrisco, 1960). The release sites should be chosen carefully. It is especially important to avoid the release of small flying insects in the middle of the day when their escape flights may carry them beyond the shelter of the habitat into winds or thermals that can transport them for miles. Of course, only apparently healthy, unharmed individuals should be released.

The release points should be scattered throughout the habitat, as it is essential that the marked animals mix freely with the remainder of the population; e.g. Muir (1958) returned the arboreal mirids he had marked to all parts of the tree. Very sedentary animals may indeed invalidate the use of the capture–recapture method if they do not move sufficiently to re-mix after marking, as Edwards (1961) found, surprisingly, with a population of the grasshopper, *Melanoplus*. The extent of the re-mixing may be checked, to some degree, by a comparison of the ratio of marked to unmarked individuals in samples from various parts of the habitat; the significance of the difference may be tested by a χ^2 (Iwao *et al.*, 1963).

CAPTURE–RECAPTURE METHODS OF ESTIMATING POPULATION PARAMETERS

Lincoln Index type methods

1. Assumptions

Various assumptions underlie all methods of capture–recapture analysis. If the particular animal does not fulfil one or more conditions it might be possible to allow for this to some extent, but a method of analysis should not be applied without ensuring, as far as is practicable, that its inherent assumptions are satisfied.

The following assumptions underlie most methods of analysis:

(1) The marked animals are not affected by being marked and the marks will not be lost.

(2) The marked animals become completely mixed in the population.

(3) The population is sampled randomly with respect to its mark status; this assumption has two aspects: firstly, that all individuals of the different age groups and of both sexes are sampled in the proportion in which they occur; secondly, that all the individuals are equally available for capture irrespective of their position in the habitat.

(4) Sampling must be at discrete time intervals and the actual time involved in taking the samples must be small in relation to the total time.

The assessment of the effects of marking, the precautions in this respect and the re-mixing of the marked animals in the population have already been discussed above.

It is often difficult to verify the assumption that sampling is completely random (De Lury, 1954), but, as Jolly (1965) points out, the important feature for capture–recapture analysis is that the probability of capturing a marked animal is the same as that of capturing any member of the population. In a multiple mark method, such as Jolly's (1965), it is also necessary that the probability of capture of the marked animals released on day i should be the same as that for other animals at liberty on day i, but marked sometime previously. Jolly (1965) discusses various implications of these requirements. In many animals differences in the probability of capture will be associated with differences in sex or age. It is indeed a good principle to enumerate and estimate males and females separately, at least in the first instance; many workers have found striking differences in their behaviour (e.g. Jackson,

1933a; Cragg & Hobart, 1955; MacLeod, 1958; Muir, 1958). Initially different stages or age classes should also be considered separately and their survival rates determined using one of the formulae given below; if their survival rates differ significantly, one must continue to consider them separately.

There may be part of the population which is never captured (see also p. 4); this non-availability may be due to peculiarities of certain individuals, e.g. trap-shy birds or mammals, or to peculiarities of certain parts of the habitat from which, for some reason, the animals cannot be sampled. This latter problem is particularly acute with subcortical, wood-boring and subterranean insects whose habitats may be described as concealing, and it is discussed in detail below.

When using the simple Lincoln Index it is also assumed that:

(5) The population is a closed one or, if not, immigration and emigration can be measured or calculated.

(6) There are no births or deaths in the period between sampling or, if there are, allowance must be made for them.

Most of the other more complex methods of estimating population by capture–recapture may be applied in situations where either migration, natality or mortality or all three are occurring. These methods, however, require a series (at least two) of occasions on which animals are marked, on the second and subsequent occasions the recaptured animals are remarked and released again. Hence these methods make the further assumption:

(7) Being captured one or more times does not affect an animal's subsequent chance of capture.

Leslie had developed a method for testing the validity of assumption 7 – this is described below.

The problem of animals with concealing habitats. As indicated above capture–recapture methods cannot be applied to animals living in a habitat whose features are such that only part of the population can be sampled. Ayre (1962) has pointed out that the number and composition of the foragers of an ant colony are so variable that unless one has a considerable knowledge of these aspects of the biology, the Lincoln Index cannot be used for absolute population estimates. The marking and recapture of foraging ants may, however, give information of a relative type and may be used to estimate the number of foragers (Holt, 1955):

$$P_f = RF \times (T_o + T_i)$$

where P_f=the population of foragers; RF=rate of flow of foragers per unit time, i.e. the average number of ants passing fixed points on all routes from a nest per minute; T_o=average time (in the same units as RF) spent outside the nest (found by marking individuals on the outward journey and timing their return); and T_i=average time spent inside the nest (found by marking ants as they enter and timing their reappearance). Golley & Gentry (1964) found in *Pogonomyrmex badius* that only about 10% of the total population forage above ground in any two-week period.

Methods for checking the random recapture of marked animals. Methods of testing for this requirement are given by Orians & Leslie (1958) and used by Turner (1960). The simplest and most efficient of these is to compare the actual and expected variance of a series of recaptures of individuals known to be alive throughout the sampling period; individual marks must be used. This test is best illustrated by a worked example taken from Leslie's appendix, based on the recaptures of shearwaters; with insects, of course, the recapture periods would be days or weeks rather than years.

EXAMPLE (after Leslie): 32 individuals marked in 1946 were recovered for the last time in 1952, therefore they were available for recapture in the years 1947–51 inclusive and the following two tables can be prepared:

Year by year analysis		All years analysis	
Year	No. of recaptures in each year (n_i)	No. of recaptures for each individual x	Frequency of x $f(x)$
1947	7	0	15
1948	7	1	7
1949	6	2	7
1950	4	3	2
1951	7	4	1
$n_i \quad = \quad \overline{31}$		5	0
		$N = \Sigma f(x) = \overline{32}$	

The actual sum of squares:

$$\Sigma (x - \bar{x})^2 = \Sigma x^2 f(x) - \frac{[\Sigma x f(x)]^2}{N}$$

$$= 69 - 30 \cdot 03 = \underline{38 \cdot 97}$$

The expected (= theoretical) variance:

$$\sigma^2 = \frac{\Sigma n_1}{N} - \frac{\Sigma (n_i{}^2)}{N^2}$$

$$= \frac{31}{32} - \frac{199}{32^2} = 0 \cdot 9688 - 0 \cdot 1943 = \underline{0 \cdot 7745}$$

Then
$$X^2 = \frac{38 \cdot 97}{0 \cdot 7745} = \underline{50 \cdot 32}$$

X^2 may be treated as equivalent to a χ^2 and for degrees of freedom $(N-1)$ of between 20 and 30 the probability of a value as great or greater than this can be assessed from χ^2 tables; probabilities of less than 0·50 imply that capture is not random. With values over 30, use can be made of the fact that $\sqrt{2\chi^2} - \sqrt{2 \mathrm{d.f.} - 1}$ is approximately normally distributed about a mean of zero without standard deviation; in other words one calculates the value for this expression and looks up its probability in the table of the normal deviate. In the present case:

$$\sqrt{2 \times 50 \cdot 32} - \sqrt{(2 \times 31) - 1} = 10 \cdot 03 - 7 \cdot 81 = +2 \cdot 22$$

The probability of a deviate as great as this is somewhere between 0·025 and 0·020 and therefore the shearwaters were not collected randomly. Leslie has suggested that the test should only be used when the number of individuals is 20 or more and the number of occasions on which recapture was possible is at least 3.

2. Methods of calculation

Although simple Lincoln Index estimates are not permissible unless conditions 5 and 6 are satisfied, the variants of the method have all been derived to allow for losses (emigration and death) from or gains (immigration and birth) to the population. Migration rate can also be measured by other means (pp. 256, 284) or it may be artificially prevented by the use of a field cage (Dobson *et al.*, 1958; Dobson & Morris, 1961). Birth and death can also be measured by other methods (chapter 9). Sometimes mortality rate may be so high that the interval between the release of the marked individuals and the recapture sampling is extremely short, a matter of hours (e.g. Coulson, 1962); this is only possible with a mobile insect and under such conditions Craig's method (p. 88) might be used as well as one based on the Lincoln Index.

a. The simple Lincoln Index

Provided the first six conditions listed above are satisfied it is legitimate to calculate the total population P from the simple index used by Lincoln (1930):

Total population ÷ Original number marked = Total second sample ÷ Total recaptured

or
$$P = \frac{an}{r}$$

where n = total number of individuals in the second sample, a = total number marked and r = total recaptures.

Strictly the size of n should be predetermined and normally is approximately equal to a, then the variance of this estimate is given by (Bailey, 1952):

$$\text{var } P = \frac{a^2 n(n-r)}{r^3}$$

If the second sample (n) consists of a series of subsamples and a large proportion of the population have been marked then it is possible to utilize the recovery ratios ($= r/n$) in each to calculate the standard error of the estimated population (Welch, 1960):

$$P = \frac{a}{R_T}$$

where R_T = the recovery ratio (r/n) based on the total animals in all of the samples; the variance is approximately:

$$\text{var } \hat{P} = \left(\frac{a}{R_T^2}\right)^2 \times R_T \frac{(1-R_T)}{y}$$

where y = total animals in subsamples. This approach is only valid if the marked individuals are distributed randomly in the subsamples, which may be tested by comparing the observed and theoretical variance (see p. 77).

Useful information can be obtained from the calculation of a series of simple Lincoln Index estimates, as Southwood & Scudder (1956) found when assessing the build-up of a lace bug population in the spring, although in this particular case such a high proportion of the population were marked that the distribution of marked and unmarked individuals in the recapture samples could not be treated as a simple binomial for maximum likelihood estimation and a modified function was devised (Gilbert, 1956).

The above methods are applicable to large samples where the value of r is fairly large (say over 20); Bailey (1951, 1952) has shown that with small samples a less biased estimate is given if 1 is added to n and r, i.e.:

$$P = \frac{a(n+1)}{r+1}$$

An approximate estimate of the variance of this is given by:

$$\text{var } P = \frac{a^2(n+1)(n-r)}{(r+1)^2(r+2)}$$

These methods are based on what is referred to as *direct sampling* in which the size of n is predetermined. If it is possible, *inverse sampling*, where the number of marked animals to be captured is predetermined, has the advantages of giving an unbiased population estimate and variance (Bailey, 1952):

$$P = \frac{n(a+1)}{r} - 1$$

$$\text{var } \hat{P} = \frac{(a-r+1)(a+1)n(n-r)}{r^2(r+1)}$$

The Lincoln Index is based on a single marking occasion; the enormous number of different mathematical developments of the method can be divided into those concerned with a single mark and those with a series of marking occasions.

b. *Other single mark methods*

This approach is extensively used in fisheries where the ecologist can mark a number of fish, but must rely on commercial fishing to provide the recapture sample; one of the major problems in this work is to distinguish mortality due to man from that due to other causes (Gulland, 1955). The methods used will not be discussed further here; some are described by Beverton & Holt (1957; p. 184 et seq.) and one, based on a stochastic model, by Seber (1962).

c. *Review of methods for a series of marking occasions*

If the animals are marked on a series of two or more occasions, then an allowance may be made for the loss of marked individuals between the time of the initial release and the time when the population is estimated. Jackson

E M—D

(1933*a*, 1937, 1939, 1940, 1944, 1948) and Dowdeswell, Fisher & Ford (1940; and Fisher & Ford, 1947) were the first to devise methods for estimating the population using the data from a series of marking and recapture occasions. Besides assumptions 1–4 and 7 listed above (p. 75), they also assumed a constant survival rate over a period of time; even though this was known to be an approximation it was considered necessary for an algebraic solution.

Jackson developed two methods in his work on the tsetse fly where he calculated a theoretical recapture immediately after release by either the 'positive method', where the loss ratio was calculated for that day over all release groups, and the 'negative method', where the loss ratio was calculated from the subsequent daily percentage losses for the two release groups. Richards & Waloff (1954) used Jackson's negative method and give worked examples. It is possible that the negative method might still be found useful in a situation, as provided by the use of radioactive isotopes, where marking is carried out on a limited number of occasions followed by a long series of recaptures.

Fisher's method is often referred to as the 'trellis method', as the data are initially set out in a trellis diagram; details of its working are given by Dowdeswell (1959). The survival rate has to be determined by trial and error. A useful discussion and summary of these methods is given by MacLeod (1958).

A slightly different method of analysis, but with the same principles, is given by Leslie & Chitty (1951) and Leslie (1952) and referred to as method A. It has been used with carabids by Grüm (1959) and trypetid flies by Sonleitner & Bateman (1963). Although these methods are of considerable historical interest and have been widely used, it is difficult to envisage a situation where their use would still be recommended in preference to the more recent methods. A possible exception to this statement is the use of Jackson's negative method under the circumstances outlined above.

An important advance was made by Bailey (1951, 1952), who introduced maximum likelihood techniques into capture–recapture analysis and so was able to calculate the variances of his estimates. The equations in Bailey's triple-catch method are simple and may be solved directly to provide estimates of various population parameters.

Another significant step was made at about the same time by Leslie (1952; Leslie & Chitty, 1951), who compared three different methods of classifying the animals according to their marks. In Leslie's method A, mentioned above, the animals were classified according to the occasion on which they were marked and thus an animal bearing several marks would give several entries in the recapture table. Jackson, Fisher and Bailey all also used this method of classification in drawing up their recapture tables, but Leslie & Chitty (1951) showed that it leads to loss of information. This loss is only slight when there are but a small number of multiple recaptures (Sonleitner & Bateman, 1963). His method B, in which the animals were classified according to the date on which they were last marked (ignoring all earlier marks), was completely efficient under the assumptions he made. Leslie (1952) gives a full account of his method and a worked example, but his formulae require solution by iterative methods when more than three sampling occasions are considered and hence the calculations are rather laborious. Jolly (1963) simplified the calculations by providing formulae for explicit solutions (i.e. direct, not 'trial and error'). This method is particularly applicable if a fairly large number of individuals have been recaptured several times (multiple recaptures) in a long series of samples, a situation that often arises with work on mammals. However, Sonleitner & Bateman (1963) used Leslie's formulae to obtain estimates of the population of a trypetid fly and Muir (1958) used Jolly's method with a mirid bug.

Working on blowflies, where the incidence of recapture was very low, MacLeod (1958) found that none of the then known methods were usable and he derived two formulae (based on the Lincoln Index) which gave estimates, albeit rather approximate, of the total population. For both methods the mortality rate had to be ascertained independently, in his case in the laboratory, and for one method the percentage of flies not immigrating over a given time was measured by a separate experiment.

All the above methods are based on deterministic models that assume that the survival rate over an interval is an exact value, whereas it would be more correct to state that in nature an animal has a probability of surviving over the interval. This probability is well expressed by a stochastic model, but initially it was thought that the computations arising from a stochastic model would be too complex. Darroch (1958, 1959) showed that under certain conditions a fully stochastic model, giving explicit solutions for the estimation of population parameters, was possible, and Seber (1965) and Jolly (1965) have, independently, extended this method to cover situations in which there is both loss (death and emigration) and dilution (births and immigration). Their methods give similar solutions, except that Jolly's makes allowance for any animals killed after capture and hence not released again, a common occurrence in entomological experiments.

Based as it is on an efficient method of grouping the data and on a fully stochastic model Jolly's method would appear to be the most appropriate method for use in studies involving three or more successive samples where both dilution and loss are occurring, that is in most studies of invertebrate populations. Parr (1965) has used Jolly's method with a dragonfly population and compared the estimates with those from other methods. When there are only three samples the methods using date-grouping (i.e. Leslie's 1952 method B, 'triangles of capture' and Jolly's 1963 and 1965 methods), all give the same estimates of population size, but Jolly's stochastically based 1965 method gives a different, and more realistic, estimate of the variance. The stochastic model affects the population estimates when a longer series of sampling occasions is considered.

The term 'multiple recapture' has been used extensively and is appropriate with mark-grouping methods (e.g. Bailey's) where the number of marks an animal bears (or the number of occasions on which it has been captured) affects its classification. However, it will be noted that in the date-grouping methods no significance is attached to any mark other than the last and hence, as Jolly (1965) points out, the term multiple recapture should not be used in connection with these methods.

d. Bailey's triple-catch method

As indicated above this method is based on a deterministic model of survival and uses an inefficient method of grouping the data, although the latter is not a serious fault if very few animals are recaptured more than once (Sonleitner & Bateman, 1963). The formulae for the calculation of the various parameters are relatively simple. De Lury (1954) has suggested that a series of only three samples is unlikely to measure the magnitude of biological variation encountered. However birth- and death-rates may well be more constant over a short period than over a larger one and furthermore, as pointed out earlier (p. 4), if these (or any) estimates can be related to other estimates based on different methods and assumptions then the reliability of the estimates is considerably strengthened. The mathematical background to this method is given by Bailey (1951) and it is described by Bailey (1952), Richards (1953) and MacLeod (1958). It was found particularly appropriate by Coulson (1962) in a study on craneflies, *Tipula*, with very short life expectancies, but series of triple-catch estimates may be used to estimate a population over a longer period (e.g. Iwao *et al.*, 1963). It seems that the results are most reliable when large numbers are marked and recaptured (Parr, 1965). For the purposes of illustration the sampling is said to take place on days 1, 2 and 3; the intervals between these sampling occasions may be of any length, provided they are long enough to allow for ample mixing of the marked individuals with the remainder of the population and not so long that a large proportion of the marked individuals have died.

With large samples the population on the second day is estimated:

$$P_2 = \frac{a_2 n_2 r_{31}}{r_{21} r_{32}}$$

Where $a_2 =$ the number of marked animals released on the second day; $n_2 =$ the total number of animals captured on the second day and $r =$ recaptures with the first subscript representing the day of capture and the second the day of marking; thus $r_{21} =$ the number of animals captured on the second day that had been marked on the first, $r_{31} =$ the number of animals captured on the third day that had been marked on the first. It is clear that we are really concerned with the number of marks and hence the same animal could contribute to r_{31} and r_{32}. The logic of the above formula may be seen as follows:

$$P_2 = \frac{\hat{a}_1 n_2}{r_{21}} \tag{1}$$

which is the simple Lincoln Index with $\hat{a}_1 =$ the estimate of the number of individuals marked on day 1 that are available for recapture on day 2. Now if the death-rate is constant:

$$\frac{\hat{a}_1}{a_2} = \frac{r_{31}}{r_{32}}$$

$$\hat{a}_1 = \frac{a_2 r_{31}}{r_{32}} \tag{2}$$

Substituting for $\hat{a}_1$ in (1) above we arrive at the formula for the population given above. The large-sample variance of the estimate is:

$$\text{var } P_2 = P_2{}^2 \left(\frac{1}{r_{21}} + \frac{1}{r_{32}} + \frac{1}{r_{31}} - \frac{1}{n_2} \right)$$

Where the numbers recaptured are fairly small there is some advantage in using 'Bailey's correction factor', i.e. the addition of 1 so that:

$$P_2 = \frac{a_2(n_2+1)r_{31}}{(r_{21}+1)(r_{32}+1)}$$

with approximate variance:

$$\text{var } P_2 = P_2{}^2 - \frac{a_2{}^2(n_2+1)(n_2+2)r_{31}(r_{31}-1)}{(r_{21}+1)(r_{21}+2)(r_{32}+1)(r_{32}+2)}$$

The loss rate, which is compounded of the numbers actually dying and the numbers emigrating, is given by:

$$\gamma_{t=0 \to 1} = -\log_e \left(\frac{a_2 r_{31}}{a_1 r_{32}} \right)^{1/t_1}$$

where $t_1 =$ the time interval between the first and second sampling occasions.

The dilution rate, which is the result of births and immigration, is given by:

$$\beta_{t=1 \to 2} = \log_e \left(\frac{r_{21} n_3}{n_2 r_{31}} \right)^{1/t_2}$$

where $t_2 =$ the time interval between the second and third sampling occasions. Both these are measures of a rate per unit of time (the unit being the units of t); Bailey (1952) gives formulae for their variance.

e. Jolly's stochastic method

The advantages of the stochastic model on which this method is based have already been discussed and its general utility has been indicated (p. 81).

The basic equation in Jolly's method is:

$$\hat{P}_i = \frac{\hat{M}_i n_i}{r_i}$$

where $\hat{P}_i =$ the estimate of population on day i, $\hat{M}_i =$ the estimate of the total number of marked animals in the population on day i (i.e. the counterpart of

Absolute Population Estimates

Table 5. The tabulation of recapture data according to the date on which the animal was last caught for analysis by Jolly's method (after Jolly, 1965)

Total captured n_i	Total released a_i	Day when last captured (j)												
54	54	*1*												
146	143	10	*2*											
169	164	3	34	*3*										
209	202	5	18	33	*4*									
220	214	2	8	13	30	*5*								
209	207	2	4	8	20	43	*6*							
250	243	1	6	5	10	34	56	*7*						
176	175	0	4	0	3	14	19	46	*8*					
172	169	0	2	4	2	11	12	28	51	*9*				
127	126	0	0	1	2	3	5	17	22	34	*10*			
123	120	1	2	3	1	0	4	8	12	16	30	*11*		
120	120	0	1	3	1	1	2	7	4	11	16	26	*12*	
142		0	1	0	2	3	3	2	10	9	12	18	35	*13*
$R_i=$			80	70	71	109	101	108	99	70	58	44	35	

'*a*' in the simple Lincoln Index), r_i=the total number of marked animals recaptured on day i and n_i=the total number captured on day i.

The procedure may be demonstrated by the following example taken from Jolly (1965). (The notation is slightly modified to conform with the rest of this chapter.)

(1) The field data are tabulated as in table 5 according to the date of capture and the date on which the animal was last captured. The columns are then summed to give the total number of the a_i ($=s_i$ of Jolly) animals subsequently recaptured (R_i), e.g. for day 7, $R=108$.

(2) Another table is drawn up (table 6) giving the total number of animals recaptured on day i bearing marks of day j or earlier (Jolly's a_{ij}); this is done by adding each row in table 5 from left to right and entering the accumulated totals. The number marked before time i which are not caught in the ith sample, but are caught subsequently (Z_i), is found by adding all but the top entry (printed in bold) in each column. Thus Z_7 is given by the figures enclosed in table 6. The figures above the dotted line, i.e. the top entry in each column, represent the number of recaptures (r_i) for the day on its right, e.g. $r_7=112$.

(3) Then the estimate of the total number of marked animals at risk in the population on the sampling day may be made:

$$\hat{M}_i = \frac{a_i Z_i}{R_i} + r_i$$

Table 6. Calculated table of the total number of marked animals recaptured on a given day (i) bearing marks of day j or earlier (after Jolly, 1965)

Day i	1	\	\	\	\	Day $i-1$	\	\	\	\	\	\	\
		2											
	10		*3*										
	3	**37**		*4*									
	5	23	**56**		*5*								
	2	10	23	**53**		*6*							
	2	6	14	34	**77**		*7*						
	1	7	12	22	56	**112**		*8*					
	0	4	4	7	21	40	**86**		*9*				
	0	2	6	8	19	31	59	**110**		*10*			
	0	0	1	3	6	11	28	50	**84**		*11*		
	1	3	6	7	7	11	19	31	47	**77**		*12*	
	0	1	4	5	6	8	15	19	30	46	**72**		*13*
	0	1	1	3	6	9	11	21	30	42	60	**95**	

$Z(i-1)+1=14$

	14	57	71	89	121	110	132	121	107	88	60
	Z_2	Z_3	Z_4	Z_5	Z_6	Z_7	Z_8	Z_9	Z_{10}	Z_{11}	Z_{12}

Thus
$$\hat{M}_7 = \frac{243 \times 110}{108} + 112 = 359 \cdot 50$$

Similarly for other $\hat{M}_i$, the results being entered in table 7 in which other population parameters are entered as calculated.

(4) The proportion of marked animals in the population at the moment of capture on day i is found and entered in the final table:

$$\alpha_i = \frac{r_i}{n_i}$$

Thus
$$\alpha_7 = \frac{112}{250} = 0 \cdot 4480$$

(5) The total population is then estimated for each day (table 7):

$$\hat{P}_i = \frac{\hat{M}_i}{\alpha_i}$$

(6) The probability that an animal alive at the moment of release of the ith sample will survive till the time of capture of the $i+1$th sample is found:

$$\hat{\phi}_i = \frac{\hat{M}_{i+1}}{\hat{M}_i - r_i + a_i}$$

This survival rate may be converted to a loss rate (the effect of death and emigration):

$$\hat{\gamma}_i = 1 - \hat{\phi}_i$$

(7) The number of new animals joining the population in the interval between the ith and $i+1$th samples and alive at time $i+1$ is given by:

$$\hat{B}_i = \hat{P}_{i+1} - \hat{\phi}_i(\hat{P}_i - n_i + a_i)$$

Table 7. The final table for a Jolly type mark and recapture analysis (after Jolly, 1965)

Day	Proportion of recaptures	No. marked animals at risk	Total population	Survival rate	No. of new animals	Standard errors			Standard errors due to errors in the estimation of parameter itself	
i	$\hat{\alpha}_i$	$\hat{M}_i$	$\hat{P}_i$	$\hat{\phi}_i$	$\hat{B}_i$	$\sqrt{\{V(\hat{P}_i)\}}$	$\sqrt{\{V(\hat{\phi}_i)\}}$	$\sqrt{\{V(\hat{B}_i)\}}$	$\sqrt{\{V(\hat{P}_i/P_i)\}}$	$\sqrt{\left\{V(\hat{\phi}_i) - \dfrac{\hat{\phi}_i^2(1-\hat{\phi}_i)}{\hat{M}_{i+1}}\right\}}$
1	—	0	—	0·649	—	—	0·114	—	—	0·093
2	0·0685	35·02	511·2	1·015	263·2	151·2	·110	179·2	150·8	·110
3	·2189	170·54	779·1	0·867	291·8	129·3	·107	137·7	128·9	·105
4	·2679	258·00	963·0	·564	406·4	140·9	·064	120·2	140·3	·059
5	·2409	227·73	945·3	·836	96·9	125·5	·075	111·4	124·3	·073
6	·3684	324·99	882·2	·790	107·0	96·1	·070	74·8	94·4	·068
7	·4480	359·50	802·5	·651	135·7	74·8	·056	55·6	72·4	·052
8	·4886	319·33	653·6	·985	−13·8	61·7	·093	52·5	58·9	·093
9	·6395	402·13	628·8	·686	49·0	61·9	·080	34·2	59·1	·077
10	·6614	316·45	478·5	·884	84·1	51·8	·120	40·2	48·9	·118
11	·6260	317·00	506·4	·771	74·5	65·8	·128	41·1	63·7	·126
12	·6000	277·71	462·8	—	—	70·2	—	—	68·4	—
13	·6690	—	—	—	—	—	—	—	—	—

This may be converted to the dilution rate $(\hat{\beta})$:

$$\frac{1}{\hat{\beta}} = 1 - \frac{\hat{B}_i}{\hat{P}_{i+1}}$$

(8) If desired the standard errors (the square roots of the variances) are obtained from:

$$\text{var}(\hat{P}_1) = P_i(P_i - n_i)\left[\frac{M_i - r_i + a_i}{M_i}\left(\frac{1}{R_i} - \frac{1}{a_i}\right) + \frac{1 - \alpha_i}{r_i}\right] + P_i - \sum_{j=0}^{i-1}\frac{P_i^2(j)}{B_j}$$

The special problems involved in the computation of the summation term are discussed by Jolly (1965).

$$\text{var}(\hat{\phi}_i) = \phi_i^2\left[\frac{(M_{i+1} - r_{i+1})(M_{i+1} - r_{i+1} + a_{+1})}{M_{i+1}^2}\left(\frac{1}{R_{i+1}} - \frac{1}{a_{i+1}}\right)\right.$$
$$\left. + \frac{M_i - r_i}{M_i - r_i + a_i}\left(\frac{1}{R_i} - \frac{1}{a_i}\right) + \frac{1 - \phi_i}{M_{i+1}}\right]$$

$$\text{var}(\hat{B}_i) = \frac{B_i^2(M_{i+1} - r_{i+1})(M_{i+1} - r_{i+1} + a_{i+1})}{M_{i+1}^2}\left(\frac{1}{R_{i+1}} - \frac{1}{a_{i+1}}\right) + \frac{M_i - r_i}{M_i - r_i - a_i}$$
$$\times \left[\frac{\phi_i a_i(1 - \alpha_i)}{\alpha_i}\right]^2\left(\frac{1}{R_i} - \frac{1}{a_i}\right) + \frac{(P_i - n_i)(P_{i+1} - B_i)(1 - \alpha_i)(1 - \phi_i)}{M_i - r_i + a_i}$$
$$+ P_{i+1}(P_{i+1} - n_{i+1})\frac{1 - \alpha_{i+1}}{r_{i+1}} + \phi_i^2 P_i(P_i - n_i)\frac{1 - \alpha_i}{r_i}$$

Jolly (1965) also gives terms for the covariance. These equations for the variance are fairly complex and if standard errors are required for a long series of estimates, then they should if possible be programmed on a computer.

(9) Jolly shows that the variances of the population and survival rate estimates given above contain an error component due to the real variation in population numbers, apart from errors of estimation. If only errors of estimation are required the formulae are:

$$\text{var}(\hat{P}_i \mid P_i) = P_i(P_i - n_i)\left\{\frac{M_i - r_i + a_i}{M_i}\left(\frac{1}{R_i} - \frac{1}{a_i}\right) + \frac{1 - \alpha_i}{r_i}\right\}$$

$$\text{var}(\hat{\phi}_i \mid \phi_i) = \text{var}(\hat{\phi}_i) - \frac{\hat{\phi}_i^2(1 - \hat{\phi}_i)}{M_{i+1}}$$

The variance due to errors of estimation will be minimal when the number of recaptures is large, and therefore Jolly suggests that when the cost of marking is high, it might be an advantage if the sampling for recaptures was separated from the sampling and marking of further animals to provide the next value of a_i. Sampling for recaptures could be carried out extensively by less experienced staff than are needed to mark.

Method based on frequency of recapture (Craig's)

If the animal is mobile but stays within the habitat and if the individuals are collected randomly, marked and immediately released, a certain number will be recaptured once; these are marked again and released and a few will be recaptured yet again. These are marked and the process continued. Then the number of animals marked once (f_1), twice (f_2), three (f_3) ... (f_x) times are part of a frequency series, the other term of which (f_0) represents those animals that have not been caught or marked at all. Craig (1953) assumed that the frequency of recapture could be described by two mathematical models: the truncated Poisson (p. 26) and the Stevens' distribution function. On the basis of these two models six different methods can be used to estimate the size of the population, three based on moments and three on maximum likelihood; Craig found, however, that they gave similar results. The two simplest are the moment estimates based on the Poisson; they are:

(1)* $$P = (\Sigma\, xf_x)^2 \div (\Sigma\, x^2 f_x - \Sigma\, xf_x)$$

where P = population, x = the number of times an individual had been marked, f_x = the frequency with which individuals marked x times had been caught and thus $\Sigma\, xf_x$ = the total number of different times animals were captured (viz. $1 \times$ the number caught once $+ 2 \times$ the number caught twice $+ 3 \times$ the number caught thrice, etc.). This method is simple, allowing a direct solution, but is subject to greater sampling error. It is useful for obtaining a trial value for use in solving the equation in method 2 (and in the other methods given by Craig).

(2) $$\log P - \log (P - \Sigma\, f_x) = \Sigma\, xf_x \div P$$

where the symbols are as above, $\Sigma\, f_x$ being the total different individual animals caught (viz. the number caught once + the number caught twice + the number caught thrice, etc.). Craig (1953) gives formulae for the variances of these estimates:

for method 1 $$\text{var}\, P = \frac{2}{P\lambda^2}$$

where $\lambda = \Sigma\, xf_x \div P$.

for method 2 $$\text{var}\, P = \frac{1}{P(e^\lambda - 1 - \lambda)}$$

where e is the base of natural (Napierian) logarithms and thus the value of e^λ is found by using a table of natural logs 'backwards'.

It is clear that this method is based on a different mathematical model to the Lincoln Index. It demands that the animals be very mobile so that their chances of recapture are virtually random almost immediately after release and yet they must not leave the habitat. It has been used with butterflies and

---

* The actual numbering of these methods is the reverse of that given by Craig, but it is most logical here to give the simplest method first.

might be applied to other large conspicuous flying or very mobile animals under certain circumstances. Its uses, however, seem to be limited.

Method based on change of composition caused by selective removal (Kelker's)
This method uses the natural marks of a population, normally the difference between the sexes, but theoretically any other recognizable distinction could be used (e.g. the different morphs of a polymorphic species). The proportion of the different forms or components are determined, a known number of one form is removed and the new ratio found; from the change in the ratio the total population can be calculated:

$$P = K_\alpha \div \left[D_{\alpha_1} - \frac{(D_{\beta_1} D_{\alpha_2})}{D_{\beta_2}} \right]$$

where α and β are the components (e.g. sexes) in a population, α is the component part of which is removed during the interval between times 1 and 2, and β is the component (or components) the members of which are not removed, then K_α = number of component α that are killed; D = the proportion of the population represented by a component at times 1 or 2; thus D_{α_1} = the proportion of α in the population as a decimal before any were removed; D_{β_2} = the proportion of the population as a decimal represented by β after K individuals of α were removed.

Such an approach is clearly most applicable with game where individuals of certain sex or age class are killed (e.g. Kelker, 1940; Scattergood, 1954; Hanson, 1963); it is sometimes referred to as the dichotomy method (Chapman, 1954).

The mathematical background has been developed by Chapman (1955), who compared the results from this method with those given by the Lincoln type capture–recapture analysis; he showed that capture–recapture estimation procedure will yield more information for the same amount of effort. A further objection to the use of this method with insect populations is that the selective removal and the resulting atypical unbalance could seriously prejudice any further study of the population; in populations of game animals such removal is one of the 'normal' mortality factors.

This method does not depend on the assumption that initial capture does not alter the probability of subsequent recapture, and this is an advantage over those methods that utilize artificial marks and might indicate conditions for its use, perhaps only as a test of estimates derived by Lincoln type methods. Chapman (1955) gives a technique for combining the two approaches.

REFERENCES

ABDEL-MALEK, A. A., 1961. The effect of radioactive phosphorus on the growth and development of *Culex pipiens molestus* Forsk. (Diptera, Culicidae). *Bull. ent. Res.* **52**, 701–8.

ABDEL-MALEK, A. A. and ABDEL-WAHAB, M. F., 1961a. Autoradiography as a technique for radioactive phosphorus, P-32, uptake in *Culex molestus* Forsk. (Diptera Culicidae). *Bull. Soc. ent. Egypt.* **45**, 409–18.

ABDEL-MALEK, A. A. and ABDEL-WAHAB, M. F., 1961b. Studies on the phosphorus-32 uptake in *Schistocerca gregaria* (Forsk.) and *Anacridium aegyptium* (L.) (Orthoptera: Acrididae). *Bull. Soc. ent. Egypt.* **45**, 419–25.

ANDREEV, S. V., et al., 1963. Radioisotopes and radiation in animal and plant insect pest control. [In Russian with Eng., Fr. and Span. sum.] *Radiation and radioisotopes applied to insects of agricultural importance. Int. atomic Energy Ag.* STI/PUB/74, 115–32.

ANON., 1961. *Proceedings of the symposium on the use of biophysics in the field of plant protection.* [In Russian.] *Vsesoyuz. Inst. Zashch. Rast. Leningrad.* (*Rev. appl. Ent.* (A) **51**, 522–3; (B) **51**, 212).

ANON., 1963. Radioisotopes and ionizing radiations in entomology. *Bibl. Ser. Int. atomic Energy Ag.* **9**, 414 pp.

AREVAD, K. and MOURIER, H., 1963. Investigations of housefly behaviour in relation to new methods of chemical fly control. *Ann. Rep. Gov. Pest Infest. Lab.* (Denmark) **1961–62**, 48–55.

AYRE, G. L., 1962. Problems in using the Lincoln Index for estimating the size of ant colonies (Hymenoptera: Formicidae). *J. N.Y. ent. Soc.* **70**, 159–66.

BABENKO, L. V., 1960. The use of radioactive isotopes for labelling ticks. [In Russian.] *Med. Parazitol.* **29**, 320–4.

BABERS, F. H., ROAN, C. C. and WALKER, R. L., 1954. Tagging boll weevils with radioactive cobalt. *J. econ. Ent.* **47**, 928–9.

BAILEY, N. T. J., 1951. On estimating the size of mobile populations from recapture data. *Biometrika* **38**, 293–306.

BAILEY, N. T., 1952. Improvements in the interpretation of recapture data. *J. anim. Ecol.* **21**, 120–7.

BAILEY, S. F., ELIASON, D. A. and ILTIS, W. C., 1962. Some marking and recovery techniques in *Culex tarsalis* Coq. flight studies. *Mosq. News* **22**, 1–10.

BALDWIN, W. F., JAMES, H. G. and WELCH, H. E., 1955. A study of predators of mosquito larvae and pupae with a radioactive tracer. *Canad. Ent.* **87**, 350–6.

BALDWIN, W. F., RIORDAN, D. F. and SMITH, R. W., 1958. Note on dispersal of radioactive grasshoppers. *Canad. Ent.* **90**, 374–6.

BANKS, C. J., 1955. The use of radioactive tantalum in studies of the behaviour of small crawling insects on plants. *Br. J. anim. Behaviour* **3**, 158–9.

BANKS, C. J., BROWN, E. S. and DEZFULIAN, A., 1961. Field studies of the daily activity and feeding behaviour of Sunn Pest, *Eurygaster integriceps* Put. (Hemiptera: Scutelleridae) on wheat in North Iran. *Ent. exp. appl.* **4**, 289–300.

BARNES, M. M., 1959. Radiotracer labelling of a natural tephritid population and flight range of the walnut husk fly. *Ann. ent. Soc. Amer.* **52**, 90–2.

BENNETT, G. F., 1963. Use of P^{32} in the study of a population of *Simulium rugglesi* (Diptera: Simuliidae) in Algonquin Park, Ontario. *Canad. J. Zool.* **41**, 831–40.

BEVERTON, R. J. H. and HOLT, S. J., 1957. On the dynamics of Exploited Fish populations. *Fishery investigations, ser. 2.* **19**, 533 pp. Min. Agric. Fish. Food Gt Britain, London. H.M.S.O.

BLACK, J. B., 1963. Observations on the home range of stream-dwelling crawfishes. *Ecology* **44**, 592–5.

BLINN, W. C., 1963. Ecology of the land snails *Mesodon thyroidus* and *Allogona profunda*. *Ecology* **44**, 498–505.

BORROR, D. J., 1934. Ecological studies of *Argia moesta* Hagen (Odonata: Coenagrionidae) by means of marking. *Ohio J. Sci.* **34**, 97–108.

BUGHER, J. and TAYLOR, M., 1949. Radiophosphorus and radiostrontium in mosquitoes. *Science* **110**, 146–7.

CALDWELL, A. H., 1956. Dry ice as an insect anaesthetic. *J. econ. Ent.* **49**, 264–5.

CHANG, H. T., 1946. Studies on the use of fluorescent dyes for marking *Anopheles quadrimaculatus* Say. *Mosq. News.* **6**, 122–5.

CHAPMAN, D. G., 1954. The estimation of biological populations. *Ann. math. stat.* **25**, 1–15.

CHAPMAN, D. G., 1955. Population estimation based on change of composition caused by a selective removal. *Biometrika* **42**, 279–90.

CLARK, D. P., 1962. An analysis of dispersal and movement in *Phaulacridium vittatum* (Sjost.) (Acrididae). *Aust. J. Zool.* **10**, 382–99.

COLLINS, C. W. and POTTS, S. F., 1932. Attractants for the flying gypsy moths as an aid to locating new infestations. *U.S.D.A. Tech. Bull.* **336**, 43 pp.

COMAR, C. L., 1955. *Radioisotopes in biology and agriculture.* New York, 481 pp.

COOK, L. M. and KETTLEWELL, H. B. D., 1960. Radioactive labelling of lepidopterous larvae: a method of estimating larval and pupal mortality in the wild. *Nature, Lond.* **187**, 301–2.

CORBET, G. B., 1956. The life-history and host-relations of a Hippoboscid fly *Ornithomyia fringillina* Curtis. *J. anim. Ecol.* **25**, 403–20.

CORBET, P. S., 1952. An adult population study of *Pyrrhosoma nymphula* (Sulzer); (Odonata: Coenagrionidae). *J. anim. Ecol.* **21**, 206–22.

CORNWELL, P. B., 1955. Techniques for labelling trees with radioactive phosphorus. *Nature, Lond.* **175**, 85–7.

CORNWELL, P. B., 1956. Some aspects of mealybug behaviour in relation to the efficiency of measures for the control of virus diseases of cacao in the Gold Coast. *Bull. ent. Res.* **47**, 137–66.

COTTAM, C., 1956. Uses of marking animals in ecological studies: marking birds for scientific purposes. *Ecology* **37**, 675–81.

COULSON, J. C., 1962. The biology of *Tipula subnodicornis* Zetterstedt, with comparative observations on *Tipula paludosa* Meigen. *J. anim. Ecol.* **31**, 1–21.

CRAGG, J. B. and HOBART, J., 1955. A study of a field population of the blowflies *Lucilia caesar* (L.) and *L. serricata* (Mg.). *Ann. appl. Biol.* **43**, 645–63.

CRAIG, C. C., 1953. On the utilisation of marked specimens in estimating populations of flying insects. *Biometrika* **40**, 170–6.

CUNNINGHAM, M. P., HARLEY, J. M. B. and GRAINGE, E. B., 1963. The labelling of animals with specific agglutinins and the detection of these agglutinins in the blood meals of *Glossina*. *Rep. E. Afr. Tryp. Res. Org.* **1961**, 23–4.

DAHMS, P. A., 1957. Uses of radioisotopes in pesticide research. *Adv. pest cont. Res.* **1**, 81–146.

DALMAT, H. T., 1950. Studies on the flight range of certain Simuliidae, with the use of aniline dye marker. *Ann. ent. Soc. Amer.* **43**, 537–45.

DARROCH, J. N., 1958. The multiple-recapture census. I. Estimation of a closed population. *Biometrika* **45**, 343–59.

DARROCH, J. N., 1959. The multiple-capture census II. Estimation when there is immigration or death. *Biometrika* **46**, 336–51.

DAVEY, J. T., 1956. A method of marking isolated adult locusts in large numbers as an aid to the study of their seasonal migrations. *Bull. ent. Res.* **46**, 797–802.

DAVEY, J. T. and O'ROURKE, F. J., 1951. Observations on *Chrysops silacea* and *C. dimidiata* at Benin, Southern Nigeria. Part II. *Ann. trop. Med. Parasit., Liverpool.* **45**, 66–72.

DAVIS, J. M. and NAGEL, R. H., 1956. A technique for tagging large numbers of live adult insects with radioisotopes. *J. econ. Ent.* **49**, 210–1.

DE LURY, D. B., 1954. On the assumptions underlying estimates of mobile populations. *In* Kempthorne, O. et al. (eds.). *Statistics and Mathematics in Biology,* 287–93.

DOBSON, R. M., 1962. Marking techniques and their application to the study of small terrestrial animals. *In* Murphy, P. W. (ed.). *Progress in Soil Zoology*, 228–39.

DOBSON, R. M. and MORRIS, M. G., 1961. Observations on emergence and life-span of wheat bulb fly, *Leptohylemyia coarctata* (Fall.) under field-cage conditions. *Bull. ent. Res.* **51**, 803–21.

DOBSON, R. M., STEPHENSON, J. W. and LOFTY, J. R., 1958. A quantitative study of a population of wheat bulb fly, *Leptohylemyia coarctata* (Fall.), in the field. *Bull. ent. Res.* **49**, 95–111.

DOW, R. P., 1959. Dispersal of adult *Hippelates pusio*, the eye gnat. *Ann. ent. Soc. Amer.* **52**, 372–81.

DOWDESWELL, W. H., 1959. *Practical animal ecology*. London, 316 pp.

DOWDESWELL, W. H., FISHER, R. A. and FORD, E. B., 1940. The quantitative study of populations in the Lepidoptera. 1. *Polyommatus icarus* Rott. *Ann. Eugen., Lond.* **10**, 123–36.

DUDLEY, J. E. and SEARLES, E. M., 1923. Color marking of the striped cucumber beetle (*Diabrotica vittata* Fab.) and preliminary experiments to determine its flight. *J. econ. Ent.* **16**, 363–8.

DUNCOMBE, W. G., 1959. An autoradiographic method for distinguishing samples labelled with phosphorus-32 and sulphur 35. *Nature, Lond.* **183**, 319.

DUNN, P. H. and MECHALAS, B. J., 1963. An easily constructed vacuum duster. *J. econ. Ent.* **56**, 899.

EDDY, G. W., ROTH, A. R. and PLAPP, F. W., 1962. Studies on the flight habits of some marked insects. *J. econ. Ent.* **55**, 603–7.

EDWARDS, R. L., 1958. Movements of individual members in a population of the shore crab, *Carcinus maenas* L., in the littoral zone. *J. anim. Ecol.* **27**, 37–45.

EDWARDS, R. L., 1961. Limited movement of individuals in a population of the migratory grasshopper, *Melanoplus bilituratus* (Walker) (Acrididae) at Kamloops, British Columbia. *Canad. Ent.* **93**, 628–31.

EVANS, W. G. and GYRISCO, G. G., 1960. The flight range of the European chafer. *J. econ. Ent.* **53**, 222–4.

FAIRES, R. A. and PARKS, B. H., 1958. *Radioisotope laboratory techniques*. London, 244 pp.

FALES, J. H., BODENSTEIN, O. F., MILLS, G. D. and WESSEL, L. H., 1964. Preliminary studies on face fly dispersion. *Ann. ent. Soc. Amer.* **57**, 135–7.

FAY, R. W., KILPATRICK, J. W. and BAKER, J. T., 1963. Rearing and isotopic labelling of *Fannia canicularis*. *J. econ. Ent.* **56**, 69–71.

FISHER, R. A. and FORD, E. B., 1947. The spread of a gene in natural conditions in a colony of the moth *Panaxia dominula* L. *Heredity* **1**, 143–74.

FITZGERALD, P. J., 1958. Autoradiography in biology and medicine. *Second U.N. int. Conf. peaceful uses of atomic energy*.

FLETCHER, T. B., 1936. Marked migrant butterflies. *Ent. Rec.* **48**, 105–6.

FRANCIS, G. E., MULLIGAN, W. and WORMALL, A., 1959. *Isotopic tracers*. 2nd ed. London.

FREDEEN, F. J. H., SPINKS, J. W. T., ANDERSON, J. R., ARNASON, A. P. and REMPEL, J. G., 1953. Mass tagging of black flies (Diptera: Simuliidae) with radio-phosphorus. *Canad. J. Zool.* **31**, 1–15.

FREDERICKSEN, C. F. and LILLY, J. H., 1955. Measuring wireworm reactions to soil insecticides by tagging with radioactive cobalt. *J. econ. Ent.* **48**, 438–42.

FREEMAN, B. E., 1964. A population study of *Tipula* species (Diptera, Tipulidae). *J. anim. Ecol.* **33**, 129–40.

FRISCH, K. VON, 1950. *Bees, their vision, chemical senses, and language*. Ithaca, New York.

GANGWERE, S. K. CHAVIN, W. and EVANS, F. C., 1964. Methods of marking insects, with especial reference to Orthoptera (Sens. lat.). *Ann. ent. Soc. Amer.* **57**, 662–9.

GARDINER, J. E., 1963. A radioactive marking ink. *Nature, Lond.* **197,** 414.

GILBERT, N. E. G., 1956. Likelihood function for capture-recapture samples. *Biometrika* **43,** 488–9.

GILLIES, M. T., 1958. A simple autoradiographic method for distinguishing insects labelled with phosphorus-32 and sulphur-35. *Nature, Lond.* **182,** 1683–4.

GILLIES, M. T., 1961. Studies on the dispersion and survival of *Anopheles gambiae* Giles in East Africa, by means of marking and release experiments. *Bull. ent. Res.* **52,** 99–127.

GODFREY, G. K., 1954. Tracing field voles (*Microtus agrestis*) with a Geiger–Müller counter. *Ecology* **35,** 5–10.

GODWIN, P. A., JAYNES, H. A. and DAVIS, J. M., 1957. The dispersion of radio-actively tagged white pine weevils in small plantations. *J. econ. Ent.* **50,** 264–6.

GOLLEY, F. B. and GENTRY, J. B., 1964. Bioenergetics of the southern harvester ant, *Pogonomyrmex badius. Ecology* **45,** 217–25.

GOODHART, C. B., 1962. Thrush predation on the snail *Cepaea hortensis. J. anim. Ecol.* **27,** 47–57.

GRAHAM, B. F., 1957. Labelling pollen of woody plants with radioactive isotopes. *Ecology* **38,** 156–8.

GREEN, G. W., BALDWIN, W. F. and SULLIVAN, C. R., 1957. The use of radioactive cobalt in studies of the dispersal of adult females of the European pine shoot moth *Rhyacionia buoliana* (Schiff.). *Canad. Ent.* **89,** 379–83.

GREENSLADE, P. J. M., 1964. The distribution, dispersal and size of a population of *Nebria brevicollis* (F.), with comparative studies on three other Carabidae. *J. anim. Ecol.* **33,** 311–33.

GRIFFIN, D. R., 1952. Radioactive tagging of animals under natural conditions. *Ecology* **33,** 329–35.

GRÜM, L., 1959. Seasonal changes of activity of the Carabidae. *Ekol. Polska A* **7,** 255–68.

GULLAND, J. A., 1955. On the estimation of population parameters from marked members. *Biometrika* **42,** 269–70.

HANSON, W. R., 1963. Calculation of productivity, survival and abundance of selected vertebrates from sex and age ratios. *Wildl. Monogr.* **9,** 60 pp.

HARTLEY, P. H. T., 1954. Back garden ornithology. *Bird Study* **1,** 18–27.

HEWLETT, P. S., 1954. A micro-drop applicator and its use for the treatment of certain small insects with liquid insecticide. *Ann. appl. Biol.* **41,** 45–64.

HINTON, H. E., 1954. Radioactive tracers in entomoligical research. *Sci. Progr., London* **42,** 292–305.

HOFFMAN, R. A., LINDQUIST, A. W. and BUTTS, J. S., 1951. Studies on treatment of flies with radioactive phosphorus. *J. econ. Ent.* **44,** 471–3.

HOLLANDER, J. M., PERLMAN, I. and SEABORG, G. T., 1953. Table of isotopes. *Rev. Mod. Physics* **25,** 469–651.

HOLT, S. J., 1955. On the foraging activity of the wood ant. *J. anim. Ecol.* **24,** 1–34.

HUBBELL, S. P., SIKORA, A. and PARIS, O. H., 1965. Radiotracer, gravimetric and calorimetric studies of ingestion and assimilation rates of an Isopod. *Health Physics* **11** (12), 1485–1501.

HUNTER, P. E., 1960. Plastic paint as a marker for mites. *Ann. ent. Soc. Amer.* **53,** 698.

IWAO, S., MIZUTA, K., NAKAMURA, H., ODA, T. and SATO, Y., 1963. Studies on a natural population of the large 28-spotted lady beetle, *Epilachna vigintioctomaculata* Motschulsky. 1. Preliminary analysis of the overwintered adult population by means of the marking and recapture method. *Jap. J. Ecol.* **13,** 109–17.

JACKSON, C. H. N., 1933*a*. On the true density of tsetse flies. *J. anim. Ecol.* **2,** 204–9.

JACKSON, C. H. N., 1933*b*. On a method of marking tsetse flies. *J. anim. Ecol.* **2,** 289–90.

JACKSON, C. H. N., 1937. Some new methods in the study of *Glossina morsitans. Proc. zool. Soc. Lond.* **1936,** 811–96.

JACKSON, C. H. N., 1939. The analysis of an animal population. *J. anim. Ecol.* **8,** 238–46.

JACKSON, C. H. N., 1940. The analysis of a tsetse fly population. *Ann. Eugen., Lond.* **10**, 332–369.

JACKSON, C. H. N., 1944. The analysis of a tsetse-fly population. II. *Ann. Eugen., Lond.* **12**, 176–205.

JACKSON, C. H. N., 1948. The analysis of a tsetse-fly population. III. *Ann. Eugen., Lond.*, **14**, 91–108.

JACKSON, C. H. N., 1953. A mixed population of *Glossina morsitans* and *G. swynnertoni*. *J. anim. Ecol.* **22**, 78–86.

JAMES, H. G., 1961. Some predators of *Aedes stimulans* (Walk.) and *Aedes trichurus* (Dyar.) (Dipt.: Culicidae) in woodland pools. *Canad. J. Zool.* **39**, 533–40.

JENKINS, D. W., 1949. A field method of marking arctic mosquitoes with radiophosphorus. *J, econ. Ent.* **40**, 988–9.

JENKINS, D. W., 1963. Use of radionuclides in ecological studies of insects. *In* Schultz, V. and Klement, A. W. (eds.), *Radioecology* 431–43.

JENKINS, D. W. and HASSETT, C. C., 1950. Radioisotopes in entomology. *Nucleonics* **6**, 5–14.

JENSEN, J. A. and FAY, R. W., 1951. Tagging of adult horse flies and flesh flies with radioactive phosphorus. *Amer. J. trop. Med.* **31**, 523–30.

JEWELL, G. R., 1956. Marking of tsetse flies for their detection at night. *Nature, Lond.* **178**, 750.

JEWELL, G. R., 1958. Detection of tsetse fly at night. *Nature, Lond.* **181**, 1354.

JOHANSSON, T. S. K., 1959. Tracking honey bees in cotton fields with fluorescent pigments. *J. econ. Ent.* **52**, 572–7.

JOHNSON, C. G., 1940. The maintenance of high atmospheric humidities for entomological work with glycerol–water mixtures. *Ann. appl. Biol.* **27**, 295–9.

JOLLY, G. M., 1963. Estimates of population parameters from multiple recapture data with both death and dilution – a deterministic model. *Biometrika* **50**, 113–28.

JOLLY, G. M., 1965. Explicit estimates from capture–recapture data with both death and immigration – stochastic model. *Biometrika* **52**, 225–47.

KELKER, G. H., 1940. Estimating deer populations by a differential hunting loss in the sexes. *Proc. Utah Acad. Sci., Arts. Lett.* **17**, 65–9.

KETTLEWELL, H. B. D., 1952. Use of radioactive tracer in the study of insect populations (Lepidoptera). *Nature, Lond.* **170**, 584.

KHUDADOV, G. D., 1959a. The method of marking insects by introducing radioactive isotopes incorporated into foodstuffs. [In Russian, with Eng. summary.] *Byull. mosk. Obshch. Ispȳt. Prir. (N.S.) Otd. Biol.* **64** (3), 35–45.

KHUDADOV, G. D., 1959b. Radioautographic method of finding insects and ticks marked with radioactive isotopes. [In Russian.] *Med. Parazitol.* **28**, 60–4.

KLOCK, J. W., PIMENTEL, D. and STENBURG, R. L., 1953. A mechanical fly-tagging device. *Science* **118**, 48–9.

KNAPP, S. E., FARINACCI, C. J., HERBERT, C. M. and SAENGER, E. L., 1956. A method for labelling the Lone Star tick with a radioactive indicator (P^{32}). *J. econ. Ent.* **49**, 393–5.

KNIGHT, R. H., and SOUTHON, H. A. W., 1963. A simple method for marking haematophagous insects during the act of feeding. *Bull. ent. Res.* **54**, 379–82.

KUENZLER, E. J., 1958. Niche relations of three species of Lycosid spiders. *Ecology* **39**, 494–500.

LE CREN, E. D., 1965. A note on the history of mark–recapture population estimates. *J. anim. Ecol.* **34**, 453–4.

LEEUWEN, E. R. VAN, 1940. The activity of adult codling moths as indicated by captures of marked moths. *J. econ. Ent.* **33**, 162–6.

LESLIE, P. H., 1952. The estimation of population parameters from data obtained by means of the capture–recapture method. II. The estimation of total numbers. *Biometrika* **39**, 363–88.

LESLIE, P. H. and CHITTY, D., 1951. The estimation of population parameters from data obtained by means of the capture–recapture method. I. The maximum likelihood equations for estimating the death-rate. *Biometrika* **38**, 269–92.

LEWIS, C. T. and WALOFF, N., 1964. The use of radioactive tracers in the study of dispersion of *Orthotylus virescens* (Douglas & Scott) (Miridae, Heteroptera). *Ent. exp. appl.* **7**, 15–24.

LINCOLN, F. C., 1930. Calculating waterfowl abundance on the basis of banding returns. *U.S.D.A. Circ.* **118**, 1–4.

LINDQUIST, A. W., 1952. Radioactive materials in entomological research. *J. econ. Ent.* **45**, 264–70.

LINDROTH, A., 1953. Internal tagging of salmon smolt. *Inst. Freshw. Res. Drottningholm* **34**, 49–57.

MACLEOD, J., 1958. The estimation of numbers of mobile insects from low-incidence recapture data. *Trans. R. ent. Soc. Lond.* **110**, 363–92.

MACLEOD, J. and DONNELLY, J., 1957. Individual and group marking methods for fly-population studies. *Bull. ent. Res.* **48**, 585–92.

MCALLAN, J. W. and NEILSON, W. T. A., 1965. Labelling the apple maggot with strontium 89. *J. econ. Ent.* **58**, 168.

MCDONALD, W. A., 1960. Nocturnal detection of tsetse flies in Nigeria with ultra-violet light. *Nature, Lond.* **185**, 867–8.

MEDER, O., 1926. Über die kennzeichnung von weisslingen zwecks Erfassung ihrer Wanderung. *Int. ent. Z.* **19**, 325–30.

MELLANBY, K., 1939. The physiology and activity of the bed-bug (*Cimex lectularius* L.) in a natural infestation. *Parasitology* **31**, 200–11.

MICHENER, C. D., CROSS, E. A., DALY, H. V., RETTENMEYER, C. W. and WILLE, A., 1955. Additional techniques for studying the behaviour of wild bees. *Insectes Sociaux* **2**, 237–46.

MITCHELL, B., 1963. Ecology of two carabid beetles, *Bembidion lampros* (Herbst.) and *Trechus quadristriatus* (Schrank). *J. anim. Ecol.* **32**, 377–92.

MUIR, R. C., 1958. On the application of the capture–recapture method to an orchard population of *Blepharidopterus angulatus* (Fall.) (Hemiptera–Heteroptera, Miridae). *Rep. E. Malling Res. Sta.* **1957**, 140–7.

MURDOCH, W. W., 1963. A method for marking Carabidae (Col.). *Ent. mon. Mag.* **99**, 22–4.

MUSGRAVE, A. J., 1949. The use of fluorescent material for marking and detecting insects. *Canad. Ent.* **81**, 173.

MUSGRAVE, A. J., 1950. A note on the dusting of crops with flurorescein to mark visiting bees. *Canad. Ent.* **82**, 195–6.

NIELSEN, E. T., 1961. On the habits of the migratory butterfly, *Ascia monuste* L. *Biol. Meddr. Dan. Vid. Selsk.* **23** (11), 81 pp.

NORRIS, K. R., 1957. A method of marking Calliphoridae (Diptera) during emergence from the puparium. *Nature, Lond.* **180**, 1002.

O'BRIEN, R. D. and WOLFE, L. S., 1964. *Radiation, radioactivity, and insects.* New York and London, 211 pp.

ODUM, E. P. and PONTIN, A. J., 1961. Population density of the underground ant, *Lasius flavus*, as determined by tagging with P^{32}. *Ecology* **42**, 186–8.

ORIANS, G. H. and LESLIE, P. H., 1958. A capture–recapture analysis of a shearwater population. *J. anim. Ecol.* **27**, 71–86.

ORPHANIDIS, P. S., SOULTANOPOULOS, C. D. and KARANEINOS, M. G., 1963. Essai préliminaire avec P^{32} sur la dispersion des adultes du *Dacus oleae* Gmel. *Radiation and radioisotopes applied to insects of agricultural importance. Int. atomic Energy Ag.* STI/PUB/**74**, 101–4.

OUGHTON, J., 1951. Tagging root maggot flies by means of radioactive phosphorus. *Ann. Rep. ent. Soc. Ontario* (81st) **1950**, 91–2.

PAJUNEN, V. I., 1962. Studies on the population ecology of *Leccorrhinia dubia* V. D. Lind. (Odon., Libellulidae). *Ann. Zool. Soc. 'vanamo'* **24** (4), 79 pp.

PAL, R., 1947. Marking mosquitoes with fluorescent compounds and watching them by ultra-violet light. *Nature, Lond.* **160**, 298–9.

PARR, M. J., 1965. A population study of a colony of imaginal *Ischnura elegans* (van der Linden) (Odonata: Coenagriidae) at Dale, Pembrokeshire. *Fld. Stud.* **2** (2), 237–82.

PEER, D. F., 1957. Further studies on the mating range of the honey bee, *Apis mellifera* L. *Canad. Ent.* **89**, 108–10.

PEFFLY, R. L. and LABRECQUE, G. C., 1956. Marking and trapping studies on dispersal and abundance of Egyptian house flies. *J. econ. Ent.*, **49**, 214–17.

PELEKASSIS, C. E. D., MOURIKIS, P. A. and BANTZIOS, D. N., 1962. Preliminary studies on the field movement of the olive fruit fly (*Dacus oleae* (Gmel.)) by labelling a natural population with radioactive phosphorus (P^{32}). *Ann. Inst. Phytopath. Benaki* (N.S.) **4**, 170–9.

PENDLETON, R. C., 1956. The uses of marking animals in ecological studies: labelling animals with radioactive isotopes. *Ecology* **37**, 686–9.

POLIVKA, J., 1949. The use of fluorescent pigments in a study of the flight of the Japanese beetle. *J. econ. Ent.* **42**, 818–21.

QUARTERMAN, K. D., MATHIS, W. and KILPATRICK, J. W., 1954. Urban fly dispersal in the area of Savannah, Georgia. *J. econ. Ent.* **47**, 405–412.

QUERCI, O., 1936. Aestivation of Lepidoptera. *Ent. Rec.* **48**, 122.

QURAISHI, M. S., 1963a. Water and food relationship of the eggs and first instar nymph of *Eurygaster integriceps* with the aid of P^{32}. *J. econ. Ent.* **56**, 666–8.

QURAISHI, M. S., 1963b. Use of isotopes for investigating the behaviour and ecology of insect pests in some recent studies. *Radiation and radioisotopes applied to insects of agricultural importance. Int. atomic Energy Ag.* STI/PUB/**74**, 93–8.

RADELEFF, R. D., BUSHLAND, R. C. and HOPKINS, D. E., 1952. Phosphorus-32 labelling of the screw-worm fly. *J. econ. Ent.* **45**, 509–14.

RADINOVSKY, S. and KRANTZ, G. W., 1962. The use of Fluon to prevent the escape of stored-product insects from glass containers. *J. econ. Ent.* **55**, 815–16.

RAKITIN, A. A., 1963. The use of radioisotopes in the marking of *Eurygaster integriceps* Put. [In Russian.] *Ent. Obozr.* **42**, 39–48. (Transl. *Ent. Rev.* **42**, 20–38).

REEVES, W. C., BROOKMAN, B. and HAMMON, W. M., 1948. Studies on the flight range of certain *Culex* mosquitoes, using a fluorescent-dye marker, with notes on *Culiseta* and *Anopheles. Mosq. News* **8**, 61–9.

RENNISON, B. D., LUMSDEN, W. H. R. and WEBB, C. J., 1958. Use of reflecting paints for locating tsetse fly at night. *Nature, Lond.* **181**, 1354.

RIBBANDS, C. R., 1950. Changes in behaviour of honeybees, following their recovery from anaesthesia. *J. exp. Biol.* **27**, 302–10.

RICHARDS, O. W., 1953. The study of the numbers of the red locust, *Nomadacris septemfasciata* (Serville). *Anti-Locust Bull.* **15**, 30 pp.

RICHARDS, O. W. and WALOFF, N., 1954. Studies on the biology and population dynamics of British grasshoppers. *Anti-Locust Bull.* **17**, 182 pp.

RICKER, W. E., 1956. Uses of marking animals in ecological studies: the marking of fish. *Ecology* **37**, 665–70.

RINGS, R. W. and LAYNE, G. W., 1953. Radioisotopes as tracers in plum curculio behaviour studies. *J. econ. Ent.* **46**, 473–7.

ROER, H., 1959. Beitrag zur Erforschung der Migrationen des Distelfalters (*Vanessa cardui* L.) im paläarktischen Raum unter besonderer Berücksichtigung der Verhältnisse des Jahres 1958. *Decheniana* **111**, 141–8.

ROER, H., 1962. Zur Erforschung der Flug- und Wandergewohnheiten mitteleuropäischer Nymphaliden (Lepidoptera). *Bonn. zool. Beitr.* **10** (1959), 286–97.

ROTH, A. R. and HOFFMAN, R. A., 1952. A new method of tagging insects with P^{32}. *J. econ. Ent.* **45**, 1091.

SCATTERGOOD, L. W., 1954. *In* Kempthorne, O., *et al.* (eds.), *Statistics and mathematics in biology* 273–85.

SCHJØTZ-CHRISTENSEN, B., 1961. Forplantngabiologien hos *Amara infirma* Dft. og *Harpalus neglectus* Serv. *Flora og Fauna* **67**, 8–12.

SCHOOF, H. F. and MAIL, G. A., 1953. The dispersal habits of *Phormia regina*, the black blowfly, in Charleston, West Virginia. *J. econ. Ent.* **46**, 258–62.

SCHOOF, H. F., SIVERLY, R. E. and JENSEN, J. A., 1952. House fly dispersion studies in metropolitan areas. *J. econ. Ent.* **45**, 675–83.

SCOTT, J. D., 1931. A practical method of marking insects in quantitative samples taken at regular intervals. *S. Afr. J. Sci.* **28**, 372–5.

SEBER, G. A. F., 1962. The multi-sample single recapture census. *Biometrika* **49**, 339–50.

SEBER, G. A. F., 1965. A note on the multiple-recapture census. *Biometrika* **52**, 249.

SHEMANCHUK, J. A., SPINKS, J. W. T. and FREDEEN, F. J. H., 1953. A method of tagging prairie mosquitoes (Diptera: Culicidae) with radio-phosphorous. *Canad. Ent.* **85**, 269–72.

SHEPPARD, P. M., 1951. Fluctuations in the selective value of certain phenotypes in the polymorphic land snail *Cepaea nemoralis* (L.). *Heredity* **5**, 125–54.

SHURA-BURA, B. L. and GRAGEAU, U. L., 1956. Fluorescent analysis studies of insect migration. [In Russian.] *Ent. Obozr.* **35**, 760–3.

SHURA-BURA, B. L., SUCHOMLINOVA, O. I. and ISAROVA, B. I., 1962. Application of the radiomarking method for studying the ability of synanthropic flies to fly over water obstacles. [In Russian.] *Ent. Obozr.* **41**, 99–108.

SIMPSON, J., 1954. Effects of some anaesthetics on honeybees: nitrous oxide, carbon dioxide, ammonium nitrate smoker fumes. *Bee World* **35**, 149–55.

SKUHRAVÝ, V., 1957. Studium pohybu některých střevlíkovitých značkováním jedinců. *Acta Soc. ent. Bohem.* **53**, 171–9.

SLACK, K. V., 1955. An injection method for marking crayfish. *Prog. Fish. Cult.* **17** (1), 36–8.

SMITH, M. V., 1958. The use of fluorescent markers as an aid in studying the forage behaviour of honeybees. *Proc. X int. Congr. Ent.* **4**, 1063.

SMITH, M. V. and TOWNSEND, G. F., 1951. A technique for mass-marking honeybees. *Canad. Ent.* **83**, 346–8.

SONLEITNER, F. J. and BATEMAN, M. A., 1963. Mark–recapture analysis of a population of Queensland fruit-fly, *Dacus tryoni* (Frogg.) in an orchard. *J. anim. Ecol.* **32**, 259–69.

SOUTH, A., 1965. Biology and ecology of *Agriolimax reticulatus* (Müll.) and other slugs: spatial distribution. *J. anim. Ecol.* **34**, 403–17.

SOUTHWOOD, T. R. E., 1965. Migration and population change in *Oscinella frit* L. (Diptera) on the oatcrop. *Proc. XII int. Congr. Ent.* 420–1.

SOUTHWOOD, T. R. E. and SCUDDER, G. G. E., 1956. The bionomics and immature stages of the thistle lace bugs (*Tingis ampliata* H.–S. and *T. cardui* L.; Hem., Tingidae). *Trans. Soc. Brit. Ent.* **12**, 93–112.

STANILAND, L. N., 1959. Fluorescent tracer techniques for the study of spray and dust deposits. *J. agric. Eng. Res.* **4**, 110–25.

SUDIA, T. W. and LINCK, A. J., 1963. Methods for introducing radionuclides into plants. *In* Schultz, V. and Klement, A. W. (eds.), *Radioecology* 417–23.

SULLIVAN, C. R., 1953. Use of radioactive cobalt in tracing the movements of the white-pine weevil, *Pissodes strobi* Peck. (Coleoptera: Curculionidae). *Canad. Ent.* **85**, 273–6

SULLIVAN, C. R., 1961. The survival of adults of the white pine weevil, *Pissodes strobi* (Peck), labelled with radioactive cobalt. *Canad. Ent.* **93**, 78–9.

TABER, R. D., 1956. Uses of marking animals in ecological studies: marking of mammals; standard methods and new developments. *Ecology* **37**, 681–5.

TAFT, H. M. and AGEE, H. R., 1962. A marking and recovery method for use in boll weevil movement studies. *J. econ. Ent.* **55**, 1018–19.

TURNER, F. B., 1960. Tests of randomness in re-captures of *Rana pipretiosa*. *Ecology* **41**, 237–9.

URQUART, F. A., 1958. *The monarch butterfly*. Toronto, 361 pp.

WALOFF, Z., 1963. Field studies on solitary and *transiens* desert locusts in the Red Sea area. *Anti-Locust Bull.* **40**, 93 pp.

WAVE, H. E., HENNEBERRY, T. J. and MASON, H. C., 1963. Fluorescent biological stains as markers for *Drosophila*. *J. econ. Ent.* **56**, 890–1.

WEATHERSBEE, A. A. and HASELL, P. G., 1938. On the recovery of stain in adults developing from anopheline larvae stained *in vitro*. *Amer. J. trop. Med.* **18**, 531–43.

WELCH, H. E., 1960. Two applications of a method of determining the error of population estimates of mosquito larvae by the mark and recapture technique. *Ecology* **41**, 228–9.

WIEGERT, R. G. and LINDEBORG, R. G., 1964. A 'stem well' method of introducing radioisotopes into plants to study food chains. *Ecology* **45**, 406–10.

WILLIAMS, C. B., COCKBILL, G. F., GIBBS, M. E. and DOWNES, J. A., 1942. Studies in the migration of Lepidoptera. *Trans. R. ent. Soc. Lond.* **92**, 101–283.

WOJTUSIAK, R. J., 1958. (New method for marking insects.) *Folia biol. Krakow* **1958**, 6, 71–8.

WOOD, G. W., 1963. The capture–recapture technique as a means of estimating populations of climbing cutworms. *Canad. J. Zool.* **41**, 47–50.

WOODBURY, A. M., 1956. Uses of marking animals in ecological studies: marking amphibians and reptiles. *Ecology* **37**, 670–4.

YATES, W. W., GJULLIN, C. M. and LINDQUIST, A. W., 1951. Treatment of mosquito larvae and adults with radioactive phosphorus. *J. econ. Ent.* **44**, 34–7.

YETTER, W. P. and STEINER, L. F., 1932. Efficiency of bait traps for the oriental fruit moth as indicated by the release and capture of marked adults. *J. econ. Ent.* **25**, 106–16.

ZAIDENOV, A. M., 1960. Study of house fly (Diptera, Muscidae) migrations in Chita by means of luminescent tagging. [In Russian.] *Ent. Obozr.* **39**, 574–84. (Transl. *Ent. Rev.* **39**, 406–14.)

ZUKEL, J. W., 1945. Marking *Anopheles* mosquitoes with fluorescent compounds. *Science* **102**, 157.

CHAPTER 4

Absolute Population Estimates by Sampling a Unit of Habitat – Air, Plants, Plant Products and Vertebrate Hosts

This is one of four approaches to the absolute population estimate; the other three being the spacing or nearest neighbour methods (p. 39), methods utilizing marked individuals (p. 75) and removal trapping (p. 181). In this approach the habitat is sampled and the contained animals along with it. Hence two separate measurements have to be made: the total number of animals in the unit of the habitat sampled and the total number of these units in the whole habitat of the population being studied. The second may involve the use of the techniques of the botanist, forester, surveyor or hydrologist and cannot be considered in detail here (see also Strickland, 1961). The first concerns the extraction of animals from the samples and sometimes the taking of samples; this and the next two chapters will be concerned mainly with these problems in two biotic (plants and vertebrate animals) and three physical habitats (air, soil and freshwater).

It is important to remember that if sampling is unbiased, the errors in the population estimates obtained by this method will nearly all lie on one side of the true value; all estimates will tend to be underestimates. This is because the efficiencies of the extraction processes will never be more than 100% – one cannot normally find more animals than are present! Usually one finds fewer. As the basis of the approach is to multiply the mean population figure per sampling unit by the number of such units in the habitat, usually a very large figure, the total final underestimation may, in terms of individuals, be large.

SAMPLING FROM THE AIR

In some ways air is the simplest of the five habitats, it is homogeneous in all environments and permits a universal solution which has now been provided by the work of C. G. Johnson & L. R. Taylor. They have developed suction traps, standardized them and measured their efficiency so precisely that aerial populations can now be assessed with a greater level of accuracy than those in most other habitats. The only environmental variable for which allowance needs to be made is wind speed. There is no evidence that insects are in any way attracted or repelled by the traps (Taylor, 1962*a*), although precautions must be taken to avoid the development of a charge of static electricity on the traps (Maw, 1964). Only a very small proportion of the insects collected in suction traps are damaged by them.

The basic features of the suction trap are an electric fan that pulls or drives air through a fine gauze cone; this filters out the insects which are collected in a jar or cylinder. The trap may be fitted with a segregating device, which separates the catch according to a predetermined time interval (normally an hour), and this provides information, not only about the numbers flying, but also about the periodicity of flight. Few insects are active equally throughout 24 hours (Lewis & Taylor, 1965) and therefore the daily catch divided by the daily intake of air of the fan does not present as realistic a picture of aerial density as if each hour is considered separately.

Sampling apparatus

a. Exposed cone type of suction trap

Here the air (and insects) pass through the fan first and subsequently into the copper gauze cone (26 mesh to the inch) (fig. 18); the cone and the mouth of the fan are both exposed to the effects of cross-winds. The most useful fan

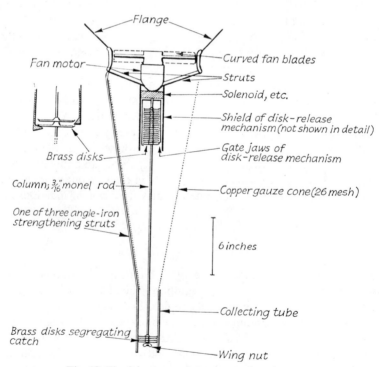

Fig. 18. The 9-in. exposed cone type of suction trap.

unit is the 9-in. Vent-Axia ('Silent Nine'). With this fan cross-winds of more than 14 m.p.h. lead to significant reductions in the air intake of the mouth of the fan, the effects of cross-winds are less at speeds of under 10 m.p.h. (Johnson, 1950a; Taylor, 1955). If the trap is standing amongst a crop, so that the cone is sheltered from the effects of the cross-winds, these only impinging on the mouth of the fan, the delivery loss is only 0·8% per m.p.h. cross-wind (Taylor, 1955).

The catch is collected in a brass tube at the base of the cone; the inside of this should be brushed with 1% solution of pyrethrum in petrol ether (Johnson, 1950; Johnson & Taylor, 1955a). If the trap is fitted with the segregating device, a series of brass discs are released by the time switch operated solenoid, one say each hour, and these accumulate in the collecting tube; the catch for each hour being retained between the appropriate pair of discs. The undersurface of the disc has a circle of muslin slightly larger than itself attached to it; this serves to brush the insects down the collecting tube and retains them between the appropriate discs; it also helps to hold a sufficient quantity of pyrethrum within the collecting tube to kill the larger insects. Various improvements to the original suction trap (Johnson, 1950), more especially to the catch-segregating mechanism and collecting tube, were described in detail by Taylor (1951). The mechanism has also been described by Horsfall (1962). 9-in. and 12-in. Vent-Axia suction traps are now commercially produced by the Burkard Manufacturing Co., Rickmansworth, England, under the name 'Johnson–Taylor traps'.

A 6-in. fan unit has also been used with an exposed cone type of trap (Johnson, 1950; Taylor, 1955, 1962a); this is a weaker fan and should only be operated in the shelter of vegetation. Bidlingmayer (1961) used a trap (referred to as 'powered aspirator') with a 5-in. fan for studying the flight of biting midges.

b. Enclosed cone types of suction trap

In these traps the fan unit is at the bottom of a metal cylinder and the metal gauze collecting cone opens to the mouth of the trap (fig. 19) so that the insects are filtered out before the air passes through the fan. More important, for the performance in higher wind speeds, the cone and mouth of the fan are protected from cross-winds. Johnson & Taylor (1955a and b) developed three traps in this class:

i. The 18-in. propeller trap, powered by a Woods 230/50 V, 50 c/s, 1-phase, 400 W, propeller fan mounted in a galvanized iron cylindrical duct; the air-filtering cone is of 32-mesh copper gauze and at its base the glass collecting jar screws into a socket; the jar contains 70% alcohol; to empty the trap the cone is removed and the jar unscrewed (fig. 19).

ii. The 12-in. aerofoil trap, powered by a Woods 230/50 V, 50 c/s, 440 W, 1-phase capacity start, capacitor run ventilator fan, mounted at the base of a sheet steel cylinder 14 in. diameter, 4·5 ft long; the air-filtering cone is of 28-mesh steel gauze. This trap is fitted with a catch-segregating device.

   iii. *The 30-in. air screw trap,* powered by a specially made light-weight fan

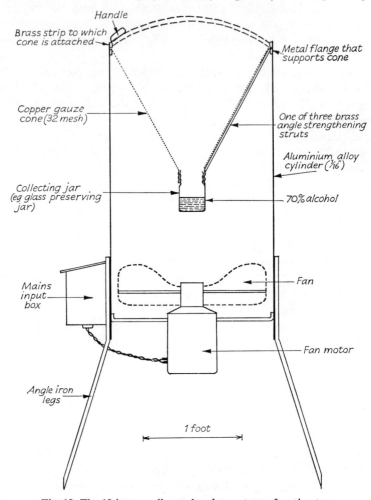

Fig. 19. The 18-in. propeller enclosed cone type of section trap.

at the base of a cylindrical cage 7·5 ft high and 2·5 ft diameter. This trap, with its light construction and enormous air delivery, was designed for operation on barrage balloons to sample the comparatively sparse aerial population at heights up to 1000 ft above ground level.

c. Rotary and other traps

The rotary or whirligig trap consists of a gauze net that is rotated at a speed of about 10 m.p.h. on the end of an arm (fig. 20); this type of trap has been developed a number of times, sometimes with a single net and sometimes with a net at each end of the arm (Williams & Milne, 1935; Chamberlin, 1940; Stage, Gjullin & Yates, 1952; Nicholls, 1960; Vité & Gara, 1961; Gara & Vité, 1962; Prescott & Newton, 1963). The greatest efficiency will be obtained if the net is built so as to sample isokinetically, that is, the airflow lines in it are straight; Taylor (1962*a*) has described such a net (fig. 20). Rotary traps sample more or less independently of wind speed, until the wind speed exceeds that of the trap; Taylor's (1962*a*) experiments indicate that they sample 85% of the flying population, but Juillet (1963) has suggested that some insects may be able to crawl out and escape; this can be prevented by adequate baffles inside the net. It is also probable that strong flyers with good vision may avoid

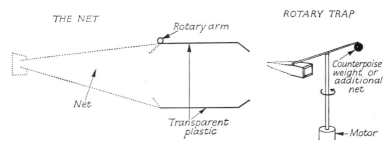

Fig. 20. A rotary trap, with an isokinetic net.

the area of the moving trap. It is not possible to segregate the catches of rotary traps, nor have their efficiencies on differently sized insects been studied; so for more precise work suction traps are to be preferred. However, the whirligig traps are of some value in comparative studies, especially in areas such as forests, where wind speeds may vary considerably from trap site to trap site.

Other traps for flying insects, sticky and water traps and suspended nets are greatly influenced by wind speed, their efficiencies being low at low wind speeds. Although Taylor (1962*b*) has shown how it is possible to convert sticky trap and suspended net catches into absolute densities if the wind speeds are known, these methods are used in general for the relative estimation of populations and are discussed in chapter 7.

d. Comparison and efficiencies of the different types of suction traps
Three factors influence the choice of the type of suction trap: the density of the insects being studied, the wind speeds in the situation where sampling is proposed and the necessity or otherwise for information on periodicity. If information is required on periodicity, then a trap with a catch-segregating mechanism must be used, and this rules out the 18-in. propeller trap. The other two factors generally give the same indications, for the sparser the insects the larger the desired air intake (so as to sample an adequate number),

and the stronger the winds the stronger (larger) the trap should be. Now at ground level and up to 3 to 4 ft amongst vegetation insect populations are usually dense and wind speeds seldom exceed 6 m.p.h.; under these conditions the 9-in. exposed cone type is generally used. In more exposed situations (e.g. above short turf) or on towers or cables many feet above the ground the enclosed cone traps should be used; the greater the height the more powerful the winds and the sparser the insects and, therefore, the stronger the fan required. Where information on periodicity can be foregone the 18-in. propeller trap provides a robust, simple and relatively inexpensive piece of equipment.

The average air deliveries of the traps given by Taylor (1955) are: 9-in. Vent-Axia, 277 cu ft/min; 12-in. aerofoil trap, 1298 cu ft/min; 18-in. propeller trap, 2730 cu ft/min; 30-in. air screw trap 7071 cu ft/min. There is, however, a certain amount of individual variation, which over a long period could lead to significant differences in catches. Taylor (1962a) has suggested that unless the actual deliveries of the traps have been checked in the field, differences in catch should exceed 6% for 9-in. traps, 2% for 12-in. traps or 10% for 18-in. traps, before they be attributed to population differences.

The effects of wind speed on the absolute efficiencies of the traps vary according to the size of the insects as well as the performance of the fan. Taylor (1962a) has shown that the efficiency of a trap for a particular insect is given by the formula:

$$E = (W+3)(0 \cdot 0082CE - 0 \cdot 123) + (0 \cdot 104 - 0 \cdot 159 \log i)$$

where E=the log efficiency of the trap, W=wind speed in m.p.h., CE=coefficient of efficiency of the trap and i=insect size in mm². The coefficient of efficiency of a trap = (vol sampled in cu ft/hr)$^{\frac{1}{3}}$ ÷ (inlet diameter of the fan in inches)$^{\frac{1}{3}}$; those for the above traps are: 9-in. 8·7, 12-in. 12·1, 18-in. 12·1, and 30-in. 13·4. Sizes (i.e. length × wing span) of various insects in mm² given by Taylor (1962a) are as follows:

Minute Phoridae and Sphaeroceridae	1–3	mm²
Oscinella, Psychodidae and small Aphididae	3–10	mm²
Drosophila, Chlorops, large Aphididae	10–30	mm²
Fannia, Musca	30–100	mm²
Calliphora, Lucilia	100–300	mm²
Sarcophaga, Tabanus	300–1000	mm²

Conversion of catch to aerial density

The numbers of insects caught is divided by the volume of air sampled; the actual crude delivery figures, given above, may be used for suction traps close to the ground if the wind speed seldom exceeds 5 m.p.h.; in other situations appropriate corrections should be made (Taylor, 1955). This figure is then corrected for the efficiency of extraction, of the particular insect, by use of the formula for efficiency given immediately above. This formula gives a negative value in logs and this is the proportion by which the actual catch is less than the real density.

Where catches have been segregated at hourly intervals the tables of conversion factors may be used (table 8); Taylor (1962a) also gives conversion

Table 8. Conversion factors for suction trap catches (after Taylor, 1962)

FOR 9-IN. VENT-AXIA TRAP

Insect size (mm²)	Wind speed (m.p.h.)				
	0–2	2–4	4–6	6–8	8–10
			$\log f$		
1– 3	1·89	2·00	2·12	2·23	2·34
3– 10	1·97	2·08	2·20	2·31	2·42
10– 30	2·05	2·16	2·28	2·39	2·50
30– 100	2·13	2·24	2·36	2·47	2·58
100– 300	2·21	2·32	2·44	2·55	2·66
300–1000	2·29	2·40	2·52	2·63	2·74

FOR 18-IN. PROPELLER TRAP

Insect size (mm²)	Wind speed (m.p.h.)						
	0–2	2–4	4–6	6–8	8–10	10–14	14–20
			$\log f$				
1– 3	0·85	0·89	0·95	1·01	1·07	1·15	1·29
3– 10	0·93	0·97	1·03	1·09	1·15	1·23	1·37
10– 30	1·01	1·05	1·11	1·17	1·23	1·31	1·45
30– 100	1·09	1·13	1·19	1·25	1·31	1·39	1·53
100– 300	1·17	1·21	1·27	1·33	1·39	1·47	1·61
300–1000	1·25	1·29	1·35	1·41	1·47	1·55	1·69

factors for 12-in. and 30-in. traps. The conversion factors are given in logs so that:

$$\log \text{catch/hour} + \text{conversion factor} = \log \text{density}/10^6 \text{ cu ft of air}$$

Conversion of density to total aerial population

Johnson (1957) has shown that the density of insects (*f*) at a particular height (*z*) is given by:

$$f_z = C(z+z_e)^{-\lambda}$$

where f_z = density at height *z*, *C* = a scale factor dependent on the general size of the population in the air, $\lambda =$ an index of the profile and of the aerial diffusion processes and $z_e =$ a constant added to the actual height and possibly related to the height of the boundary layer: the height at which the insects' flight speed is exceeded by the wind speed (Taylor 1958).

These values should be determined as follows (Johnson, 1957). Firstly z_e must be found. The data are plotted on double logarithmic paper, when a curve will be obtained (fig. 21). The observed heights are each increased by a constant until a straight line is obtained; the value that gives the greatest linearity is taken as z_e.

To find λ the densities at two heights near the ends of the graph are read off. Now:

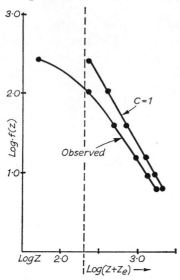

Fig. 21. The plotting of insect aerial density against height on a double logarithmic transformation. The observed curve is not linear until the constant z_e has been added to the height (after Johnson, 1957).

$$\lambda = \log\left(\frac{f_{z_1}}{f_{z_2}}\right) \div \log\left(\frac{z_2 + z_e}{z_1 + z_e}\right)$$

where $f_{z_1} =$ density of insects at height z_1 which is near or at the minimum height of observations and $f_{z_2} =$ density at height z_2 which is near or at the maximum height of observations.

Then:

$$\log C = f_z + \lambda \log (z + z_e)$$

where $f_z =$ density of insects at height z (which may be z_1 or z_2 or another).

The total number of insects between heights z_1 and z_2 (P) may then be integrated as follows

$$P = \frac{C}{1 - \lambda}[(z_2 + z_e)^{1-\lambda} - (z_1 + z_e)^{1-\lambda}]$$

where the symbols are as above.

With individual species of insect, the profiles may be found to be rather irregular and approximate integrations may then be made graphically (Johnson, Taylor & Southwood, 1962). The density at each height sampled should be plotted on double logarithmic paper (i.e. plot log density against log height) and curves drawn in by eye. Then density estimates at various heights can be read off and these plotted against height on ordinary arithmetic graph paper, and the area under each curve, between say ground level and cloud base, may easily be found. Such an approach will, of course, give only approximate values and some measure of the variation can be obtained by drawing alternative curves, if they are possible, on the log/log plot and comparing the population figures derived from them.

In many ways this is the most difficult habitat to sample from; it differs from the soil and the air both in being much more heterogeneous and in continually changing. It is frequently convenient to take a part of the plant as the sampling unit; the resulting population estimate is not an absolute one, but a measure of *population intensity*. The distinction between these terms has already been discussed (p. 2), but the point is so vital that some further elaboration here is justified. If the amount of damage to the plant is the primary concern it may seem reasonable to make all estimates in terms of numbers of, say, mites per leaf. This is the intensity of mites that the tree has to withstand, and if mite populations were being related to some index of the health of the tree such an estimate of 'population intensity' is probably the most relevant. But if the study is concerned with the changes in the numbers of mites in a season a series of estimates of population intensity could easily be misleading. If the number of mites per leaf fell throughout the summer this could be due to an actual reduction in the mite population or to an increase in the numbers of leaves. In order to determine which of these explanations is correct the number of leaves per branch would have to be counted on each sampling date, and the mite population could then be expressed in terms of numbers per branch. This is sometimes called a 'basic population estimate', but it differs from the measure of population intensity only in degree and not fundamentally, for from year to year the number of branches or indeed the number of trees in the forest or orchard will alter. It is only when these units are also counted and the whole converted into numbers per unit surface area of soil, commonly per square metre, square yard or acre, that it is possible to make a valid comparison between populations differing in time (and space), which is the essence of life-table or budget construction.

The labour of obtaining the additional data on the density of the plant unit is often comparatively slight, and it cannot be stressed too strongly that this should always be done wherever possible as it makes the resulting data so much more meaningful.

Assessing the plant

The simplest condition is found in annual crops where the regular spacing and uniform age of the plants makes the estimation of the number of shoots or plants per length of row a relatively easy matter: the variance of even a few samples is often small and the determination of the number of row length units per unit of area (e.g. per m^2), is also straightforward. With natural herbaceous vegetation there will usually be far more variability in the number of individual plants of the species that is the insect's host, per unit area and in their age. Although the number of plants per unit area is sometimes an adequate measure, the variation in size and age often means that weight of plant or the number of some part of the plant frequented by the insect (e.g. flower head) gives a more adequate measure. Occasionally botanical measures such as frequency, as measured by a point quadrat (Greig-Smith, 1964), are useful.

The most complex situation is found when one attempts to assess the habit of arboreal insects. The leaf is often, but not always the sampling unit (Harris, 1960; Richards & Waloff, 1961); in this case its age, aspect and height above the ground need to be considered as well as the age of the tree. With a citrus mealy bug Browning (1959) found the variance was minimal if each aspect of the tree was sampled in turn and individual leaves picked haphazardly rather than sampling the mealy bugs on all the leaves on a single branch.

The precise estimation of the number of leaves per branch is often a minor piece of research on its own. Actual numbers may be counted or dry weight used as the measure. In some trees the actual weight of the foliage may continue to increase after the leaves have ceased elongating (Ives, 1959). The diameter of the trunk may be taken as a cruder measure of foliage weight and of shoot number in young growing trees, especially conifers (Harris, 1960).

Determining the numbers of insects

Although a certain method may be suitable for a given insect, it is difficult to devise an 'all-species method' for synecological work, the more mobile insects frequently escaping (Chauvin, 1957).

1. Direct counting

With large conspicuous insects it is sometimes possible to count all the individuals, for example Moore (1964) was able to make a census of the male dragonflies over a pond using binoculars. Direct counts may also be used to follow a particular cohort (see p. 247) and they have the great advantage that the results are known to be true for that population; the difficulties of determining the true mean and other parameters, which may be severe in highly aggregated populations, are avoided.

More often a part of the habitat is delimited and the insects within the sample counted. Quadrats may be placed upon the ground and used to estimate fairly mobile, but relatively large, insects like grasshoppers (Richards & Waloff, 1954) or froghoppers (cercopids). These quadrats are made of wire and it is often useful to attach white marker-ribbons. They are placed in the field and are left undisturbed for some while before a count is made. Each quadrat is approached carefully and the numbers of insects within it counted as they fly or hop out. For smaller and less mobile animals the quadrat often needs wood or metal sides that may be driven into the soil to prevent the animals running out of the area whilst collecting or counting is in progress (Balogh & Loksa, 1956); in such cases and with other relatively immobile large insects, e.g. the sunn pest, *Eurygaster integriceps* (Banks & Brown, 1962), or lepidopterous larvae and pupae (Arthur, 1962), a count is made as soon as the quadrat is in position.

Where the insects are restricted to particular plants or trees, leaves or other portions of these may be collected or examined and the numbers on each sample counted, but care must be exercised as many insects can be dislodged as the samples are taken (Satchell & Mountford, 1962). Forest and orchard pests are often assessed as numbers per shoot (e.g. Wildholtz *et al.*, 1956); crop insects as numbers per plant (Richards, 1940) or per leaf. It will commonly be found that the position of the shoot or leaf – whether it is in the upper, middle or lower part of the tree or plant – influences the numbers of insects upon it, and due allowance should be made for this stratification by a subdivision of the habitat (p. 16). When small abundant insects are actually being counted it is desirable that the sampling unit should be as small as possible; Shands, Simpson & Reed (1954) showed that various aphids on potatoes could be adequately estimated by counting, not every aphid on a selected leaf, but only those on the terminal and two basal leaflets; even a count based on those on a half of each of those leaflets could be satisfactory. Insects in stored products, especially cacao, are often estimated by 'snaking'. The bag is opened and the contents tipped on to a floor in a long wavy line; the insects may be counted directly and a large number will often be found in the last piece tipped out, known as the 'tail'. This method, although technically providing an absolute type of sample, is really more properly regarded as a relative method.

2. The separation of exposed small animals from the foliage on which they are living

a. *Knockdown – by chemicals, jarring and heat*
Knockdown by chemicals and jarring are discussed more fully below, as they are more generally used when the whole twig or tree is the sampling unit. Here we are concerned with their use with animals on herbaceous plants and with animals on trees when the leaf is the sampling unit. Some insects can be made to drop off foliage by exposing them to the vapours of certain chemicals. With the wide range of organic substances available this approach could undoubtedly be extended. Aphids can be made to withdraw their stylets and will mostly drop off the plant if exposed to the vapour of methyl isobutyl ketone (Gray & Schuh, 1941; Helson, 1958; Alikhan, 1961). Aphids that do not cover the host plant with a thick deposit of honey dew and are fairly active may be separated from the foliage by exposing them to this vapour and then shaking them in the type of sampling can described by Gray & Schuh (1941) (fig. 22a). With the pea aphid *Acyrthosiphon pisum*, these authors

shook the can 50 times following a 5-minute interval and found that after one such treatment an average of 89·3% of the aphids were extracted, after 10 minutes (and 100 shakes) 97% and after 15 minutes 99·1%. In the six samples tested the lowest extraction rate was 98·5% after 15 minutes; the numbers extracted from each sample in the can were between 3000 and 7000. Laster & Furr (1962) found that the fauna of sorghum heads could be killed by insecticide and collected in a paper cone strapped round the stem and stabilized with a little sand in the base.

Thrips may be extracted from flowers and grassheads, as well as foliage, by exposing them to turpentine vapour (Evans, 1933; Lewis, 1960). A convenient apparatus has been described by Lewis who found the method was over 80% efficient for adults, but confirmed Taylor & Smith's (1955) conclusion that it

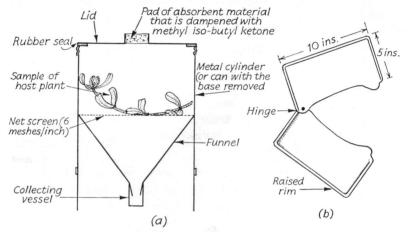

Fig. 22. *a*. Aphid sampling can (modified from Gray & Schuh, 1941). *b*. Sampling tray for flea-beetle, weevils and others on small crop plants (after la Croix, 1961).

was unsatisfactory for larvae. Lewis & Navas (1962) obtained thrips and some other insects that were overwintering in bark crevices by breaking the bark sample into small pieces and sieving; this dislodges the majority, but to obtain 97–100% extraction efficiencies the fragments were exposed to turpentine vapour.

Heat was used by Hughes (1963) to stimulate *Brevicoryne brassicae* to leave cabbage leaves, and Hoerner's (1947) onion thrips extractor worked on the same principle; these techniques can be considered modifications of the Berlese funnel (p. 145).

Insects that fall from their host plant when disturbed, e.g. some beetles, can be sampled from young field crops by enclosing the base of the plant in a hinged metal tray (fig. 22*b*). The plant is then tapped (jarred) and beetles from it may be counted as they fall on to the tray. This method was developed by la Croix (1961) for flea beetles, *Podagrica*, on cotton seedlings; they must be counted quickly before they hop off the tray. This is facilitated by painting the tray white.

b. Brushing

Mites, and apparently other small animals apart from insects, are removed from leaves if these are passed between two spiral brushes revolving at high speed in opposite directions (Henderson & McBurnie, 1943; Morgan *et al.*, 1955; Chant & Muir, 1955; Chant. 1962). The mites are collected on a glass plate, covered with adhesive, below the machine. Clear varnish was the original adhesive, but various surface-active agents have been found more satisfactory if the mites are to be examined at once; e.g. Emcol 5100, an alkanolamine condensate (Morgan *et al.*, 1955), Tween 20 (polyoxyethylene sorbitan monolaurate) and span (sorbitan monolaurate) (Cleveland, 1962). For permanent storage Muir in Chant (1962) recommends replacing the glass plate with a cardboard disc, repeatedly coated with varnish. Adult mites are usually removed slightly more efficiently than the eggs; in general the efficiency for fruit-tree mites has been found to be between 95 and 100% (Morgan *et al.*, 1955; Chant & Muir, 1955).*

c. Washing

Small animals, principally mites, aphids and thrips, can be washed off herbaceous plants or single leaves with various solutions. With aphids the extraction will be facilitated if they are first exposed to the vapour of methyl isobutyl ketone (=4-methyl 2-pentanone) (Gray & Shuh, 1941; Pielou, 1961). Dilute soap detergent or alcohol solutions are often adequate for washing (e.g. Newell, 1947; Taylor & Smith, 1955; Szalay-Marzsó, 1957), but with eggs a solvent must be used that will dissolve the cement. Benzene heated almost to boiling point, removes many of the eggs of mites on fruit-tree twigs (Morgan *et al.*, 1955), as does hot sodium hydroxide solution (Jones & Prendergast, 1937); whilst petrol has been found satisfactory for washing eggs of the corn earworm (*Heliothis zea*) from the silks of maize (Connell, 1959). Thrips may be washed off foliage with ethanol (Le Pelley, 1942), the solution filtered and the thrips separated from the other material by shaking in benzene and water; the thrips pass into the benzene where they may be counted (see also p. 141) (Bullock, 1963).

The animals removed by washing are often too numerous to be counted directly by eye, and electronic counters have been devised by Lowe & Dromgoole (1958) and Hughes & Woolcock (1963). An alternative approach is to count a sample; this may be done by means of a counting grid or disc (fig. 23) (Strickland, 1954; Morgan *et al.*, 1955). The animals are mixed with 70% alcohol or some other solution, agitated in a Petri dish and allowed to settle. The dish is stood above a photographically produced counting disc (on celluloid) and illuminated from below. Strickland (1954) found that the

---

* Mite eggs on peach leaves are much less efficiently removed (Putnam, W. L., 1966. *J. econ. Ent.* **59**, 224–5).

E M—E

percentage error of the count for aphids using the disc in fig. 23 ranged from 5 (with about 3000 aphids/dish) to 15 (with less than 500 aphids/dish).

If the number of animals is too great for the counting grid to be used directly the 'suspension' of the animals in a solution may be aliquoted (Newell, 1947). The diluted samples may then be estimated with a counting disc or volumetrically or the two methods combined. In the volumetric method the animals are allowed to settle or are filtered out of the solution; they are then estimated as, for example, so many small specimen-tubefuls, the

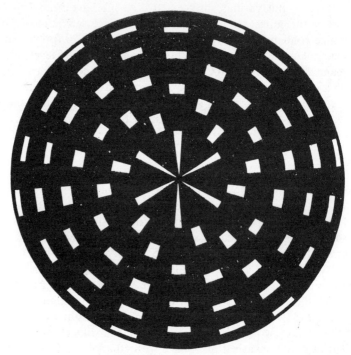

Fig. 23. A counting grid (after Strickland, 1954). All animals that are wholly within the clear areas or overlap the left-hand or outer margins should be counted and these will be one-sixth of the total.

numbers in a few of the tubes are counted partially by the use of a counting disc or *in toto* (Banks, 1954). If the population consists of very different sized individuals the volumetric method may lead to inaccuracies, unless special care is taken. This variation can, however, be used to aid estimation: Pielou (1961) showed that if apple aphids (*Aphis pomi*) were shaken with alcohol and the solution placed in Imhoff sedimentation cones (wide-mouthed graduates), the sediment stratifies into layers, firstly the larger living aphids, then the smaller living aphids, and finally dead aphids and cast skins; the volumes of these can easily be read off and this calibrated for the various categories.

Another method of separating the instars based on the same principle has been developed by Kershaw (1964).

d. *Imprinting*

This technique has been used only with mites and their eggs; the infested leaves are placed between sheets of glossy absorbent paper and passed between a pair of rubber rollers (e.g. a household wringer); where each mite or its egg has been squashed a stain is left (Venables & Dennys, 1941; Austin & Massee, 1947). Summers & Baker (1952) used the same method to record the mites beaten from almond twigs, and the advantage of this method is its speed and the provision of a permanent record; furthermore, with certain precautions, nearest neighbour type techniques (p. 39) might be applied to the resulting marks. However, Chant & Muir (1955) found with the fruit-tree red spider mite (*Panonychus ulmi*) that the number recorded by the imprinting method was significantly less than the number recorded by the brushing method (see above), which is therefore to be preferred in general.

3. The expulsion of animals from trees or shrubs

a. *Jarring or beating*

This is a collector's method and originally the tree was hit sharply with a stick and the insects collected in an umbrella held upside down under the tree! The umbrella is now replaced by a beating tray which is basically a cloth-covered frame, flat or slightly sloping towards the centre, that is large enough to collect all the insects that drop off the tree. The colour of the cloth should produce the maximum contrast with that of the insect being studied, and the insects are rapidly collected from the tray by an aspirator or pooter (fig. 52). In general this is only a relative method, but with some insects such as leaf beetles (Chrysomelids), many weevils and lepidopterous larvae that fall from the host plant, if disturbed, a sufficiently high proportion may be collected for it to be regarded as an absolute method (e.g. Richards & Waloff, 1961; Legner & Oatman, 1962; Gibb & Betts, 1963). As very small animals, like mites, may be overlooked on a beating tray and active ones may escape, more accurate counts can sometimes be obtained by fastening a screen over a large funnel. The twigs are tapped on the screen and mites and insects funnelled into a container (Boudreaux, 1953; Steiner, 1962).

The beating tray and funnel methods may be combined: Wilson (1962) attached a removal jar below a hole in the centre of the tray and Coineau (1962) placed a grid above a funnel in the centre of a net tray; this grid helps to separate twigs and other debris from the insects.

Although the tree is generally hit sharply with a stick, Legner & Oatman (1962) suggest the use of a rubber mallet, and Richards & Waloff (1961) found that some host plants (e.g. *Sarothamnus*) could be damaged by such violence (so leading to a change in the habitat); they recommended vigorous shaking by hand.

A different approach was developed by Lord (1965) for sampling the mirid predators on apple trees: branches were cut from the tree over a cloth tray and then divided into smaller portions which were put in a 'shaker' sampler, a revolving rectangular cage. The animals are dislodged by this treatment; Lord found that 60–100% of those present were dislodged after 500 revolutions in the sampler.

b. Chemical knockdown

The total number of insects on a fruit tree have been estimated by shrouding the tree with polythene sheets or screens and applying an insecticide with a rapid knockdown (e.g. pyrethrum) as a mist or aerosol; the dead insects are collected on a groundsheet below (Collyer, 1951). Tests in which a known number of marked insects were released indicated, however, that this method led to the recovery of only 48–78% of a mirid, the variety of the tree appearing to influence the result (Muir & Gambrill, 1960). In spite of these results, this might be a reliable absolute method for certain insects.

A method of estimating the population of leaf-feeding caterpillars on large forest trees was devised by Satchell & Mountford (1962). A systemic insecticide, phosdrin, was introduced into the tree and the falling caterpillars collected on a sheet. A watertight collar was formed round the trunk by a strip of rubber sheet attached at its lower end to a ring of smoothed bark by rubber solution, and supported by a wire ring held in position by skewers driven into the bark below the collar. A ring of horizontal chisel cuts at 2-cm intervals was made through the bark into the xylem near the bottom of this collar, and this was filled with the insecticide solution. Between 70 and 95% of the larvae of the trees fell on to the sheets after this treatment, and therefore it is necessary to count the remaining larvae on a proportion of the shoots on the tree to obtain a complete estimate. A possible source of error in this type of method is the consumption by birds of moribund larvae.

Besides the objections to the above methods due to their only partial efficiency, it is seldom desirable in long-term ecological work to destroy all the insects from a sampling unit as large as a whole tree. The fauna of part of a tree or bush or from the tops of herbaceous plants may be sampled by the use of a hinged metal box (fig. 24), whose leading edges are faced with sponge rubber – this will accommodate branches up to $\frac{1}{2}$ in. thick (Adam *in* Chauvin, 1957; Dempster, 1961). Once the branch is enclosed the insects are killed by a chemical: Adam used ethyl acetate, Dempster carbon dioxide from a small cylinder, released into the closed box through a small hole. The fauna becomes momentarily more active and then drops to the floor of the box, anaesthetized. The box may then be opened and the animals collected by a mouth-operated or an electric aspirator or pooter. This method is least efficient with those insects that tend to 'hang on' to the plant, e.g. mirid larvae, caterpillars.

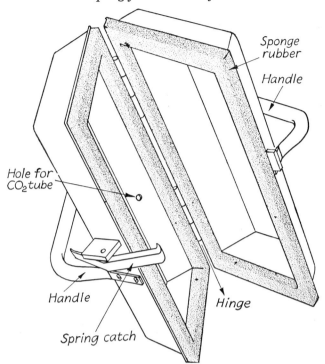

Fig. 24. A sampler for insects on woody vegetation (after Dempster, 1961).

c. Collection of naturally descending animals
Many arboreal larvae pupate in the soil and these may be collected as they descend to provide a population estimate of the total numbers at that particular developmental stage (see p. 246). Cone (1963) found that the vine weevil (*Otiorrhynchus sulcatus*) dropped off its host plant at daybreak and the population could therefore be determined by placing funnel-type traps under the grape vines.

4. The extraction of animals from herbage and debris
Here one is concerned with animals living in the herbage layer just above the soil and the problem is not, as in the above section, to make them fall down, but to get them to 'come up', either artificially or naturally.

a. Suction apparatus
A number of types of machine have been devised to sample, by suction, the animals living on or amongst the herbage down to the soil surface. There are basically two types (fig. 25); the narrow suction-hose type developed by Johnson *et al.* (1957) and others (table 9), and the wide hose type of Dietrick

et al. (1959). In the narrow suction-hose model the area to be sampled is enclosed by forcing a small metal cylinder (e.g. a bottomless bucket) into the soil; the area delimited is then systematically worked over with the nozzle and a mixture of animals and plant debris are trapped in the collecting bag (fig. 25). This may be sorted by hand or further extracted in a Berlese type apparatus (Dietrick, Schlinger & van den Bosch, 1959), but any further extraction,

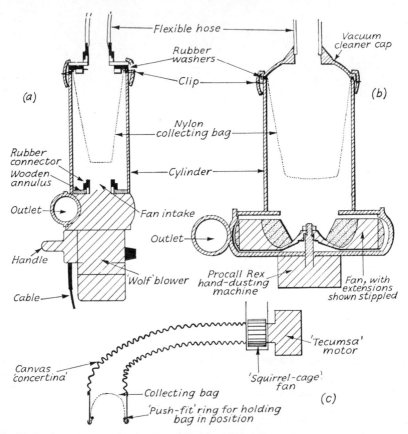

Fig. 25. Suction apparatus: *a.* electric model (after Johnson, Southwood & Entwistle, 1957); *b.* hand-operated model (after Southwood & Pleasance, 1962); *c.* the Dietrick model.

of course, introduces further errors. The suction is provided by a fan which can be driven by hand, by an electric motor or by a large or a small petrol motor (see table 9); if high rates of extraction are to be obtained the wind speed at the nozzle must be in the order of at least 60 m.p.h. (A low nozzle wind speed was probably the reason for the lack of success of this method for sampling apple-tree fauna reported by Lord (1965).) Extraction rates of 95–100% are obtained by Johnson *et al.* (1957) for groups such as Hemiptera, adult Diptera, adult Hymenoptera and surface-dwelling Collembola, and the

Table 9. Basic features of various types of suction apparatus. (Note: Ordinary vacuum-cleaner motors are not usually satisfactory as they tend to race when the nozzle is impeded and models based on them are not claimed to give absolute estimates)

| Authors | Fan unit and power source | Diameter of (in in.) | | Position of collecting chamber |
		Nozzle	Suction hose	
Dietrick, Schlinger & van den Bosch (1959)	20B 'Homelite' blower (single-cylinder, air-cooled petrol motor)		15	Separated from motor by 15-in. diameter extensible (to about 5 ft) air hose
Dietrick (1961) ('D-vac' model)	'Tecumsa' (single-cylinder, air-cooled petrol motor)	6½–13½	8	ditto
Weekman & Ball (1963)	Hoover 'Pixie' vacuum cleaner		1¼	ditto
Johnson, Southwood & Entwistle (1957)	Wolf portable electric blower (Type NWBE) mains electricity	1¼	2	Fixed to motor casing
Southwood & Pleasance (1962)	Gear box, fan and casing of Procall Rex dusting machine (with blades of fan enlarged to increase air flow), hand-operated	1	2	ditto
Cross & Southwood (unpublished)	British vacuum cleaner Ltd, T172 with petrol engine	2	2½	ditto
Whittaker (1965)	Smith's F350 centrifugal blower, operated from a 12-V battery	—	—	ditto
Remane (1958)	Blasator (Leer) 50-c.c petrol motor	—	—	—
Levi *et al.* (1959)	Pemz – 1 vacuum cleaner with 'Kiev' motor	1¼		Separated from fan by air hose

lowest rates (about 70–75%) for larval Diptera and Coleoptera. Using a battery-operated model Whittaker (1965) obtained an extraction rate of 87% for Auchenorrhyncha (Hemiptera).

Owing to the formation of a water film, in which animals may become trapped, inside the suction hose, it is difficult to sample damp herbage with the narrow suction-hose types of apparatus, but the substitution of a wide polythene tube for the more normal wire and canvas hose at least enables a check to be kept on this potential source of error. When sampling arable habitats it may be an advantage to use two bags, one of nylon net which retains the insects and outside this a larger cloth bag to prevent the soil passing through the fan. The narrow suction-hose type of sampler, with its high nozzle wind speed and fan whose efficiency does not fall off when impeded, is particularly suited for work with the fauna of the lower parts of vegetation and the soil surface.

In the Dietrick (1961) sampler, which is available commercially from D-vac Ltd, Ventura, California, the area to be sampled is delimited by the head of the suction tube which also contains the collecting bag; a squirrel-cage type of fan produces a strong air current so long as it is not impeded. This model is therefore particularly suited for use with animals on herbage; the elimination of the long suction hose before the collecting bag overcomes the problem of insects being trapped in a water film inside this hose, and therefore this suction apparatus may be used on damp foliage.

A suction apparatus samples more or less absolutely habitats where the only other available method is sweeping (p. 189), which can under certain conditions give a biased picture (Johnson *et al.*, 1957; Heikinheimo & Raatikainen, 1962). The suction apparatus can be used under different weather conditions and from herbage at different stages of growth, but because the estimates are absolute ones per unit area, all can be directly compared. It can also be used for sampling the fauna of bark or of underground rodents' nests (Levi *et al.*, 1959), or, a lighter model, for insects in the flowers of trees (Kennard & Spencer, 1955).

The main disadvantage of this method arises from the patchy distribution of animals in many natural habitats; the variance of 4-in. diameter samples from some habitats has been found to be very high; whereas in contrast sweep net samples from the same habitat were far more uniform, for here a much larger part of the habitat is sampled, albeit only partially. The theoretical answer lies in taking far more suction apparatus samples, but each sample must be from a very small area if the worker is not to become overburdened with sorting the catches.

Santa (1961) has described a method for sampling the leafhoppers on rice stubble by blowing them off the plants with a mechanical blower into a collecting bag.

b. Cylinder or covering method

The basis of this method is the enclosure of an area of herbage within a covered cylinder; the animals are knocked down with an insecticide and collected by some method. Kretzschmar (1948) used a modification of Romney's (1945) technique for sampling soya-bean insects; he placed plastic transparent base plates beneath the plants the day before sampling. These greatly facilitate the subsequent collection of the insects, but I would suggest that tests should be made to ensure that their presence does not influence the density of insects on the plants above. In order to prevent the escape of active insects, Balogh & Loksa (1956) attached the sampling cylinder to the end of a long pole and rapidly brought this down on to the crop. These workers killed the insects with powerful fumigants (carbon disulphide, hydrogen cyanide) and then removed them by hand. As it is difficult to reach and search the base of a tall cylinder Skuhravý *et al.* (1959, 1961) used two cylinders and removed the tall outer one after the insects had been knocked down.

The combination of some of these improvements with a suction apparatus for collection (a hand-operated model would probably be adequate), might provide a valuable absolute method for synecological work.

c. Tents for sampling strongly phototactic animals
A large muslin covered cage or 'tent' (fig. 26) is quickly put into position when the animals are least active, usually at dusk. When they are active again, the following morning, the animals (if large) may be directly collected from the sides of the tent; alternatively it may be covered with a black shroud leaving

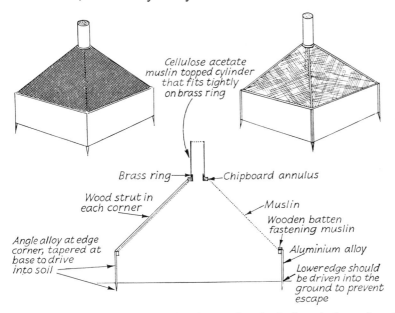

Fig. 26. A 'tent' for sampling strongly phototactic animals from herbage. A sagittal section through one corner and a side, with sketches of its appearance, shrouded and unshrouded.

only the muslin-topped celluloid collecting cylinder exposed at the apex. After some time, about 15 minutes in bright sunshine, the majority of the animals will be in the cylinder, which can be quickly removed and is conveniently carried back to the laboratory by pushing its base into appropriately sized rings of 'Plasticine' on a metal tray. If possible someone should then get inside the 'tent' and remove the remaining animals from the insides of the walls; on a dull day quite a large proportion of the total population may fail to enter the collecting cylinder. This method has been used successfully with blowflies (*Lucilia*) (MacLeod & Donnelly, 1957), mosquitoes (Chinaev, 1959) and frit flies (*Oscinella frit*) (Southwood *et al.*, 1961). A miniature tent for use with mites is described by Jones (1950).

An apparatus that is intermediate between a cylinder and a tent has been devised by Wiegert (1961) for sampling grasshoppers, cercopids and other insects that readily leave the vegetation if disturbed. It consists of a truncated nylon-covered strap-iron cone, topped with a metal funnel and a collecting jar. As with the tent or cylinder, this is placed rapidly over the vegetation which is then agitated. The sampling cone is then gradually moved on to a flat sheet, of wood or other substance, that is placed adjacent to it. Eventually most of the vegetation can be slid out of the cone whilst the active insects remain; it is then inverted and the insects jarred down into the collecting container. Wiegert considered the efficiency for the froghopper, *Philaenus*, greater than 90%.

d. *Extraction by heat and drying*
A further extension of the use of the animal's reactions to certain physical conditions leads logically to the removal of samples of herbage or debris to the laboratory, where they are subjected to drying by heat. This is the basis of the Berlese/Tullgren funnel and the many modifications of it that are discussed in chapter 5 (p. 145); although principally a method for soil and litter, it may be used with herbage (e.g. Dietrick *et al.*, 1959).

5. Methods for animals in plant tissues
Although leaf-miners may be directly counted (p. 233), it is seldom possible to estimate eggs imbedded in plant tissue or larval or adult insects boring into the stems of herbaceous plants or trees so simply. The main impetus for the development of techniques for such animals has been provided by work on insect pests of stored grain and timber. Doubtless considerable advances will be made when the approaches developed in this field are applied and extended with insects in the tissues of herbaceous plants.

a. *Dissection*
This method is widely applicable, if tedious. Sometimes it is possible to limit the dissection of stems, fruits or other parts to those that are obviously damaged.

b. *Bleaching and/or selective staining*
The plant tissue may be rendered transparent by treatment in 'Eau de Javelle', lactophenol (Koura, 1958; Carlson & Hibbs, 1962) or 10% sodium hydroxide solution (Apt, 1950) so that the insects become visible; this method

has been used with grains and lentils. Plant parasitic nematodes are assessed by simultaneously bleaching the plant tissues and staining the worms in a mixture of lactophenol and cotton blue (Goodey, 1957). The eggs of various Hemiptera in potato leaves can be detected by bleaching the leaves (boiled in water until limp and then in 95% alcohol over a water bath) and then staining in saturated solution of methyl red and differentiating in a slightly alkaline solution (containing sodium hydroxide) of the same dye; the leaf tissues become orange or yellow, but the eggs remain bright red and may be counted by transmitted light (Curtis, 1942). However, Carlson & Hibbs (1962) found that the same eggs could be counted after merely boiling for one minute in lactophenol, when the leaf tissues become bleached and egg proteins coagulated. Insect egg plugs in grains have been found to be stained selectively by gentian violet (when moist) (Goosens, 1949) or by various alkaloids, derberine sulphate, chelidonium and primuline that fluoresce yellow, orange and light blue under ultra-violet light (Milner, Barney & Shellenberger, 1950). If the grain is crushed the insect protein may be recognized by the ninhydrin test (Dennis & Decker, 1962).

c. X-rays
In 1924 Yaghi suggested that these rays could be used in the detection of wood-boring insects, but it is only recently that the principle has been extensively applied, more particularly to insects in homogeneously textured materials: in grain (Milner *et al.*, 1950, 1953; Pedersen & Brown, 1960) and other seeds (Simak, 1955); it is also of wide applicability to the assessment of insects in moist plant tissues: for wood-borers (Berryman & Stark, 1962; Bletchly & Baldwin, 1962), stem-borers (Goodhue & van Emden, 1960) and bollworms (Graham *et al.*, 1964). The cavity made by the larva or adult is much more easily detected in the radiographs than the difference between animal and plant tissues. Where one has to rely on the latter distinction, as with the blackcurrant gall mite, *Cecidophytopsis ribis*, then the value of the method may be limited; for long exposures to maximize the distinction will lead to blurred images (Smith, 1960). It has generally been found that 'soft' X-rays (5–35 kV) are best for the work; the thicker the plant material the greater the kilovoltage required for the same exposure time. Small portable X-ray units (e.g. 'Picker') with a thin (*c.* 2 mm) beryllium window are particularly suitable for ecological work. Further technical details are given in the papers cited above. It has been shown by De Mars (1963) that X-ray detection of a bark beetle, *Dendroctonus*, is virtually as efficient as dissection, eight times faster and less than a quarter the cost, even when allowance is made for materials. Wickman (1964) reached similar conclusions for its use with Siricidae. The interpretation of X-rays of bark insects is discussed by Berryman (1964).

d. Methods based on the different mass of the whole and the infested material
Where the plant material is of fairly uniform weight, e.g. grain, advantage
may be taken of the fact that material in which insects have, or are, feeding
will be lighter. The lighter grain can be made to float (e.g. in 2% ferric nitrate
solution – Apt, 1952) or to fall more rapidly when projected (Katz, Farrell &
Milner, 1954). Such an approach naturally leads on to flotation techniques
that are discussed in chapter 5.

Special sampling problems with animals in plant material

a. The marking of turf samples
Van Emden (1963) has described a method whereby small areas of turf may
be marked and subsequently found and recognized without impairing mowing
or grazing or attracting the attention of vandals. Wire rings, marked with a
colour code, were sunk into the soil around the samples and here they could
remain for weeks or even years. Their approximate positions were recorded
by reference to a grid and a diagonal tape, and their condition or other
relevant ecological information noted. After the desired period, the rings may
be rediscovered and the ecological changes in the precise area observed, by
plotting the approximate position with reference to the grid and finding the
actual ring with a mine-detector.

b. The sampling of bulk grain
When studying insect populations in stored grain, it is often desired to draw
samples from known depths ensuring that they are not contaminated by
insects or grain from the outer layers. Burges (1960) has developed a method
for doing this: a hollow spear with a lateral aperture is forced into the required
position and then the desired sample sucked out through its shaft by a domestic vacuum cleaner. Other types of aspirator for sampling grain have been
described by Chao & Peterson (1952) and Ristich & Lockard (1953).

c. The sampling of bark
A circular punch that cuts 0·1 sq ft samples from bark has been devised by
Furniss (1962). The punch is made from a segment of a 4-in. diameter steel
pipe fitted with a central handle so that it can be rapidly and symmetrically
hammered into the bark. Very thick bark may need to have the outer layer
shaved off first if Scolytidae are being sampled and the phloem layer required;
but not, of course, if the crevice fauna is being studied (Lewis & Navas, 1962).

SAMPLING FROM VERTEBRATE HOSTS

There are two important variables to be considered when attempting to
obtain complete samples of vertebrate ectoparasites from their hosts. Firstly
the readiness or otherwise with which they will leave their hosts, and secondly

whether the host can be killed or not. Furthermore, if the host is killed, can the skin be destroyed whilst obtaining the parasites or must it be retained in good condition? Sampling from living animals will generally be more likely to provide absolute population counts of those parasites that are readily dislodged from the host (e.g. fleas, hippoboscids) than for those that are more firmly attached (e.g. lice, mites); to estimate these the host will often need to be killed and even the skin destroyed.

Sampling from living hosts

Care must be taken in handling the host, for Stark & Kinney (1962) found that many fleas would rapidly leave a struggling or agitated host.

a. Searching
This method is usually satisfactory only with relatively large parasites (e.g. ticks), active ones (e.g. hippoboscids – Ash, 1952) or those that sit on exposed and hairless parts of the body. In the rare cases where the host is almost completely hairless minute parasites can be counted by this method, e.g. on man (Johnson & Mellanby, 1942). Nelson, Slen & Banky (1957) compared various relative sampling techniques for the sheep ked, *Melophagus ovinus*, with the 'total live counts' (MacLeod, 1948) and with the 'picked-off' count; in the latter method every ked that can be found on the sheep is picked off. They showed that the 'total live count', in which the living keds are counted as the fleece is parted, underestimated the total population; the actual mean estimates for different breeds of sheep ranging from 61 to 81% of the 'picked-off' count. This experiment emphasizes the importance of confirming that apparently absolute methods are really giving estimates of the total population. Ash (1960) sampled lice from living birds by removing a proportion of the feathers from the area frequented; the lice on these were determined and the total feathers in the area counted. Buxton (1947) determined the head louse populations of men by shaving the scalp and dissolving the hair.

b. Combing
A fine-toothed comb may be used to remove the ectoparasites on living mammals; but with lice, only a small part of the population is removed (see below). It is often an advantage if the host is anaesthetized with ether (Mosolov, 1959), but this also affects the parasites and is strictly a combination of combing and fumigation (see below).

c. Fumigation
This technique is particularly successful for Hippoboscidae and fleas (Siphonaptera) and is used for obtaining these parasites from birds at ringing stations

and elsewhere during ecological studies on vertebrates. The hosts are collected from a trap and immediately placed in a white cloth (linen) bag for transportation to the laboratory. Here they may be exposed to the vapour of ether (Mosolov, 1959; Janion, 1960) or chloroform (Williamson, 1954) that will dislodge the parasites. Janion merely sprinkled the bags containing the hosts (mice in his work) with ether and after a few seconds of gentle squeezing the mouse was released, the fleas remaining in the bag; Mosolov removed the rodents from the bag and shook and combed them with forceps and obtained a wide range of parasites. He points out that as larval ectoparasites are often

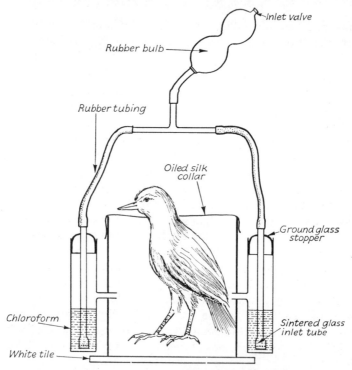

Fig. 27. The 'Fair Isle' apparatus for collecting bird ectoparasites.

pale and the adults dark they are most readily seen if they are shaken on to coloured paper. Malcomson (1960) dusted the plumage with pyrethrum powder and allowed the bird to flutter for about 5 minutes under an inverted paper cone.

In the 'Fair Isle apparatus' described by Williamson (1954) the bird is placed in an open-ended cylinder with its head projecting from one end and protected by a collar of oiled silk which also seals the top. The base of the cylinder is stood on a white tile and chloroform vapour is pumped into the cylinder. This is conveniently produced by bubbling air with a rubber bulb from inlet tubes (with ends of sintered glass) through chloroform (fig. 27). The bird should be encouraged to flutter during this process, that lasts for about one minute. The parasites will be found on the tile and in the bag in which the bird was carried; in view of Mosolov's (1959) observations a pink or light blue tile might be preferable to the white tile of the original model.

Kalamarz (1963) found that lice were efficiently removed from the host after fumigation if it was vacuum cleaned with a special brush nozzle.

Sampling from dead hosts

Mohr (1959) recommends the preservation of the host by formalin injection and its storage in a closed black cloth bag if the collection of ectoparasites cannot be carried out immediately.

a. Searching and combing

These methods combined with brushing in all directions with a stiff brush will provide many specimens from mammal pelts (Spencer, 1956), but often this is really only a relative method. With birds, however, Ash (1960) considered that a feather-by-feather search was the only efficient method for lice. Janzen (1963) used a novel principle, that may be of wider application, to obtain almost absolute samples of the beaver beetle (*Platypsyllus castoris*). The host's pelts were first frozen and then brought into a warm environment, the beetles would move away from the chilled pelts and the majority were found by searching; most of the remainder were extracted by combing.

b. Fumigation

If the mammals are trapped live, but can be sacrificed, fumigation with hydrogen cyanide (produced from calcium cyanide) for about 15 minutes followed by combing will yield most parasites (Ellis, 1955; Murray, 1957). Bird lice on hens have been sampled by fumigation with methyl bromide followed by fluffing the feathers (Harshbarger & Raffensperger, 1959).

c. Dissolving

The pelt of the host is dissolved, most conveniently by incubating with the proteolytic enzyme trypsin for two days, followed by boiling in 10% caustic potash for some minutes (Cook, 1954). After such treatment virtually only the ectoparasites remain and even minute Listrophorid mites can be recovered. This method is generally associated with Hopkins (1949), who records the following comparison with searching and beating; the latter method had yielded 31 lice (larvae and adults) from three pelts; when these were dissolved a further 1208 specimens were recovered. Although this method is very useful for mammal ectoparasites, Ash (1960) found it unsatisfactory for those on birds.

d. Clearing

The pelt is shaved and the hair placed in lysol or some other cleaning medium when the lice and their eggs may be counted under a microscope (Murray, 1961). If the exact distribution of the parasites is to be determined Murray recommends stunning the animals, soaking their coats with ether or chloroform to kill all lice *in situ* and then placing the animal in a closed jar until dead. The hair is then shaved from each area (these may be delimited by a grid) and mounted in Berlese's mounting medium.

e. Washing

Large numbers of ectoparasites, especially mites, can be removed by washing the pelt or the animal in a solution (<5%) of detergent (Lipovsky, 1951).

Sampling from vertebrate 'homes'

Birds' and rodents' nests, bat roosts and other vertebrate 'homes' may usually be treated as litter and their fauna extracted by modified Berlese funnels (Sealander & Hoffman, 1956) and the other methods described in the next chapter; however, Woodroffe (1953) concluded that there was no absolute method, he found a combination of warming and sieving most efficient. Drummond (1957) and Wasylik (1963) collected continuous samples of the mites in mammal and avian nests by placing funnels or gauze-covered tubes below the nests; such traps basically resemble pitfall traps (p. 195) and provide relative estimates.

REFERENCES

ALIKHAN, M. A., 1961. Population estimation techniques for studies on the black bean aphid, *Aphis fabae* Scop. *Annls. Univ. Mariae Curie-Sklodowska* (*C*) **14**, (1959), 83–92.

APT, A. C., 1950. A method for detecting hidden infestation in wheat. *Milling Production* **15** (5), 1.

APT, A. C., 1952. A rapid method of examining wheat samples for infestation. *Milling Production* **17** (5), 4.

ARTHUR, A. P., 1962. A skipper, *Thymelicus lineola* (Ochs.) (Lepidoptera: Hesperiidae) and its parasites in Ontario. *Canad. Ent.* **94**, 1082–9.

ASH, J. S., 1952. Records of Hippoboscidae (Dipt.) from Berkshire and Co. Durham in 1950, with notes on their bionomics. *Ent. mon. Mag.* **88**, 25–30.

ASH, J. S., 1960. A study of the Mallophaga of birds with particular reference to their ecology. *Ibis* **102**, 93–110.

AUSTIN, M. D. and MASSEE, A. M., 1947. Investigations on the control of the fruit tree red spider mite (*Metatetranychus ulmi* Koch) during the dormant season. *J. Hort. Sci.* **23**, 227–53.

BALOGH, J. and LOKSA, I., 1956. Untersuchungen über die Zoozönose des Luzernenfeldes. Strukturzönologische Abhandlung. *Acta Zool. Hung.* **2**, 17–114.

BANKS, C. J., 1954. A method for estimating populations and counting large numbers of *Aphis fabae* Scop. *Bull. ent. Res.* **45**, 751–6.

BANKS, C. J. and BROWN, E. S., 1962. A comparison of methods of estimating population density of adult Sunn Pest, *Eurygaster integriceps* Put. (Hemiptera, Scutelleridae) in wheat fields. *Ent. exp. appl.* **5**, 255–60.

BERRYMAN, A. A., 1964. Identification of insect inclusions in X-rays of Ponderosa pine bark infested by western pine beetle, *Dentroctonus brevicornis* Le Conte. *Canad. Ent.* **96**, 883–8.

BERRYMAN, A. A. and STARK, R. W., 1962. Radiography in forest entomology. *Ann. ent. Soc. Amer.* **55**, 456–66.

BIDLINGMAYER, W. L., 1961. Field activity studies of adult *Culicoides furens*. *Ann. ent. Soc. Amer.* **54**, 149–56.

BLETCHLY, J. D. and BALDWIN, W. J., 1962. Use of X-rays in studies of wood boring insects. *Wood* **27**, 485–8.

BOUDREAUX, H. B., 1953. A simple method of collecting spider mites. *J. econ. Ent.* **46**, 1102–3.

BROWNING, T. O., 1959. The long-tailed mealybug *Pseudococcus adonidium* L. in South Australia. *Aust. J. Agric. Res.* **10**, 322–39.

BULLOCK, J. A., 1963. Extraction of Thysanoptera from samples of foliage. *J. econ. Ent.* **56**, 612–14.

BURGES, H. D., 1960. A spear for sampling bulk grain by suction. *Bull. ent. Res.* **51**, 1–5.

BUXTON, P. A., 1947. *The Louse*. 2nd ed. London, 164 pp.

CARLSON, O. V. and HIBBS, E. T., 1962. Direct counts of potato leafhopper, *Empoasca fabae*, eggs in *Solanum* leaves. *Ann. ent. Soc. Amer.* **55**, 512–15.

CHAMBERLIN, J. C., 1940. A mechanical trap for the sampling of aerial insect populations. *U.S.D.A. Bur. Ent. Pl. Quar. E.T.* **163**, 12 pp.

CHANT, D. A., 1962. A brushing method for collecting mites and small insects from leaves. *Progress in Soil Zoology* **1**, 222–5.

CHANT, D. A. and MUIR, R. C., 1955. A comparison of the imprint and brushing machine methods for estimating the numbers of the fruit tree red spider mite, *Metatetranychus ulmi* (Koch), on apple leaves. *Rep. E. Malling Res. Sta.* (A) **1954**, 141–5.

CHAO, Y. and PETERSON, A., 1952. A new type of aspirator. *J. econ. Ent.* **45**, 751.

CHAUVIN, R., 1957. *Réflexions sur l'écologie entomologique*. Soc. Zool. Agricole Talence, 79 pp. [extract *Rev. Zool. Agric. appl.* 1956 (4–6, 7–9) and 1957 (1–3, 4–6)].

CHINAEV, P. P., 1959. Methods in quantitative sampling of bloodsucking mosquitoes (Diptera, Culicidae). [In Russian.] *Ent. Obozr.* **38**, 757–65 (transl. *Ent. Rev.* **38**, 679–86).

CLEVELAND, M. L., 1962. Adhesives for holding mites to glass plates. *J. econ. Ent.* **55**, 570–1.

COINEAU, Y., 1962. Nouvelles méthodes de prospection de la faune entomologique des plantes herbacées et ligneuses. *Bull. Soc. ent. Fr.* **67**, 115–19.

COLLYER, E., 1951. A method for the estimation of insect populations on fruit trees. *Rep. E. Malling, Res. Sta.* **1949-50**, 148–51.

CONE, W. W., 1963. The black vine weevil, *Brachyrhinus sulcatus*, as a pest of grapes in South Central Washington. *J. econ. Ent.* **56**, 677–80.

CONNELL, W. A., 1959. Estimating the abundance of corn earworm eggs. *J. econ. Ent.* **52**, 747–9.

COOK, E. F., 1954. A modification of Hopkins' technique for collecting ectoparasites from mammal skins. *Ent. News* **15**, 35–7.

CROIX, E. A. S. LA, 1961. Observations on the ecology of the cotton-flea-beetles in the Sudan Gezira and the effect of sowing date on the level of population in cotton. *Bull. ent. Res.* **52**, 773–83.

CURTIS, W. E., 1942. A method of locating insect eggs in plant tissues. *J. econ. Ent.* **35**, 286.

DE MARS, C. J., 1963. A comparison of radiograph analysis and bark dissection in estimating numbers of western pine beetle. *Canad. Ent.* **95**, 1112–16.

DEMPSTER, J. P., 1961. A sampler for estimating populations of active insects upon vegetation. *J. anim. Ecol.* **30**, 425–7.

DENNIS, N. M. and DECKER, R. W., 1962. A method and machine for detecting living internal insect infestation in wheat. *J. econ. Ent.* **55**, 199–203.

DIETRICK, E. J., 1961. An improved back pack motor fan for suction sampling of insect populations. *J. econ. Ent.* **54**, 394–5.

DIETRICK, E. J., SCHLINGER, E. I. and BOSCH, R. VAN DEN, 1959. A new method for sampling arthropods using a suction collecting machine and modified Berlese funnel separator. *J. econ. Ent.* **52**, 1085–91.

DRUMMOND, R. O., 1957. Observations on fluctuations of acarine populations from nests of *Peromyscus leucopus*. *Ecol. Monogr.* **27**, 137–52.

ELLIS, L. L., 1955. A survey of the ectoparasites of certain mammals in Oklahoma. *Ecology* **36**, 12–18.

EMDEN, H. F. VAN, 1963. A technique for the marking and recovery of turf samples in stem borer investigations. *Ent. exp. appl.* **6**, 194–8.

EVANS, J. W., 1933. A simple method of collecting thrips and other insects from blossom. *Bull. ent. Res.* **24**, 349–50.

FURNISS, M. M., 1962. A circular punch for cutting samples of bark infested with beetles. *Canad. Ent.* **94**, 959–63.

GARA, R. I. and VITÉ, J. P., 1962. Studies on the flight patterns of bark beetles (Coleoptera: Scolytidae) in second growth Ponderosa pine forests. *Contrib. Boyce Thompson Inst.* **21**, 275–90.

GIBB, J. A. and BETTS, M. M., 1963. Food and food supply of nestling tits (Paridae) in Breckland pine. *J. anim. Ecol.* **32**, 489–533.

GOODEY, J. B., 1957. Laboratory methods for work with plant and soil nematodes. *Tech. Bull. Min. Agric., Lond.* **2** (3rd ed.). London. H.M.S.O.

GOODHUE, R. D. and EMDEN, H. F. VAN, 1960. Detection of stem borers in Gramineae by X-rays. *Plant Path.* **9**, 194.

GOOSENS, H. J., 1949. A method for staining insect egg plugs in wheat. *Cereal Chem.* **26** (5), 419–20.

GRAHAM, H. M., ROBERTSON, O. T. and MARTIN, D. F., 1964. Radiographic detection of pink bollworm larvae in cottonseed. *J. econ. Ent.* **57**, 419–20.

GRAY, K. W. and SCHUH, J., 1941. A method and contrivance for sampling pea aphid populations. *J. econ. Ent.* **34**, 411–15.

GREIG-SMITH, P., 1964. *Quantitative plant ecology.* 2nd ed. London, 256 pp.

HARRIS, P., 1960. Number of *Rhyacionia buoliana* per pine shoot as a population index, with a rapid determination method of this index at low population levels. *Canad. J. Zool.* **38**, 475–8.

HARSHBARGER, J. C. and RAFFENSPERGER, E. M., 1959. A method for collecting and counting populations of the shaft louse. *J. econ. Ent.* **52**, 1215–16.

HEIKINHEIMO, O. and RAATIKAINEN, M., 1962. Comparison of suction and netting methods in population investigations concerning the fauna of grass leys and cereal fields, particularly in those concerning the leafhopper, *Calligypona pellucida* (F.). *Valt. Maatalousk. Julk. Helsingfors* **191**, 31 pp.

HELSON, G. A. H., 1958. Aphid populations: ecology and methods of sampling aphids *Myzus persicae* (Sulz.) and *Aulacorthum solani* (Kltb). *N.Z. Entomologist* **2**, 20–3.

HENDERSON, C. F. and MCBURNIE, H. V., 1943. Sampling technique for determining populations of the citrus red mite and its predators. *U.S.D.A. Circ.* **671**, 11 pp.

HOERNER, J. L., 1947. A separator for onion thrips. *J. econ. Ent.* **40**, 755.

HOPKINS, G., 1949. The host associations of the lice of mammals. *Proc. zool. Soc. Lond.* **119**, 387–604.

HORSFALL, W. R., 1962. Trap for separating collections of insects by interval. *J. econ. Ent.* **55**, 808–11.

HUGHES, R. D., 1963. Population dynamics of the cabbage aphid *Brevicoryne brassicae* (L.). *J. anim. Ecol.* **32**, 393-424.

HUGHES, R. D. and WOOLCOCK, L. T., 1963. The use of an electronic counter in population studies of the cabbage aphid (*Brevicoryne brassicae* (L.)). *N.Z. J. agric. Res.* **6**, 320-7.

IVES, W. G. H., 1959. A technique for estimating Tamarack foliage production, a basis for detailed population studies of the larch sawfly. *Canad. Ent.* **91**, 513-19.

JANION, S. M., 1960. Quantitative dynamics in fleas (Aphaniptera) infesting mice of Puszcza Kampinoska Forest. *Bull. acad. Pol. Sci.* II, **8** (5), 213-18.

JANZEN, D. H., 1963. Observations on populations of adult beaver-beetles, *Platypsyllus castoris* (Platypsyllidae: Coleoptera). *Pan. Pacif. Ent.* **32**, 215-28.

JOHNSON, C. G., 1950. A suction trap for small airborne insects which automatically segregates the catch into successive hourly samples. *Ann. appl. Biol.* **37**, 80-91.

JOHNSON, C. G., 1957. The distribution of insects in the air and the empirical relation of density to height. *J. anim. Ecol.* **26**, 479-94.

JOHNSON, C. G. and MELLANBY, K., 1942. The parasitology of human scabies. *Parasitology* **34**, 285-90.

JOHNSON, C. G., SOUTHWOOD, T. R. E. and ENTWISTLE, H. M., 1957. A new method of extracting arthropods and Molluscs from grassland and herbage with a suction apparatus. *Bull. ent. Res.* **48**, 211-18.

JOHNSON, C. G. and TAYLOR, L. R., 1955a. The development of large suction traps for airborne insects. *Ann. appl. Biol.* **43**, 51-61.

JOHNSON, C. G. and TAYLOR, L. R., 1955b. The measurement of insect density in the air. *Lab. Pract.* **4**, 187-92, 235-9.

JOHNSON, C. G., TAYLOR, L. R. and SOUTHWOOD, T. R. E., 1962. High altitude migration of *Oscinella frit* L. (Diptera: Chloropidae). *J. anim. Ecol.* **31**, 373-83.

JONES, B. M., 1950. A new method for studying the distribution and bionomics of trombiculid mites (Acarina: Trombidiidae). *Parasitology* **40**, 1-13.

JONES, L. S. and PRENDERGAST, D. T., 1937. Method of obtaining an index to density of field populations of citrus red mite. *J. econ. Ent.* **30**, 934-40.

JUILLET, J. A., 1963. A comparison of four types of traps used for capturing flying insects. *Canad. J. Zool.* **41**, 219-23.

KALAMARZ, E., 1963. Badania nad biologia Mallophaga IV. Nowe methody zbierania ektopasozytów. *Ekol. Polska B* **9**, 321-5.

KATZ, R., FARRELL, E. P. and MILNER, M., 1954. The separation of grain by projection I. *Cereal Chem.* **31**, 316-25.

KENNARD, W. C. and SPENCER, J. L., 1955. A mechanical insect collector with high manœuverability. *J. econ. Ent.* **48**, 478-9.

KERSHAW, W. J. S., 1964. Aphid sampling in sugar beet. *Plant. Path.* **13**, 101-6.

KOURA, A., 1958. A new transparency method for detecting internal infestation in grains. *Agric. Res. Rev.* **36**, 110-13.

KRETZSCHMAR, G. P., 1948. Soy bean insects in Minnesota with special reference to sampling techniques. *J. econ. Ent.* **41**, 586-91.

LASTER, M. L. and FURR, R. E., 1962. A simple technique for recovering insects from sorghum heads in insecticide tests. *J. econ. Ent.* **55**, 798.

LEGNER, E. F. and OATMAN, E. R., 1962. Foliage-feeding Lepidoptera on young non-bearing apple trees in Wisconsin. *J. econ. Ent.* **55**, 552-4.

LE PELLEY, R. H., 1942. A new method of sampling thrips populations. *Bull. ent. Res.* **33**, 147-8.

LEVI, M. I., CHERNOV, S. G., LABUNETS, N. F. and KOSMINSKII, R. B., 1959. Aspiration method for the collection of fleas from rodents' nests. [In Russian.] *Med. Parazitol.* **28**, 64-9.

LEWIS, T., 1960. A method for collecting *Thysanoptera* from Gramineae. *Entomologist* **93**, 27–8.

LEWIS, T. and NAVAS, D. E., 1962. Thysanopteran populations overwintering in hedge bottoms, grass litter and bark. *Ann. appl. Biol.* **50**, 299–311.

LEWIS, T. and TAYLOR, L. R., 1965. Diurnal periodicity of flight by insects. *Trans. R. ent. Soc. Lond.* **116**, 393–469.

LIPOVSKY, L. J., 1951. A washing method of ectoparasite recovery with particular reference to chiggers. *J. Kansas ent. Soc.* **24**, 151–6.

LORD, F. T., 1965. Sampling predator populations on apple trees in Nova Scotia. *Canad. Ent.* **97**, 287–98.

LOWE, A. D. and DROMGOOLE, W. V., 1958. The development of an electronic aphid counter. *N.Z. J. agric. Res.* **1**, 903–12.

MACLEOD, J., 1948. The distribution and dynamics of ked populations, *Melophagus ovinus* Linn. *Parasitology* **39**, 61–8.

MACLEOD, J. and DONNELLY, J., 1957. Some ecological relationships of natural populations of Calliphorine blowflies. *J. anim. Ecol.* **26**, 135–70.

MALCOLMSON, R. O., 1960. Mallophaga from birds of North America. *Wilson Bull.* **72** (2), 182–97.

MAW, M. G., 1964. An effect of static electricity on captures in insect traps. *Canad. Ent.* **96**, 1482.

MILNER, M., BARNEY, D. L. and SHELLENBERGER, J. A., 1950. Use of selective fluorescent stains to detect egg plugs on grain kernels. *Science* **112**, 791–2.

MILNER, M., KATZ, R., LEE, M. R. and PYLE, W. B., 1953. Application of the Polaroid-Land process to radiographic inspection of wheat. *Cereal Chem.* **30**, 169–70.

MILNER, M., LEE, M. R. and KATZ, R., 1950. Application of X-ray technique to the detection of insects infesting grain. *J. econ. Ent.* **43**, 933–5.

MOHR, C. O., 1959. A procedure for delayed collecting of ectoparasites from small captured hosts. *J. Parasit.* **45** (2), 154.

MOORE, N. W., 1964. Intra- and interspecific competition among dragonflies (Odonata). *J. anim. Ecol.* **33**, 49–71.

MORGAN, C. V. G., CHANT, D. A., ANDERSON, N. H. and AYRE, G. L., 1955. Methods for estimating orchard mite populations, especially with the mite brushing machine. *Canad. Ent.* **87**, 189–200.

MOSOLOV, L. P., 1959. A method of collecting the ectoparasites of rodents, without destroying the host population. [In Russian, Eng. summary.] *Med. Parazitol.* **28**, 189–192.

MUIR, R. C. and GAMBRILL, R. G., 1960. A note on the knockdown method for estimating numbers of insect predators on fruit trees. *Ann. Rep. E. Malling Res. Sta.* **1959**, 109–11.

MURRAY, K. F., 1957. An ecological appraisal of host–ectoparasite relationships in a zone of epizootic plague in central California. *Amer. J. trop. Med. Hyg.* **6**, 1068–86.

MURRAY, M. D., 1961. The ecology of the louse *Polyplax serrata* (Burm.) on the mouse *Mus musculus* L. *Aust. J. Zool.* **9**, 1–13.

NELSON, W. A., SLEN, S. B. and BANKY, E. C., 1957. Evaluation of methods of estimating populations of the sheep ked, *Melophagus ovinus* (L.) (Diptera: Hippoboscidae), on mature ewes and young lambs. *Canad. J. anim. Sci.* **33**, 8–13.

NEWELL, I. M., 1947. Quantitative methods in biological and control studies of orchard mites. *J. econ. Ent.* **40**, 683–9.

NICHOLLS, C. F., 1960. A portable mechanical insect trap. *Canad. Ent.* **92**, 48–51.

PEDERSEN, J. R. and BROWN, R. A., 1960. X-ray microscope to study behaviour of internal-infesting grain insects. *J. econ. Ent.* **53**, 678–9.

PIELOU, D. P., 1961. Note on a volumetric method for the determination of numbers of apple aphid, *Aphis pomi* DeG., on samples of apple foliage. *Canad. J. Pl. Sci.* **41**, 442–3.

PRESCOTT, H. W. and NEWTON, R. C., 1963. Flight study of the clover root Curculio. *J. econ. Ent.* **56**, 368–70.

REMANE, R., 1958. Die Besiedlung von Grünlandflächen verschiedener Herkunft durch Wanzen und Zikaden im Weser – Ems – Gebiet. *Z. angew. Ent.* **42**, 353–400.

RICHARDS, O. W., 1940. The biology of the small white butterfly (*Pieris rapae*) with special reference to the factors controlling abundance. *J. anim. Ecol.* **9**, 243–88.

RICHARDS, O. W. and WALOFF, N., 1954. Studies on the biology and population dynamics of British grasshoppers. *Anti-Locust Bull.* **17**, 184 pp.

RICHARDS, O. W. and WALOFF, N., 1961. A study of a natural population of *Phytodecta olivacea* (Forster) (Coleoptera, Chrysomeloidea). *Phil. Trans.* **244**, 205–57.

RISTICH, S. and LOCKARD, D., 1953. An aspirator modified for sampling large populations. *J. econ. Ent.* **46**, 711–12.

ROMNEY, V. E., 1945. The effect of physical factors upon catch of the beet leafhopper (*Eutettix tenellus* (Bak.)) by a cylinder and two sweep methods. *Ecology* **26**, 135–47.

SANTA, H., 1961. [A method for sampling plant and leaf-hopper density in winter and early Spring.] [In Japanese.] *Plant Protection, Tokyo* **8**, 353–5.

SATCHELL, J. E. and MOUNTFORD, M. D., 1962. A method of assessing caterpillar populations on large forest trees, using a systemic insecticide. *Ann. appl. Biol.* **50**, 443–50.

SEALANDER, J. A. and HOFFMAN, C. E., 1956. A modified Berlese funnel for collecting mammalian and avian ectoparasites. *Southw. Nat., Dallas* **1**, 134–6.

SHANDS, W. A., SIMPSON, G. W. and REED, L. B., 1954. Subunits of sample for estimating aphid abundance on potatoes. *J. econ. Ent.* **47**, 1024–7.

SIMAK, M., 1955. Insect damage on seeds of Norway spruce determined by X-ray photography. *Medd. Stat. Skogsforsknings-Inst.*, Uppsala **41**, 299–310.

SKUHRAVÝ, V., NOVÁK, K. and STARÝ, P., 1959. Entomofauna jetele (*Trifolium pratense* L.) a její vývoj. *Rozpr. čsl. Akad. Věd.* **69** (7), 3–82.

SKUHRAVÝ, V. and NOVÁK, V., 1961. The study of field crop entomocenoses. [In Russian.] *Ent. Obozr.* **41**, 807–14 (transl. *Ent. Rev.* **41**, 454–8).

SMITH, B. D., 1960. Population studies of the black currant gall mite (*Phytoptus ribis* Nal.). *Rep. agric. hort. Res. Sta. Bristol* **1960**, 120–4.

SOUTHWOOD, T. R. E., JEPSON, W. F. and VAN EMDEN, H. F., 1961. Studies on the behaviour of *Oscinella frit* L. (Diptera) adults of the panical generation. *Ent. exp. appl.* **4**, 196–210.

SOUTHWOOD, T. R. E. and PLEASANCE, H. J., 1962. A hand-operated suction apparatus for the extraction of Arthropods from grassland and similar habitats, with notes on other models. *Bull. ent. Res.* **53**, 125–8.

SPENCER, G. J., 1956. Some records of ectoparasites from flying squirrels. *Proc. ent. Soc. B.C.* **52**, 32–4.

STAGE, H. H., GJULLIN, C. M. and YATES, W. W., 1952. Mosquitoes of the Northwestern states. *U.S.D.A., Agric. Handb.* no. **46**, 95 pp.

STARK, H. E. and KINNEY, A. R., 1962. Abandonment of disturbed hosts by their fleas. *Pan. Pacif. Ent.* **38**, 249–51.

STEINER, H., 1962. Methoden zur untersuchung der Populationsdynamik in Obstanlagen (inc. Musternahme und Sammeln). *Entomophaga* **7**, 207–14.

STRICKLAND, A. H., 1954. An aphid counting grid. *Plant Path.* **3**, 73–5.

STRICKLAND, A. H., 1961. Sampling crop pests and their hosts. *A. Rev. Ent.* **6**, 201–20.

SUMMERS, F. M. and BAKER, G. A., 1952 A procedure for determining relative densities of brown almond mite populations on almond trees. *Hilgardia* **21**, 369–82.

SZALAY-MARZSÓ, L., 1957. Populációsdinamikai vizsgálatok egy répaöfld répalevéltetü (*Dorsalis fabae* Scop.) állományén. *Ann. Inst. Prot. Plant Hung.* **7** (1952–6), 91–101.

TAYLOR, E. A. and SMITH, F. F., 1955. Three methods for extracting thrips and other insects from rose flowers. *J. econ. Ent.* **48**, 767–8.

TAYLOR, L. R., 1951. An improved suction trap for insects. *Ann. appl. Biol.* **38**, 582–91.

TAYLOR, L. R., 1955. The standardization of air flow in insect suction traps. *Ann. appl. Biol.* **43**, 390–408.

TAYLOR, L. R., 1958. Aphid dispersal and diurnal periodicity. *Proc. Linn. Soc. Lond.* **169**, 67–73.

TAYLOR, L. R., 1962*a*. The absolute efficiency of insect suction traps. *Ann. appl. Biol.* **50**, 405–21.

TAYLOR, L. R., 1962*b*. The efficiency of cylindrical sticky insect traps and suspended nets. *Ann. appl. Biol.* **50**, 681–5.

VENABLES, E. P. and DENNYS, A. A., 1941. A new method of counting orchard mites. *J. econ. Ent.* **34**, 324.

VITÉ, J. P. and GARA, R. I., 1961. A field method for observation on olfactory responses of bark beetles (Scolytidae) to volatile materials. *Contrib. Boyce Thompson Inst.* **21**, 175–82.

WASYLIK, A., 1963. Metoda analizy ciaglej roztoczy gniazd ptasich. *Ekol. Polska B* **9**, 219–24.

WEEKMAN, G. T. and BALL, H. J., 1963. A portable electrically operated collecting device. *J. econ. Ent.* **56**, 708–9.

WHITTAKER, J. B., 1965. The distribution and population dynamics of *Neophilaenus lineatus* (L.) and *N. exclamationis* (Thun.) (Homoptera, Cercopidae) on Pennine Moorland. *J. anim. Ecol.* **34**, 277–97.

WICKMAN, B. E., 1964. A comparison of radiographic and dissection methods for measuring siricid populations in wood. *Canad. Ent.* **96**, 508–10.

WIEGERT, R. G., 1961. A simple apparatus for measuring density of insect population. *Ann. ent. Soc. Amer.* **54**, 926–7.

WILDHOLTZ, T., VOGEL, W., STRAUB, A. and GESLER, B., 1956. Befallskontrolle an apfelbaümen im Frühjahr 1955. *Schwiez. Z. Obst. u. Weinb.* **65**, 85–8.

WILLIAMS, C. B. and MILNE, P. S., 1935. A mechanical insect trap. *Bull. ent. Res.* **26**, 543–51.

WILLIAMSON, K., 1954. The Fair Isle apparatus for collecting bird ectoparasites. *Brit. Birds* **47**, 234–5.

WILSON, L. F., 1962. A portable device for mass-collecting or sampling foliage-inhabiting arthropods. *J. econ. Ent.* **55**, 807–8.

WOODROFFE, G. E., 1953. An ecological study of the insects and mites in the nests of certain birds in Britain. *Bull. ent. Res.* **44**, 739–72.

YAGHI, N., 1924. Application of the Roentgen ray tube to detection of boring insects. *J. econ. Ent.* **17**, 662–3.

CHAPTER 5

Absolute Population Estimates by Sampling a Unit of Habitat — Soil and Litter

The extraction methods described here can be used not only with soil and with plant and animal debris, litter and dung, but also with plant material collected by suction apparatus or other means, the nests of vertebrates and the mud from ponds and rivers. The actual methods for obtaining the samples from these other habitats are discussed in chapters 4 and 6.

Much of the work in soil zoology was originally aimed at the extraction of a large segment of the fauna by a single method; however, most workers have now concluded that a method that will give an almost absolute estimate of one species or group, will give at the most a rather poor relative estimate for another. Not only does the efficiency of extraction vary with the animal, but also with the soil, its nature, its water content and the amount of vegetable matter in it. Therefore, although with certain animals under certain conditions each of these methods will give absolute population estimates, none of them will provide such data under all conditions.

Further information on ecological methods in soil zoology is given in reviews by Balogh (1958), Murphy (1962b and c), Macfadyen (1955, 1962) and Kevan (1962) and in the collections of research papers edited by Kevan (1955) and Murphy (1962a).

Bees, cicindelid and *Bledius* larvae, and other comparatively large insects that make holes or casts in bare ground, may be counted directly *in situ*. Small animals may be examined in soil sections: Haarløv & Weis-Fogh (1953, 1955) have devised a method of fixing and freezing a soil core and then impregnating with agar and sectioning. A similar method using gelatine for impregnation has been described by Minderman (1957). In most studies, however, it is necessary both to take a sample and to extract the animals.

SAMPLING

The number and size of the samples and the sampling pattern in relation to statistical considerations have been discussed in chapter 2 and by Macfadyen (1962). The soil samples are usually taken with a corer; golf-hole borers or metal tubing sharpened at one end make simple corers, but it has been suggested that some animals may be killed by compression when the core is forced from such 'instruments', and furthermore it is highly desirable to keep the core undisturbed (especially for extraction by behavioural methods), so more elaborate corers have been developed. In general the larger the animal and the sparser its population the bigger the sample (e.g. Frick (1962) took 8-in. diameter cores for *Nomia* bees). The depth to which it is necessary to sample varies with the animal and the condition of the soil (e.g. Paris & Pitelka, 1962).

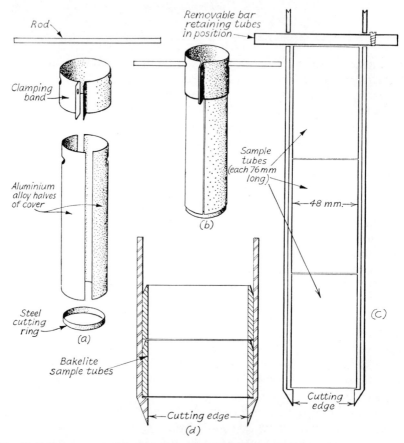

Fig. 28. Soil corers. *a* and *b*. The O'Connor split corer: *a*. showing compartments (after O'Connor, 1957); *b*. assembled. *c*. Soil corer with sample tubes (after Dhillon & Gibson, 1962). *d*. Soil corer for the canister extractor (after Macfadyen, 1961).

With the O'Connor (1957) split corer (fig. 28) the risk of compressing the sample by forcing it out of the corer is avoided. After the core has been taken the clamping band can be loosened, the two aluminium halves of the cover separated and the sample exposed. Furthermore the sample can then be easily divided into the different soil layers: litter, humus, upper 2 cm soil, etc. Plastic or metal rings may be inserted inside the metal sheath of the corer, just behind the cutting ring (Macfadyen, 1961; Dhillon & Gibson, 1962) (fig. 28); these will enable the core to be extracted with its natural structure intact (see p. 144).

In order to penetrate hard tropical or frozen tundra soils it may be necessary to have equipment of the types described by Belfield (1956) and Potzger (1955). In contrast in soft humus rich situations, such as manure heaps, it is difficult to take an undisturbed sample; von Törne (1962b) has devised a sampler for these habitats consisting of two concentric tubes each with cutting teeth. The inner tube is pushed down firmly and held still, thereby protecting the sample, while the outer one is rotated and cuts through the compost.

Many pests of field crops lay their eggs on the bases of the plants and on the soil; the number of eggs usually falls off very rapidly with distance away from the plant (e.g. Lincoln & Palm, 1941; Abu Yaman, 1960). Suitable samples of young plants and the soil around them can be taken by the scissor type of sampler described by Webley (1957).

Fallen leaves and other debris are usually sampled with quadrats, such as a metal box with top and bottom missing and the lower edge sharpened (Gabbutt, 1959).

MECHANICAL METHODS OF EXTRACTION

Mechanical methods have the advantages that theoretically they extract all stages, mobile and sedentary, and are in no way dependent on the behaviour of the animal or the condition of the substrate; samples for mechanical extraction may be stored frozen for long periods before use. Their disadvantages are that compared with behavioural methods the operator must expend a great deal of time and energy on each sample, that sometimes they damage the animals and that, as mobile and immobile animals are extracted, it may be difficult to distinguish animals that were dead at the time of sampling from those that were alive.

There are a number of distinct mechanical processes that can be used to separate animals from the soil and vegetable material: sieving, flotation, sedimentation, elutriation and differential wetting. The following account, however, is intended to be functional, rather than classificatory or historical; only the main types of processes will be outlined and it must be stressed that although there are already many different combinations and variants (see Murphy's, 1962c review) others will need to be developed for particular animals and substrates.

Dry sieving

This method may be of use for the separation of fairly large (and occasionally small) animals, from friable soil or fallen leaves. Its disadvantages are that small specimens are often lost and a considerable amount of time needs to be spent in hand-sorting the sieved material. The Reitter sifter (see Kevan, 1962) is a simple device, but this is really more a collector's tool than a means of estimating populations. Lane & Shirck's (1928) was the first mechanical sieve with a to-and-fro motion although it was worked by hand. The most complex apparatus of this type is the fully motorized self-propelled model of Lange, Akesson & Carlson (1955), which was used for surveying elaterid larvae in California.

Molluscs have been extracted by dry sieving methods (Økland, 1929; Jacot, 1935), but these have been shown to be inaccurate, some snails remaining in the leaves (Williamson, 1959).

Dry sieving has also been used to separate mosquito eggs from mud (Stage, Gjullin & Yates, 1952). A modified grain drier is the basis of this method; the samples are dried until almost dusty, passed through a mesh sieve and then into the top of four shaker sieves of the grain drier. Coarser particles are removed by the first three sieves, but the eggs and similar sized soil particles are held on the last one (80-mesh); they then fall through an opening on to a 60-mesh roll screen; a carefully adjusted air current blows away the lighter particles during the fall. Because of their spindle shape the eggs, with only a very small quantity of soil, eventually pass 'end-on' through the roll screen into the 'catch pan'. Such a degree of mechanization is possible because only a single organism with a constant and regular shape and a uniform weight was required.

The active red-legged earth mite (*Halotydeus destructor*) lives amongst the grass and plant debris in Australian pastures; Wallace (1956) has shown that it can be very accurately sampled by taking shallow cores which are then inverted and rotated, still within the corer, over a sieve in a funnel. The sides of the metal corer are tapped a number of times and the mites fall through the sieve and may be collected in tubes below the funnel.

Soil washing (or wet sieving)

This technique is most often used in conjunction with other methods (see below); on its own it is of particular value where the organisms are much smaller than the particles of the substrate (e.g. small snails amongst freshly fallen leaves) or much larger (e.g. many mud-dwellers), and hence separation by size alone is sufficient.

The sieves may be of two basic designs: flat or revolving. Flat sieves may be built up into a tower (see fig. 30) and a series of sieves was the basis of early uses of this method by N. A. Cobb and H. M. Morris. Sieving is often used in studies on the bottom animals of aquatic habitats for the separation of the mud from the organisms and stones that are retained by the sieve (Berg, 1938; Brundin, 1949; Jonasson, 1955; Hairston *et al.*, 1958); a single frame is used into which frames with different mesh phosphor-bronze screens may be fitted. Jonasson (1955) has shown that many benthic organisms pass through the 0·6-mm mesh gauge sieves frequently employed in such studies; with insect larvae the size of the head capsule determined whether or not it would pass through the mesh of a sieve and there was no evidence that a significant proportion would roll up and so be retained by coarse sieves. The smallest sieve used by Jonasson had a mesh gauze of 0·2 mm, but clearly in any particular study its size would be determined by the diameter of the organism being sampled.

Although most soil nematodes can be separated by elutriation or the Baermann funnel (p. 149), for those in marine habitats these methods may not give good results (Capstick, 1959) and sieving is recommended to separate the largest worms, followed by agitation, to make a suspension of the remainder, which is subsampled volumetrically. The subsamples are examined directly.

Gastropod molluscs and possibly other small animals may be efficiently separated from fresh leaf litter by wet sieving, but here it is the organisms that pass through the sieve and the unwanted material that is retained (Williamson,

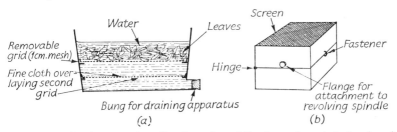

Fig. 29. *a*. Tank for the separation of molluscs from fallen leaves by wet sieving, based on Williamson's design. *b*. Simple sieve box for wet sieving sawfly cocoons, based on McLeod's design.

1959). The leaves are placed on a coarse sieve (mesh size 1 cm), above a fine cloth-covered grid, the whole immersed in a vessel of water (fig. 29*a*) and the leaves are stirred from time to time; after about 15 minutes the vessel can be drained from below and the molluscs will be found on the cloth sheet, which is then inspected under the microscope. Clearly this method is not satisfactory for molluscs amongst soil or humus as much of these materials will pass through the upper sieve.

Simple revolving sieves were used by McLeod (1961) for the extraction of sawfly cocoons. They consisted of wooden boxes, hinged in the middle and with screen tops and bottoms (fig. 29*b*); they were revolved once or twice while a jet of water from a hose was played on to them. More elaborate revolving models were designed by Horsfall (1956) and Read (1958); these are discussed below.

Soil washing and flotation

When the organisms to be extracted and the rest of the sample are of different particle-size sieving alone is sufficient for extraction; however, in most situations after sieving the animals required remain mixed with a mass of similar sized mineral and vegetable matter. As the specific gravity of mineral and biotic material is frequently different the extraction may be taken a stage further by flotation of the animals; unfortunately plant material usually floats equally well. The combination of flotation, devised by A. Berlese many years before, with soil washing is usually associated with Ladell (1936). This approach, much modified and improved by Salt & Hollick (1944) and Raw (1955, 1962), is the basis of one of the most widely used, versatile and efficient techniques; it consists of four stages, three of which will be discussed under this heading.

i. Pretreatment. In order to disperse the soil particles, particularly important if there is a high clay content, the cores may be soaked in water and deep frozen. Chemical dispersion may also be used: the core soaked in solutions of sodium citrate (d'Aguilar, Benard & Bessard, 1957) or sodium oxalate (Seinhorst, 1962). For the heavy clay soils it may be necessary to combine chemical and physical methods: the core is gently crumbled into a plastic container and covered with a solution of sodium hexametaphosphate (50 g) and sodium carbonate (20 g) in one litre of water (sold commercially as 'Calgon'); the whole is then placed under reduced pressure in a vacuum desiccator for a time. After the restoration of atmospheric pressure the sample is frozen for at least 48 hours and may be stored in this condition (Raw, 1955).

ii. Soil washing. The sample is placed in the upper and coarsest, sieve of the washing apparatus (fig. 30*a*); it may be washed through by slow jets of water or single sieves 'dunked' in the settling can. The material retained in the sieves must be carefully teased apart, and thoroughly washed; a few large animals may be removed at this stage. The mesh of the lowest sieve* is such as to allow the animals required to pass through into the settling can, which is pivoted and is then tipped into the 'Ladell can'. The Ladell, which resembles an inverted bottomless paraffin can, has a fine phosphor-bronze sieve and its lower opening immersed in the drainage tank; this tank should be arranged so that the level of water maintained in it, and hence in the Ladell, is slightly above the sieve of the latter – this minimizes blockage of the sieve. The Ladell is allowed to drain; this, often tedious, process may be aided by tapping the side of the can with the hand from time to time. The standard Ladell has a fine sieve (mesh size about 0·2 mm); for many animals this may be much finer than is necessary and to overcome this Stephenson (1962) has designed a Ladell, with a set of interchangeable sieve plates of various mesh sizes.

In conclusion it must be warned that soil washing is an invariably wet operation and is best carried out in a room with a concrete floor and the operator wearing rubber boots and suitable apparel.

iii. Flotation. The Ladell is removed from the tank to a stand (fig. 30*b*), allowed to drain completely and then the process of flotation is begun. The lower opening of the Ladell is closed with a bung and the flotation liquid introduced until the Ladell is about two-thirds full (fig. 30*b*). Concentrated magnesium sulphate solution (specific gravity *c.* 1.2) is the most usual flotation liquid, but solutions of sodium chloride (Lincoln & Palm, 1941; Cockbill *et al.*, 1945; Golightly, 1952; Cohen, 1955), potassium bromide (d'Aguilar *et al.*, 1957) or zinc chloride (Sellmer, 1956) may be used.

---

* If this sieve is finer its contents must also be tipped into the settling tank, its function being to aid dispersion.

Air is then bubbled up from the bottom of the Ladell; this agitation is continued for 2–3 minutes and serves to free any animal matter that may have been trapped on the sieve. More of the flotation solution is introduced from below until the liquid and

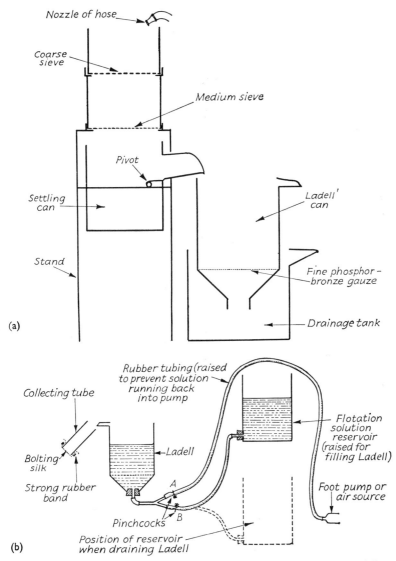

Fig. 30. *a.* Soil washing apparatus (modified from Salt & Hollick, 1944). *b.* Ladell can and associated equipment during the air agitation phase of flotation (diagrammatic).

'float' passes over the lip and the latter is retained on the collecting tube, which usually consists of a glass tube with a piece of bolting silk held in place with a rubber band. A wash bottle may be used to help direct the float out of the Ladell. When the surface and sides of the Ladell are completely clean, the animal and plant material will all be in the collecting tube and the process is complete. The flotation liquid is then drained from the Ladell, for further use, by appropriate manipulations of the reservoir and pinchclips (see fig. 30*b*).

The animals may now be separated from the plant material by direct examination under the microscope or it may be necessary to carry out a further separation based on differential wetting and/or centrifuging (see below). However, before these are discussed other washing and flotation techniques must be reviewed.

The apparatus of d'Aguilar *et al.* (1957) first removes the smallest silt particles by agitating the sample with a water current in a cylinder with a fine gauze side; subsequently the material is passed through a series of sieves, followed by flotation.

The eggs and puparia of the cabbage root fly (*Erioischia brassicae*) may be separated from the soil by sieving and flotation in water (Abu Yaman, 1960; Hughes, 1960); with such insects therefore there is no need for the Ladell – the final sieve should be fine enough to retain them; this is immersed in water and the insects float to the surface. A certain amount of foam often develops in soil washing and hinders examination of the float; it may be dispersed with a small quantity of caprylic acid (Abu Yaman, 1960). To separate relatively large insects (root maggots) Read (1958) used a cylindrical aluminium screen sieve that was sprayed with water and rotated and half submerged in a tank; all the fine soil passed out of the sieve, which could then be opened and the floating insects removed.

A revolving sieve was also used by Horsfall (1956) for mosquito eggs. Here the function of the drum, which consisted of three concentric sieves, was to disintegrate the sample and retain the larger materials, the eggs passing out and being collected in the finest of a series of sieves.

Flotation

If the sample is first dried flotation alone may be used for molluscs (Vágvölgyi, 1953) and nematode cysts (Goodey, 1957). Vágvölgyi recommends soaking in weak detergent and potassium hydroxide, drying and floating again in water. With nematode cysts drying, dry sieving and flotation in water is the usual sequence; various details and modifications are given by Goodey (1957) and in papers in Kevan (1955) and Murphy (1962*a*).

A very large range of benthic marine animals are efficiently extracted from grab-samples by merely stirring in a glass beaker with carbon tetrachloride (Birkett, 1957). The mineral matter remains as a sediment, but the animals float. This technique would seem to have many applications for the extraction of annelids and molluscs from freshwater and terrestrial substrates, so long as there is not a great quantity of plant matter. Indeed there is a range of heavy organic solvents whose potentialities have been little explored for ecological work; but care should be taken over ventilation when working with them (Solomon, 1962). Sellmer (1956) used a 75% solution of zinc chloride (sp.

gravity 2·1) to float *Gemma*, a small bivalve mollusc, from marine sediment. Laurence (1954) separated insect larvae from dung by merely stirring the samples in a 25% solution of magnesium sulphate.

The separation of plant and animal matter by differential wetting

A mixture of animal and plant material results from soil washing and flotation and also from various methods of sampling animals on vegetation (chapter 4).

There are two possible approaches to their separation, both due to the lipoid and waterproof cuticle of arthropods; either the arthropod cuticle can be wetted by a hydrocarbon 'oil' or the plant material can be waterlogged so that it will sink in aqueous solutions.

i. Wetting the arthropod cuticle. If arthropods and plant material are shaken up in a mixture of petrol or other hydrocarbon and water and then allowed to settle, the arthropods, whose cuticles are wetted by the petrol, will lie in the petrol layer above the water and the plant material in the water. As Murphy (1962c) has pointed out this separation will be imperfect if the plant material contains much air or if the specific gravities of the two phases are either too dissimilar or too close. The former may be overcome by boiling the suspension in water first (Cockbill *et al.*, 1945); the second by the choice of appropriate solutions. 60% ethyl alcohol may be used for the aqueous phase with a light oil. This concept was originally introduced into soil faunal studies by Salt & Hollick (1944). The float from the collection tube (see above) is placed in a wide-necked vessel with a little water, benzene is added, the whole shaken vigorously and allowed to settle. The arthropods will be in the benzene phase, which may be washed over into an outer vessel by adding further water below the surface from a pipette or wash bottle. Raw (1955) introduced the idea of freezing the benzene (m.p. 50°C); the plug plus animals may then be removed and the benzene evaporated in a sintered glass crucible. (The fumes should be carried away by an exhaust fan as they are an accumulative poison.) Xylene and paraffin have also been used for the oil phase and gelatine, that solidifies on cooling, for the aqueous phase; in the latter case, it is the plant material that is removed in a plug.

ii. Waterlogging the plant material. This process, by boiling under reduced pressure (Hale, 1964) or vacuum extraction, may be used as part of the above technique. Repeated freezing and thawing also serves to impregnate the vegetable matter with water.

Danthanarayana (1966) has devised a method for the separation of the eggs of the weevil *Sitona* from the float by waterlogging the plant material by repeated freezing, filtering and transferring the whole float to a tube containing saturated sodium chloride solution; this is then centrifuged for five minutes (1500 r/m) and the eggs, and other animal matter, come to the surface whilst the plant material sinks.

Centrifugation

Although used widely in parasitological and pathological work, this technique has not been utilized to any extent in ecology, probably because only small samples can be treated at any time. However, it seems likely that it will be found to be of value in the final separation when the initial extraction concentration has been by another method (see above). Müller (1962) found that Acarina and Collembola could be more efficiently extracted from soil by centrifugal flotation in saturated salt (sodium chloride) solution than by certain funnels. A similar technique has been used to separate nematode cysts from plant debris. Murphy (1962c) gives a useful summary, in tabular form, of previous work using centrifugal flotation to separate animals from foodstuffs, soil and excreta.

Sedimentation

The principle of this technique is to utilize the difference in settling rates between animal matter and the substrate. It is the basis of an unpublished method of Davies (*in* Macfadyen, 1955) for cleaning samples already separated from the soil; the sample is added to the top of a very long (4 m) glass tube, the base of which is in a rotating trough. However, the method is not very efficient as some mites settle at the same rate as soil particles. Seinhorst (1962) describes a sedimentation method ('Two Erlenmeyer method') for soil nematodes in which the flask containing the suspension was moved across a series of collecting vessels; the first of which was also inverted and the sediment in it further precipitated. The efficiency of the method was, however, only 60–75%.

Elutriation

This is an extension of the sedimentation process in which the sedimentation takes place against a water current flowing in the opposite direction and the principle is incorporated in two widely used methods for the extraction of soil nematodes: the Oostenbrink and Seinhorst elutriators. In the Oostenbrink model (fig. 31a) the nematodes are washed out of the sample and carried in suspension by the opposing water currents out of the overflow and through a series of sieves (Oostenbrink, 1954; Goffart, 1959; Murphy, 1962c).

The Seinhorst elutriator is also part of a combined elutriation and sieving process; the soil is first passed through a coarse sieve and the suspension retained in a flask. This is inverted on top of the elutriator and the cork removed *in situ* (fig. 31b); the upward flow of water (45 ml/min) coupled with the narrow sections A_2 and B_2 ensures that the nematodes are retained in sections A and B. After about half an hour the flask and the sections A and B may be drained through stopcocks A_3 and B_3. This material and that collected from the overflow is then wet sieved. A few large worms may pass into the soil-collecting container and this should be re-elutriated, but only for a brief period so that they will still be retained in vessel A (Goodey, 1957; Seinhorst, 1962). This method might well be adapted for single species studies on other organisms: those of a comparatively uniform size and mass, e.g. eggs, would

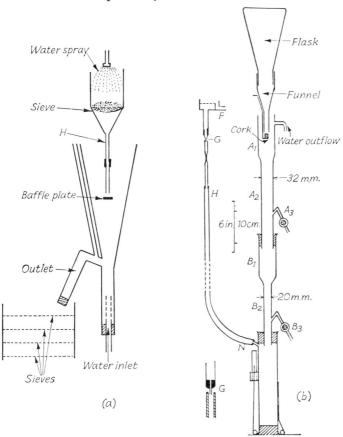

Fig. 31. Elutriators: *a*. Oostenbrink's model; *b*. Seinhorst's model (after Murphy, 1962*a*)

be easily separated at a single level, whereas healthy, parasitized and dead individuals having different masses would separate at different levels.

Small arthropods such as Pauropoda and some Collembola that float in water may be extracted by von Törne's (1962*a*) elutriator and sieving process in which they are carried to the top of apparatus.

BEHAVIOURAL OR DYNAMIC METHODS

In these methods the animals are made to leave the substrate under some stimuli, e.g. heat, moisture (lack or excess) or a chemical. Their great advantage is that unlike the mechanical methods once the extraction has been set up it may usually be left, virtually unattended, and thus large quantities of material may be extracted simultaneously in batteries of extractors. Another important advantage is the ability to extract animals from substrates containing a large amount of vegetable material. The disadvantage is that, being based on the animal's behaviour, the extraction efficiency will vary with the condition of the animals and be influenced by changes in climate, water content, etc., experienced before sampling as well as by variations in these conditions in the apparatus itself. Obviously eggs and other immobile stages cannot be extracted by this method.

As it is desired that the animals leave the substrate under the stimuli, the primary desiderata of behaviour extractors are that the gradient should be well marked, thus insuring that the animals all move in the right direction, but that it should not be so fierce that any slow-moving individuals are overtaken and killed before leaving the substrate. With the diversity of soil organisms it is not surprising that it is impossible to construct an extractor that is optimal in these respects for all animals. Therefore although dry funnels, in particular, have been used extensively in the past for community studies, it must be remembered that their efficiency varies from taxa to taxa and soil to soil (Nef, 1960; Macfadyen, 1961; Satchell & Nelson, 1962).

Dry extractors*

The basic apparatus is the Berlese–Tullgren funnel, a combination of the heated copper funnel designed at the turn of the century by the Italian entomologist, A. Berlese, and subsequently modified by the Swede, A. Tullgren, who used a light-bulb as a heat source. The funnel has been considerably modified and improved by many workers, as described in the reviews of Macfadyen (1955, 1962) and Murphy (1962a). Some of the most important innovations have been the demonstration by Hammer (1944) that when soil is being extracted the core should be retained intact and inverted, thereby enabling the animals to leave the sample by the natural passageways, and discovery by Haarløv (1947) that serious losses could result from the animals becoming trapped in condensation from the core on the sides of the funnel; he recommended that the core should never touch the sides of the funnel and subsequent workers have sometimes referred to the space between the core and the sides of the funnel as the 'Haarløv passage'. When litter is being extracted and the 'passage' is difficult to maintain, it may be helpful to increase air circulation with wide plastic piping (Paris & Pitelka, 1962). Large numbers of small funnels were first grouped together by Ford (1937) and this approach has been much developed and improved by Macfadyen (1953, 1955, 1961, 1962), who also introduced the concepts of steepening the heat gradient and arranging a humidity gradient. Murphy (1955), Newell (1955), Dietrick,

* As Milne *et al.* (1958) correctly pointed out in connection with their hot water process, such methods really expel rather than extract the animals.

Schlinger & van den Bosch (1959) and Kempson, Lloyd & Ghelardi (1963) have all introduced devices to reduce the fall of soil into the sample, thereby ensuring a cleaner extraction. A simple folding Berlese funnel for use on expeditions has been developed by Saunders (1959).

There are many variants of the dry funnel in use, but most of them approximate to one of the following types.

a. Large Berlese funnel

This is used for extracting large arthropods. e.g. Isopoda, Coleoptera, from bulky soil or litter samples (Macfadyen, 1961) and also for the extraction of insects from suction apparatus and other samples containing much vegetation (Clark, Williamson & Richmond, 1959; Dietrick, Schlinger & van den Bosch, 1959). Desirable features are an air circulation system, introduced by Macfadyen, which may be opened to ensure a rapid drying for the extraction of

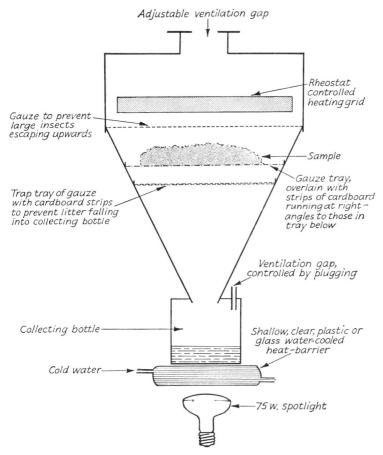

Fig. 32. A large Berlese funnel with modification.

desiccation-resistant animals, such as beetles and ants, or partly closed for a slower 'wet regime' (but avoid condensation) for beetle larvae, *Campodea* and other animals that are susceptible to desiccation. Macfadyen recommends testing the humidity below the sample by cobalt thiocyanate papers; for the resistant animals humidities down to 70% are tolerable, for the others it should not fall below 90%. As phototactic animals, e.g. Halticine beetles, are often attracted upwards towards the light-bulb of the funnel and so fail to be extracted, this is replaced as a heat source by a Nichrome or similar wire-grid heating element – this also heats the sample more uniformly (Clark *et al.*, 1959). The extraction of positively phototactic animals has been further improved by Dietrick *et al.* (1959) who placed a 75 W spotlight below the collecting jar; this was switched on intermittently. An apparatus incorporating these and other features is illustrated in fig. 32. As Macfadyen and others have frequently stressed, for most animals the heat should be applied slowly and therefore it may be useful to be able to control the voltage of the heating element through a rheostat (Dietrick *et al.*, 1959) or 'Simmerstat'. Extraction time will vary from a few days to over a month (e.g. Park & Auerbach, 1954) depending on the substrate and the animal.

b. Horizontal extractor

Designed by Duffey (1962) for extracting spiders from grass samples, this extractor (fig. 33) would probably serve equally well for any rapidly moving litter animal. It has the advantages that steep gradients are built up and that debris cannot fall into the collecting trough; it is also relatively compact and

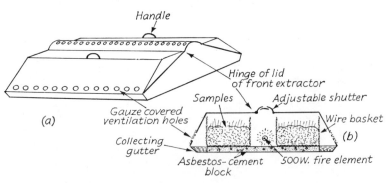

Fig. 33. A pair of horizontal extractors, based on Duffey's (1962) design: *a*. sketch; *b*. sectional view.

built in paired units. Heat is provided by a 500-W fire heating element controlled by a 'Simmerstat'. Air passes in through the ventilation holes just above the aqueous solution of the collecting gutters; this helps to prevent too rapid desiccation. Duffey recommended a 0·001% solution of phenylmercuric acetate, a fungicide and bactericide, with a few drops of a surface-active agent

Wet extractors

The principle of this method is similar to that of the dry extractors, the animals being driven out of their natural substrate under the influence of a stimulus, possibly heat or, as the observations of Williams (1960*a*) would suggest for some cases, reduced oxygen tension. As the substrate is flooded with water in all variants of the method there is no risk of desiccation and the method is particularly successful with those groups that are but poorly extracted by the Berlese-type funnels, that is nematode and enchytraeid worms, insect larvae and various aquatic groups (Williams, 1960*a*). The method which is faster than dry extraction seems to have been discovered independently at least three times.

a. Baermann funnel
As originally designed this consisted of a glass funnel with a piece of metal gauze or screen resting in the funnel and a piece of rubber tubing with a pinchcock on the stem (fig. 36*a*); the sample, contained in a piece of muslin, partly flooded with warm water. Nematode worms leave the sample, and fall to the bottom of the funnel where they collect in the stem. They may be drawn off, in a little water, by opening the pinchcock (Peters, 1955). A number of

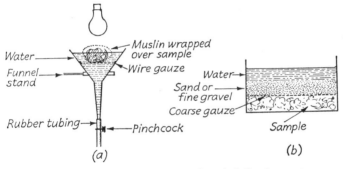

Fig. 36. *a*. Simple heated Baermann funnel. *b*. Sand extractor.

refinements of this method have been introduced: Nielsen (Overgaard, 1947–1948) ran a battery of Baermann funnels within a box with a lamp above; this heated the surface of the water in the funnels which was initially cold. Nematodes and rotifers could be extracted from soil and moss by this method, but it was not satisfactory for tardigrades. In order to extract Enchytraeidae, O'Connor (1955, 1962) used larger polythene funnels, spread the sample directly on to the gauze, without muslin, and submerged it completely; a powerful shrouded lamp heated the surface of the water to 45°C in three hours; dry samples must be moistened before being placed in the funnel and if the soil temperature is low samples must be gradually warmed to room temperature for a day. Extraction usually takes about three hours. In a series of tests O'Connor (1962) and Peachey (1962) have shown this method to be as efficient as the Nielsen inverted extractor (see below) for grassland soils and more efficient for peat and woodland soils.

Minderman (1962) found that the extraction of nematodes from forest soils could be improved if the gauze on which the sample rested was shaken from time to time, by an alarm clock mechanism.

b. Hot water extractors

These have been developed by Nielsen (1952–53) for Enchytraeidae and by Milne, Coggins & Laughlin (1958) for tipulid larvae. Nielsen's apparatus involved the heating of the lower surface of the sample, contained in an earthenware vessel, by hot water; the animals moved up and entered a layer of sand, kept cool by a cold water coil, that was placed above the sample. The only advantage of this method over O'Connor's funnel (see above) is that it seems to extract more of the young worms (Peachey, 1962); under conditions with a large amount of humus it is less efficient (see above).

The larvae of many insects, notably of some Coleoptera and Diptera, earthworms, molluscs, and most motile animals seem to be efficiently and rapidly extracted from soil samples if these are heated from below. Schjøtz-Christensen

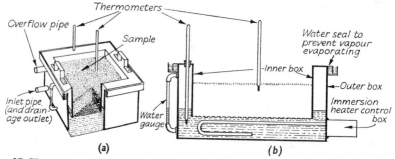

Fig. 37. Hot water extractor (after Milne *et al.*, 1958): *a*. sketch with segment 'removed'; *b*. sectional diagram.

(1957) recorded 85% extraction of Elateridae using Nielsen's apparatus, modified by heating more strongly and omitting the cooling coil. Such an apparatus is not very different from that of Milne *et al.* (1958) (fig. 37), which was found to be virtually 100% efficient for active larvae and pupae. Essentially their device consists of two galvanized boxes, one within the other; the space between is a water bath heated by a thermostatically controlled immersion heater. The water temperature should not rise above 90°C. The inner box has a wire gauze base and holds the sample. The initial mode of operation is to fill the water bath until the level is just above the base of the sample, the heater is switched on until the temperature registered by the thermometer in the centre of the turf is 40°C; the water level is then raised to the level where it would just, eventually, flood the surface of the sample. Heating and observation is continued, the insects being picked up as they leave the turf (but not before or they will retreat). The light above the extraction apparatus should not be too bright; Milne and co-workers recommended as a maximum, a 4-ft 40-W natural fluorescent tube 3 ft above the sample; however, other species of insect might be more or less sensitive. Extraction times varied from an hour in a light soil to nearly three hours in heavy peat-covered clay. The chief disadvantage of this method as at present designed is that the apparatus must be watched continuously and the animals removed as they appear; however, equivalent mechanical methods take about as long.

c. Sand extractors

Extremely simple in design, consisting of a metal can, a piece of wire gauze and some sand (fig. 36b), these devices seem to be remarkably efficient for extracting aquatic and semi-aquatic insect larvae and other animals from mud and debris. The method was described by Bidlingmayer (1957) for the extraction of ceratopogonid midge larvae from salt marshes and has been improved and extended by Williams (1960a and b), who has found that the following freshwater invertebrates could be extracted from their soil substrate by this technique: Coelenterata, Turbellaria, Nematoda, Oligochaeta, Ostracoda, Acarina, Dipterous larvae, Gastropoda and Plecopoda. The sample, about 2 in. thick, is cut so as to fill the container completely: it is then covered with 2 in. of dry clean sand and the whole flooded with water. After 24 hours the sand may be scooped off and will contain large numbers of animals, but for 100% extraction of *Culicoides* larvae it should be left for 40 hours (Williams, 1960b) and for other groups tests would need to be made. The animals may be separated from the sand as Bidlingmayer and Williams recommend by stirring in a black photographic tray when the pale moving objects easily show up against the dark background. If the promise of this method is justified it will clearly repay further development. The final separation might be facilitated by the adoption of a sedimentation, elutriation or flotation method, aided perhaps by the replacement of the sand by fine washed gravel as used by Nielsen (1952–53) in his extractor (see above – that really combines this method with the hot water process). The chief disadvantages of the method in its present form is that it is difficult to make a clean separation of the sand from the soil after extraction; the placing of a piece of wide-mesh wire gauze between the two substrates might aid this operation, or if the extraction was done in a square vessel a plate could be pushed across between the layers at the end of extraction and the top layer poured off.

d. Cold water extractor

South (1964) found that slugs could be efficiently extracted from 1-ft deep turves by slowly immersing these in water. Initially they are stood in 1 in. of water; after about 17 hours the water level is raised to half the depth of the turf (i.e. 6 in.); after 2 days the water level is again raised, this time in several stages, until at the end of another 24 hours it is within $\frac{1}{2}$ in. of the top of the turf.

Chemical extraction

Chemical fumes may be used to drive animals from vegetation (p. 109); the extension of such methods to soil and litter animals has been successful only with aphids and thrips (Macfadyen, 1953 – who used dimethyl phthalate and 2-cyclohexyl-4,6-dinitrophenol). Chemicals in a liquid form, notably potassium permanganate solution, orthodichlorobenzene and formalin, often with a 'wetter', have been used for the extraction of insect larvae and earthworms (Svendsen, 1955; Milne *et al.*, 1958; Raw, 1959). Milne *et al.* showed these methods to be only 85% efficient for tipulid larvae and Satchell (1955) and Svendsen (1955) showed that, owing to differential penetration, potassium permanganate is unsuitable for absolute samples of earthworms. Boyd (1958) has, however, claimed that on shallow porous soils satisfactory data can be obtained with potassium permanganate and Raw (1959) found formalin (25 ml of 4% formaldehyde/1 gal water/4 sq ft ground) applied twice, with a 20-minute interval, efficient for *Lumbricus terrestris*, but not for other species.

Electrical extraction

By discharging a current from a water-cooled electrode driven into the soil, Satchell (1955) was able to expel large numbers of earthworms; but, as he has pointed out, this method suffers from the disadvantage that the exact limits of the volume of soil treated are unknown (Nelson & Satchell, 1962).

SUMMARY OF THE APPLICABILITY OF THE METHODS

It has already been pointed out that the efficiency of the different methods varies greatly with the animal group and the substrate, as is shown for example by the studies of Nef (1960), Raw (1959, 1960), Macfadyen (1961), O'Connor (1962) and Satchell & Nelson (1962). Some suggestions for different groups are given in a tabular form by Macfadyen (1962). The comments made here should only be taken as general indications; more specific information is given under each method.

i. *Substrate type*. Because of the difficulties of separating plant and animal material the mechanical methods have generally been considered unsuitable for litter and for soils, pond mud and other substrates containing a large amount of organic matter. For these media behavioural methods are likely to be the most satisfactory, and the hot water and sand extraction techniques may well repay further development. There are, however, some exceptions; flotation is suitable for dung-dwelling insects (Laurence, 1954), Williamson's wet sieving (which may contain a behavioural element) works well for snails in fresh litter and Satchell & Nelson (1962) found that flotation was more efficient than dry funnels for the extraction of Scutacarid mites from a moder soil.

With friable and sandy soils or aquatic sediments mechanical methods are much to be preferred and techniques as simple as wet sieving or flotation, perhaps using a heavy organic solvent, may be satisfactory for the study of a single species.

ii. Animal type. Obviously immobile stages can only be extracted by mechanical methods. Comparatively large and robust animals can often be estimated simply by sieving. When the specific gravity of the animal is very different from that of the substrate particles, possible techniques include elutriation and centrifugal separation, as well as the more widely used flotation. The two first named methods might also be useful for the separation of parasitized and unhealthy individuals from healthy ones and for the extraction of the eggs of a single species.

Behavioural methods must naturally be adopted to fit the behaviour of the animal; fast-moving animals comparatively resistant to desiccation need to be extracted by the horizontal extractor or the large Berlese funnel; the last named, when modified as described here, is also the only method really suitable for positively phototactic species such as Lygaeid bugs and phytophagous beetles. Groups such as Collembola and most mites need a slower extraction in the Kempson or multiple canister extractors. Those animals that are very sensitive to desiccation (e.g. nematode and enchytraeid worms, dipterous and probably many coleopterous larvae) should be separated in wet extractors, which is also, of course, the behavioural method appropriate for animals in aquatic sediments. The degree of complexity for a single group is well illustrated by the earthworms, for while *Lumbricus terrestris*, but not other species, may be efficiently extracted from orchard soils by a surface application of formalin and several species from shallow soils by wet sieving and flotation, in other habitats even hand-sorting fails (Raw, 1959, 1960; Nelson & Satchell, 1962).

iii. Cost. Mechanical methods are usually more efficient and are generally to be preferred whenever possible; however, they do involve more work and time considerations may rule them out for an extensive survey. Hand-sorting, which is the 'last resort', is the most time-consuming method of all and suffers from human error.

REFERENCES

ABU YAMAN, I. K., 1960. Natural control in cabbage root fly populations and influence of chemicals. *Meded. LandbHoogesch. Wageningen* **60** (1), 1–57.

AGUILAR, J. D', BENARD, R. and BESSARD, A., 1957. Une méthode de lavage pour l'extraction des arthropodes terricoles. *Ann. Epiphyt. C* **8,** 91–9.

BALOGH, J., 1958. *Lebensgemeinschaften der Landtiere.* Budapest, 560 pp.

BELFIELD, W., 1956. The arthropoda of the soil in a West African pasture. *J. anim. Ecol.* **25,** 275–87.

BERG, K., 1938. Studies on the bottom animals of Esrom Lake. *K. danske Vidensk. Selsk., Skr. Nat. Math. Afd. 9, Raekke* **8,** 1–255.

BIDLINGMAYER, W. L., 1957. Studies on *Culicoides furens* (Poey) at Vero Beach. *Mosq. News* **17,** 292–4.

BIRKETT, L., 1957. Flotation technique for sorting grab samples. *J. Cons. perm. int. Explor. Mer.* **22,** 289–92.

BOYD, J. M., 1958. The ecology of earthworms in cattle-grazed machair in Tiree, Argyll. *J. anim. Ecol.* **27,** 147–57.

BRUNDIN, L., 1949. Chironomiden und andere Bodentiere der Südschwedischen Urgebirgsseen. *Rep. Inst. Freshw. Res. Drottningholm* **30,** 915 pp.

CAPSTICK, C. K., 1959. The distribution of free-living nematodes in relation to salinity and the middle and upper reaches of the river Blyth estuary. *J. anim. Ecol.* **28,** 189–210.

CLARK, E. W., WILLIAMSON, A. L. and RICHMOND, C. A., 1959. A collecting technique for pink bollworms and other insects using a Berlese funnel with an improved heater. *J. econ. Ent.* **52,** 1010–12.

COCKBILL, G. F., HENDERSON, V. E., ROSS, D. M. and STAPLEY, J. H., 1945. Wireworm populations in relation to crop production. 1. A large-scale flotation method for extracting wireworms from soil samples and results from a survey of 600 fields. *Ann. appl. Biol.* **32,** 148–63.

COHEN, M., 1955. Soil sampling in the national agricultural advisory service. *In* Kevan, D. K. McE. (ed.), *Soil Zoology*, 347–50.

DANTHANARAYANA, W., 1966. Extraction of arthropod eggs from soil. *Ent. exp. appl.* **9,** 124–5.

DHILLON, B. S. and GIBSON, N. H. E., 1962. A study of the Acarina and Collembola of agricultural soils. 1. Numbers and distribution in undisturbed grassland. *Pedobiologia* **1,** 189–209.

DIETRICK, E. J., SCHLINGER, E. I. and VAN DEN BOSCH, R., 1959. A new method for sampling arthropods using a suction collecting machine and modified Berlese funnel separator. *J. econ. Ent.* **52,** 1085–91.

DUFFEY, E. (A. G.)., 1962. A population study of spiders in limestone grassland. Description of study area, sampling methods and population characteristics. *J. anim. Ecol.* **31,** 571–99.

FORD, J., 1937. Fluctuations in natural populations of Collembola and Acarina. *J. anim. Ecol.* **6,** 98–111.

FRICK, K. E., 1962. Ecological studies on the alkali bee, *Nomia melanderi*, and its Bombyliid parasite, *Heterostylum robustum* in Washington. *Ann. ent. Soc. Amer.* **55,** 5–15.

GABBUTT, P. D., 1959. The bionomics of the wood cricket, *Nemobius sylvestris* (Orthoptera: Gryllidae). *J. anim. Ecol.* **28,** 15–42.

GOFFART, H., 1959. Methoden zur Bodenuntersuchung auf nichtzystenbildende Nematoden. *NachrBl. dtsch. PflSchDienst, Stuttgart* **11,** 49–54.

GOLIGHTLY, W. H., 1952. Soil sampling for wheat-blossom midges. *Ann. appl. Biol.* **39,** 379–84.

GOODEY, J. B., 1957. Laboratory methods for work with plant and soil nematodes. *Tech. Bull. Min. Agric., Lond.* **2** (3rd ed.). H.M.S.O.

HAARLØV, N., 1947. A new modification of the Tullgren apparatus. *J. anim. Ecol.* **16,** 115–21.

HAARLØV, N. and WEIS-FOGH, T., 1953. A microscopical technique for studying the undisturbed texture of soils. *Oikos* **4,** 44–7.

HAARLØV, N. and WEIS-FOGH, T., 1955. A microscopical technique for studying the undisturbed texture of soils. *In* Kevan, D. K. McE. (ed.), *Soil Zoology* 429–32.

HAIRSTON, N. G., HUBENDICK, B., WATSON, J. M. and OLIVER, L. J., 1958. An evaluation of techniques used in estimating snail populations. *Bull. Wld Hlth Org.* **19,** 661–72.

HALE, W. G., 1964. A flotation method for extracting Collembola from organic soils. *J. anim. Ecol.* **33,** 363–9

HAMMER, M., 1944. Studies on the Oribatids and Collemboles of Greenland. *Medd. Grønland* **141,** 1–210.

HORSFALL, W. R., 1956. A method for making a survey of floodwater mosquitoes. *Mosq. News* **16,** 66–71.

HUGHES, R. D., 1960. A method of estimating the numbers of cabbage root fly pupae in the soil. *Plant Path.* **9,** 15–17.

JACOT, A. P., 1935. Molluscan populations of old growth forests and rewooded fields in the Asheville basin of N. Carolina. *Ecology* **16,** 603–5.

JONASSON, P. M., 1955. The efficiency of sieving techniques for sampling freshwater bottom fauna. *Oikos* **6,** 183–207.

KEMPSON, D., LLOYD, M. and GHELARDI, R., 1963. A new extractor for woodland litter. *Pedobiologia* **3,** 1–21.

KEVAN, D. K. MCE. (ed.), 1955. *Soil Zoology, Proceedings of the University of Nottingham second Easter School in Agricultural Science, 1955.* London, 512 pp.

KEVAN, D.K. MCE., 1962. *Soil animals,* London, 237 pp.

LADELL, W. R. S., 1936. A new apparatus for separating insects and other arthropods from the soil. *Ann. appl. Biol.* **23,** 862–79.

LANE, M. and SHIRCK, F., 1928. A soil sifter for subterranean insect investigations. *J. econ. Ent.* **21,** 934–6.

LANGE, W. H., AKESSON, N. B. and CARLSON, E. C., 1955. A power-driven self-propelled soil sifter for subterranean insects. *In* Kevan, D. K. McE. (ed.), *Soil Zoology* 351–5.

LAURENCE, B. R., 1954. The larval inhabitants of cow pats. *J. anim. Ecol.* **23,** 234–60.

LINCOLN, C. and PALM, C. E., 1941. Biology and ecology of the Alfalfa Snout beetle. *Mem. Cornell Univ. agric. Exp. Sta.* **236,** 3–45.

MACFADYEN, A., 1953. Notes on methods for the extraction of small soil arthropods. *J. anim. Ecol.* **22,** 65–78.

MACFADYEN, A., 1955. A comparison of methods for extracting soil arthropods. *In* Kevan, D. K. McE. (ed.). *Soil Zoology* 315–32.

MACFADYEN, A., 1961. Improved funnel-type extractors for soil arthropods. *J. anim. Ecol.* **30,** 171–84.

MACFADYEN, A., 1962. Soil arthropod sampling. *Adv. Ecol. Res.* **1,** 1–34.

MCLEOD, J. M., 1961. A technique for the extraction of cocoons from soil samples during population studies of the Swaine sawfly, *Neodiprion swainei* Midd. (Hymenoptera: Diprionidae). *Canad. Ent.* **91,** 888–90.

MILNE, A., COGGINS, R. E. and LAUGHLIN, R., 1958. The determination of numbers of leatherjackets in sample turves. *J. anim. Ecol.* **27,** 125–45.

MINDERMAN, G., 1957. The preparation of microtome sections of unaltered soil for the study of soil organisms in situ. *Plant Soil* **8,** 42–8.

MINDERMAN, G., 1962. Nematode extraction methods for forest soils. *In* Murphy, P. W. (ed.), *Progress in Soil Zoology* 257–60.

MÜLLER, G., 1962. A centrifugal-flotation extraction technique and its comparison with two funnel extractors. *In* Murphy, P.W. (ed.), *Progress in Soil Zoology* 207–11.

MURPHY, P. W., 1955. Notes on processes used in sampling, extraction and assessment of the meiofauna of heathland. *In* Kevan, D. K. McE. (ed.), *Soil Zoology* 338–40.

MURPHY, P. W. (ed.), 1962a. *Progress in Soil Zoology. Papers from a colloquium on Research methods organised by the Soil Zoology Committee of the International Society of Soil Science held at Rothamsted Experimental Station Hertfordshire 10–14th July, 1958.* London, 398 pp.

MURPHY, P. W., 1962*b*. Extraction methods for soil animals. I. Dynamic methods with particular reference to funnel processes. *In* Murphy, P. W. (ed.), *Progress in Soil Zoology* 75–114.

MURPHY, P. W., 1962*c*. Extraction methods for soil animals. II. Mechanical methods. *In* Murphy, P. W. (ed.), *Progress in Soil Zoology* 115–55.

NEF, L., 1960. Comparaison de l'efficacité de différentes variantes de l'appareil de Berlese-Tullgren. *Z. angew. Ent.* **46**, 178–99.

NELSON, J. M. and SATCHELL, J. E., 1962. The extraction of Lumbricidae from soil with special reference to the hand-sorting method. *In* Murphy, P. W. (ed.), *Progress in Soil Zoology* 294–9.

NEWELL, I., 1955. An autosegregator for use in collecting soil-inhabiting arthropods. *Trans. Amer. Microsc. Soc.* **74**, 389–92.

NIELSEN, C. OVERGAARD, 1952–53. Studies on Enchytraeidae 1. A technique for extracting Enchytraeidae from soil samples. *Oikos* **4**, 187–96.

O'CONNOR, F. B., 1955. Extraction of enchytraeid worms from a coniferous forest soil. *Nature, Lond.* **175**, 815–17.

O'CONNOR, F. B., 1957. An ecological study of the Enchytraeid worm population of a coniferous forest soil. *Oikos* **8**, 162–99.

O'CONNOR, F. B., 1962. The extraction of Enchytraeidae from soil. *In* Murphy, P. W. (ed.), *Progress in Soil Zoology* 279–85.

ØKLAND, F., 1929. Methodik einer quantitativen Untersuchung der Landschneckenfauna. *Arch. Molluskenk.* **61**, 121–36.

OOSTENBRINK, M., 1954. Een doelmatige methode voor het toetsen van aaltjesbestrijdingsmiddelen in grond met *Hoplolaimus uniformis* als proefdier. *Meded. LandbHoogesch. Gent.* **19**, 377–408.

OVERGAARD, C. [NIELSEN, C. OVERGAARD], 1947–48. An apparatus for quantitative extraction of nematodes and rotifers from soil and moss. *Natura jutl.* **1**, 271–8.

PARIS, O. H. and PITELKA, F. A., 1962. Population characteristics of the terrestrial Isopod *Armadillidium vulgare* in California grassland. *Ecology* **43**, 229–48.

PARK, O. and AUERBACH, S., 1954. Further study of the tree-hole complex with emphasis on quantitative aspects of the fauna. *Ecology* **35**, 208–22.

PEACHEY, J. E., 1962. A comparison of two techniques for extracting Enchytraeidae from moorland soils. *In* Murphy, P. W. (ed.), *Progress in Soil Zoology* 286–93.

PETERS, B. G., 1955. A note on simple methods of recovering nematodes from soil. *In* Kevan, D. K. McE. (ed.), *Soil Zoology* 373–4.

POTZGER, J. E., 1955. A borer for sampling in permafrost. *Ecology* **36**, 161.

RAW, F., 1955. A flotation extraction process for soil micro-arthropods. *In* Kevan, D. K. McE. (ed.), *Soil Zoology* 341–6.

RAW, F., 1959. Estimating earthworm populations by using formalin. *Nature, Lond.* **184**, 1661–2.

RAW, F., 1960. Earthworm population studies: a comparison of sampling methods. *Nature, Lond.* **187**, 257.

RAW, F., 1962. Flotation methods for extracting soil arthropods. *In* Murphy, P. W. (ed.), *Progress in Soil Zoology* 199–201.

READ, D. C., 1958. Note on a flotation apparatus for removing insects from soil. *Canad. J. Pl. Sci.* **38**, 511–14.

SALT, G. and HOLLICK, F. S. J., 1944. Studies of wireworm populations. 1. A census of wireworms in pasture. *Ann. appl. Biol.* **31**, 53–64.

SATCHELL, J. E., 1955. An electrical method of sampling earthworm populations. *In* Kevan, D. K. McE. (ed.), *Soil Zoology* 356–64.

SATCHELL, J. E. and NELSON, J. M., 1962. A comparison of the Tullgren-funnel and flotation methods of extracting acarina from woodland soil. *In* Murphy, P. W. (ed.), *Progress in Soil Zoology* 212–16.

SAUNDERS, L. G., 1959. Methods for studying *Forcipomyia* midges, with special reference to cacao-pollinating species (Diptera, Ceratopogonidae). *Canad. J. Zool.* **37**, 33–51.

SCHJØTZ-CHRISTENSEN, B., 1957. The beetle fauna of the Corynephoretum in the ground of the Mols Laboratory, with special reference to *Cardiophorus asellus* Er. (Elateridae). *Natura jutl.* **6–7**, 1–120.

SEINHORST, J. W., 1962. Extraction methods for nematodes inhabiting soil. In Murphy, P. W. (ed.), *Progress in Soil Zoology* 243–56.

SELLMER, G. P., 1956. A method for the separation of small bivalve molluscs from sediments. *Ecology* **37**, 206.

SOLOMON, M. E., 1962. Notes on the extraction and quantitative estimation of Acaridiae (Acarina). In Murphy, P. W. (ed.), *Progress in Soil Zoology* 305–7.

SOUTH, A., 1964. Estimation of slug populations. *Ann. appl. Biol.* **53**, 251–8.

STAGE, H. H., GJULLIN, C. M. and YATES, W. W., 1952. Mosquitoes of the Northwestern States. *U.S.D.A., Agric. Handb.* **46**, 95 pp.

STEPHENSON, J. W., 1962. An improved final sieve for use with the Salt and Hollick soil-washing apparatus. In Murphy, P. W. (ed.), *Progress in Soil Zoology* 202–3.

SVENDSEN, J. A., 1955. Earthworm population studies: a comparison of sampling methods. *Nature, Lond.* **175**, 864.

TÖRNE, E. VON, 1962a. An elutriation and sieving apparatus for extracting micro-arthropods from soil. In Murphy, P. W. (ed.), *Progress in Soil Zoology* 204–6.

TÖRNE, E. VON, 1962b. A cylindrical tool for sampling manure and compost. In Murphy, P. W. (ed.), *Progress in Soil Zoology* 240–2.

VÁGVÖLGYI, J., 1953 (1952). A new sorting method for snails, applicable also for quantitative researches. *Ann. Hist. Nat. Mus. Nat. Hung.* **44** (N.S. 3), 101–4.

WALLACE, M. M. H., 1956. A rapid method of sampling small free-living pasture insects and mites. *J. Aust. Inst. agric. Sci.* **22**, 283–4.

WEBLEY, D., 1957. A method of estimating the density of frit fly eggs in the field. *Plant Path.* **6**, 49–51.

WILLIAMS, R. W., 1960a. A new and simple method for the isolation of fresh water invertebrates from soil samples. *Ecology* **41**, 573–4.

WILLIAMS, R. W., 1960b. Quantitative studies on populations of biting midge larvae in saturated soil from two types of Michigan bogs (Diptera: Ceratopogonidae). *J. Parasit.* **46**, 565–6.

WILLIAMSON, M. H., 1959. The separation of molluscs from woodland leaf-litter. *J. anim. Ecol.* **28**, 153–5.

CHAPTER 6

Absolute Population Estimates by Sampling a Unit of Habitat – Freshwater Habitats

Phyla other than the Arthropoda are well represented in this habitat, but it is not the intention of this chapter to detail the methods for the study of the microfauna of inland waters; these are described in works such as Welch (1948). In contrast to terrestrial habitats, major difficulties in making absolute estimates lie in actually taking a sample of a known unit, as well as in the separation of the animals from the media. The problems of extraction are similar to those in terrestrial habitats and reference should therefore be made to chapters 4 and 5.

Many of the methods described in this chapter have comparatively low efficiencies, so that the emphasis in the chapter heading must be on the use of a unit of habitat, rather than on the absoluteness of the estimate. When a method has been calibrated the data from it could be multiplied by an appropriate conversion factor to give an absolute estimate.

It is convenient to divide the freshwater habitat and its animals into:

I. Open water – inhabited by surface dwellers and by plankton-type animals.
II. Vegetation – animals living on or around submerged plants.
III. Bottom fauna – animals living on or in the substrate.

OPEN WATER

No absolute quantitative method has been devised for estimating surface-dwelling insects. The larger forms may be counted directly *in situ*; their numbers and dispersion might also be studied by photography and possibly nearest neighbour techniques used in their estimation (p. 39).

Small free-swimming animals may be sampled by the many methods that have been developed in plankton studies. A full account of these is given by Welch (1948); there are four main types that are of significance in entomological studies.

a. Nets

The simplest type of plankton net, a bolting silk bag on a metal frame, is easy to construct; towed behind a boat or hauled across a pond on a line, it collects and separates the animals in one operation. It is possible to calculate the volume of water that has to be filtered through the net, i.e. from which the insects have been extracted. Care must be taken to ensure that the net is not moved too fast so that it 'pushes aside' some water and the animals in it; this is particularly important with fine-mesh nets (Ricker, 1938; Fujita, 1956); however, if the net is moved too slowly the more agile animals with good vision may be able to avoid it. One should always use the coarsest net consistent with the size of the animal being studied.

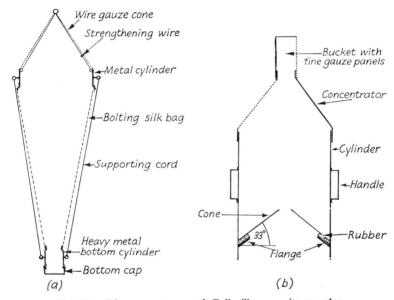

Fig. 38. *a.* Birge cone tow-net. *b.* Belleville mosquito sampler.

The Birge cone net, as modified by Wolcott (1901) (fig. 38*a*), is a convenient tow-net: the anterior wire-mesh cone ensures that water weed and other large debris do not clog the net, which is easily emptied by the removal of the bottom cap, conveniently made from the screw cap of a metal can.

If nets are to be used to sample animals in the lower layers of water, then they must have a mechanism for closing them as they pass through the surface layer. Wickstead (1953) has described one for sampling the animals in the immediate vicinity of the sea or lake bottom.

b. Pumps and baling

If a pump is used, a hose is inserted in the water to a known depth, the water pumped out and the organisms extracted by sieves or screens. The disadvantages of this technique are that the precise depth from which the water is drawn is unknown and some animals may react to the current and so avoid capture (Welch, 1948). A portable unit, fitting exactly into a small boat, has been described by Griffith (1957).

With small bodies of water, e.g. mosquito breeding pools, it may be possible to empty the complete pond, carefully separating the animals by a series of sieves, the contents of each sieve being sorted in a large pan. As developed by Christie (1954), the method allows the mosquito larvae to be returned to the pond after enumeration; although the water level is lowered with a pump, the residue containing the insects is baled out and the sieves are kept full of water so that the larvae are not damaged by violent contact with them.

c. The Clarke–Bumpus plankton sampler

This apparatus consists of a normal cone-shaped plankton net; in its mouth is a metal cylinder with a propeller blade (that records the throughput of water), two stabilizing vanes and a shutter mechanism. It is described in detail by Clarke & Bumpus (1940) and Welch (1948).

d. The Belleville mosquito sampler

Because mosquito larvae dive to the bottom of a pond when disturbed and then gradually make their way up to the surface again, sampling by dipping with a net or strainer will give variable results depending on the skill of the collector. Welch & James (1960) have, however, used this habit in the Belleville mosquito sampler (fig. 38b). The sampler consists of a cylinder, a cone, a concentrator and a bucket. The cylinder is placed in the pond, its base firmly pushed on to the substrate, the cone slipped inside and the apparatus left for 20 minutes. The concentrator and bucket are then fixed to the top; the whole rapidly reversed. Most of the larvae are collected in the bucket, as the water drains out through it and the concentrator; a few may remain stuck on the sides, so the apparatus should be rinsed.

The angle of the cone may have to be adjusted for different species; for Canadian *Aedes* Welch & James found the minimum was 33°. The greater the angle of the cone, the greater its height; as the water must always be deeper than the height of the cone this value will limit the depth of water in which the sampler can be used. Since the samplers need to be left for some time, a practical set of equipment for field work would consist of ten cylinders and cones with a single concentrator and bucket. Laboratory tests gave disappointingly low efficiencies, in the region of 30–40%; and increasing the 'rising time' from 5 to 20 minutes did not markedly increase the number of larvae extracted. Welch & James suggest that the sampler be standardized by comparing the catch for a 24-hour period with that for a shorter time. The series of catches may then be corrected to give an absolute estimate.

VEGETATION

Animals among floating vegetation are frequently sampled by dipping with a pond net or a strainer; such methods, however, give only relative estimates of population density. For absolute estimates it is necessary to enclose a unit

volume of the vegetation and associated water; when this has been strained
the organisms are usually separated by hand-sorting; however, some of the
methods described in chapter 4 might be found useful (e.g. clearing and staining for eggs in water plants). Extraction by spraying the material with a fine
mist, as used in plant nematode work (Goodey, 1957), might also be found
applicable.*

a. Sampling cylinder for floating vegetation

This was described by Hess (1941); it consists of a stout galvanized cylinder
with copper mesh screening (fig. 39*b*) and is lowered under the vegetation,
moved into position, raised and any plant stems crossing its edge cut by

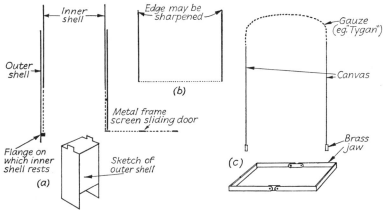

Fig. 39. *a*. Gerking sampler, sketch of outer shell and section. *b*. Hess's sampling cylinder
for floating vegetation. *c*. Wisconsin trap, sketch of jaws and section.

striking the edges of the cylinder with a wooden paddle. If necessary this could
be aided by sharpening the upper edges of the cylinder. The cylinder is then
raised from the water and the plants and animals retained within it.

b. Wisconsin trap

As described by Welch (1948) this is simply a canvas and gauze net with a
closable mouth (fig. 39*c*). The trap is lowered over the vegetation; the jaws of
the trap are closed just above the substrate, the plants being uprooted or cut
off. The whole is then raised from the water and drained.

c. The Gerking sampler

Designed by Gerking (1957) for the sampling of littoral macrofauna, this
equipment would seem to be satisfactory, apart from the labour involved, for
obtaining absolute samples of all but the most active animals. It consists of
two galvanized iron shells, each with a square cross-section; they may be
nearly 1 m high if necessary (fig. 39*a*). The two shells of the sampler are placed

* Originally described by Seinhorst, J. W. (1950) *Tijdschr. Pl. Ziekt.* **56**, 289.

in position, the lower edges of the outer shell being forced into the mud. One side of the base of the outer shell is open (see sketch, fig. 39) and through this opening the stems of the water plants are quickly cut with a pair of grass-clippers. The metal and screen sliding door is then inserted and this effectively closes the inner shell, which may be slowly raised. The outer cylinder is left in position and Gerking used an Ekman dredge to remove the substrate from within the same area; alternatively it could be scooped out (see *d.* below). If it is not desired to sample the substrate simultaneously then only a single shell need be used; it should correspond in shape to the outer shell, but have a number of gauze panels. In some ways this apparatus is a modification of the Wilding (1940) square foot sampler.

d. Sampling cages

A simpler approach along the same lines as the Gerking sampler, that is enclosing a column of water of a known volume, is the sampling cage of James & Nicholls (1961). It is a screen cage that is pushed down into the mud, the enclosed water is hand-sieved and then the substrate dredged up and sorted on sorting trays attached to the sides of the cage. There is always the danger with this method that some animals will be missed in the hand-sieving. Earlier versions of this sampling device are described by Bates (1941) and Goodwin & Eyles (1942).

BOTTOM FAUNA

A large number of methods have been developed for sampling the bottom fauna of freshwater habitats; one reviewer has commented that the number of samplers is nearly proportional to the number of investigators (Cummins, 1962)! This fact arises because five variables affect the choice of sampler:

(1) The animal
(2) The nature of the bottom substrate – soft or hard
(3) The current
(4) The depth of the water
(5) The object of the study, e.g. a routine survey for pollution, an assessment of the food potentially available for fish or an intensive ecological investigation for the development of a life-table for a single species.

A few generalizations are possible. Fast-flowing water has the advantage that the current may be used to carry animals, disturbed from the substrate, into a sampler (as with the Surber sampler, p. 165); however, it limits the use of devices that enclose a unit area, for as these are lowered the increased current immediately beneath them may scour the organisms from the very area that is to be sampled.

After the sample has been taken the problem remains of separating the animals from the substrate. Most workers have done this by hand-sorting, but some of the methods described in chapter 5 may be applicable: wet sieving, flotation in saturated solutions of various salts (e.g. $MgSO_4$, NaCl, $CaCl_2$, $ZnCl_2$) or heavy chlorinated hydrocarbons; elutriation and the sand extractor have been used to a limited extent by freshwater ecologists.

Sampling in stony streams has recently been reviewed by Macan (1958) and the general problem of benthic sampling by Albrecht (1959), Longhurst (1959) and Cummins (1962). Cummins discusses the type of sampling programme and pattern; he stresses the importance of simultaneous sampling and characterizing the substrate in any study of the distribution of benthic animals. Kajak (1963) discusses the problems of sample unit size and the number of samples (see chapter 2); with the tremendous variability of microhabitats within a small area of stream bottom the variance of a series of samples is often extremely large (Usinger & Needham, 1954).

a. The 'planting' of removable portions of the substrate

One of the most accurate methods of sampling the bottom fauna is to place a bag, tray or box in the stream or pond bed and either replace the substrate or allow the sediment to accumulate naturally (Moon, 1935; Wene & Wickliff, 1940; Usinger & Needham, 1954; Ford, 1962). The most elaborate apparatus of this type is the box of Ford. This has two fixed wooden sides and a bottom and is placed in a hole in the bed of the stream, the two sides being parallel to the course of the water. After a suitable time (Ford left it for 6 weeks) the other two sides, which are made of 'Perspex',* are slid into position, the box is then made watertight and may be lifted from the stream bed with the sample undisturbed. In Ford's model it was possible to divide the sample horizontally so that each stratum could be separately analysed: one of the wooden sides had a series of slots in it; the egress of mud and water through these was prevented by rubber flaps on the inside, the other sides were grooved at the corresponding level; 'Perspex' sheets could then be pushed through these slots dividing the sample.

The fauna of rocks or concrete substrates may be studied by placing easily removable blocks or plates of similar composition. Britt (1955) placed blocks of concrete, heavily scored on the undersurface, on a rubble and gravel bottom in deep water. The blocks can be easily located and raised with the help of the buoy and cord, but some animals may be lost as the block is raised. This loss is overcome in Mundie's (1956) method, devised for the study of Chironomidae on the sloping slides of artificial reservoirs. The artificial substrate is a plate of asbestos–cement composition (fig. 40); attached to the centre of the plate is a guide wire which must be attached to a line above the water surface. The plates are left for the period of time necessary for them to be indistinguishable from the surrounding substrate (1–3 months) and then retrieved. Mundie's ingenious method of retrieval was as follows: a retrieving cone (fig. 40b) is slid down the guide line; this cone has flap-valves on the upper surface and

* 'Plexiglass' is a similar transparent plastic material.

these open as it descends ensuring that there is no surge of water to disturb the sample as the cone settles; rubber flanges around these valves and the base of the cone protect the sample from disturbance as the plate is gradually hauled up by the guide wire. Before the sample breaks the surface a gauze-bottomed bucket (fig. 40c) is placed below it; this retains any organisms

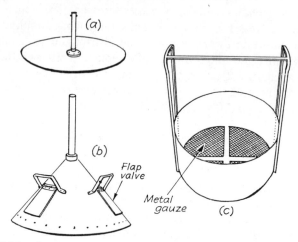

Fig. 40. Artificial substrate and sampling apparatus (after Mundie, 1956): *a.* artificial substrate-plate with central pipe to which wire is attached; *b.* retrieving cone; *c.* gauze-bottomed landing bucket.

washed out as the water in the sampler drains through the flap-valves of the cone.

   Completely artificial substrates may also be used, but these give only relative estimates as settlement on them will be different to that on the natural substrate. Metal cones, polythene funnels and tapes have been used in this way to estimate relative changes in the number of blackfly (Simuliidae) larvae (Wolfe & Peterson, 1958; Williams & Obeng, 1962).

b. Lifting stones

The majority of the animals in fast-flowing streams will be underneath the stones on the bottom. Scott & Rushforth (1959) have investigated from the mathematical angle the influence of stone size and spacing on the area of the stream bed covered by stones. They propose the symbol C_v for this parameter and discuss its value. An estimate of the absolute population of animals may be obtained by picking up the stones from an area of the bottom; a net should be held on the downstream side to catch those animals washed off (Macan, 1958). However, some animals may be especially difficult to remove from the stones and Britt (1955) found that these would become active if placed in a very weak acid alcohol solution (2–5% alcohol, 0·03–0·06% hydrochloric acid). A flotation solution (p. 138) might serve the same purpose and separate the animals as well.

Alternatively a net may be fixed in position; the stones and remainder of the substrate are disturbed from a unit area (one square foot) upstream and the animals caught in the net. This is the principle of the Surber sampler (Surber, 1936) (fig. 41). The variability of this technique, with operator and stream conditions, and its efficiency have been tested by Usinger & Needham (1954; and Needham & Usinger, 1956). As some stones will lie partly inside and

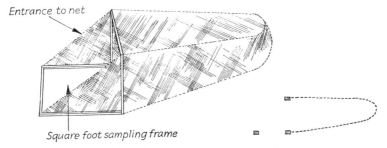

Entrance to net

Square foot sampling frame

Fig. 41. Surber sampler; sketch and section.

partly outside the square-foot frame the selection and rejection of these is a matter of personal judgement, and Usinger & Needham found that one operator continually sampled half as much area again as the other four operators, but the latter were consistent. Comparison of the results from the Surber sampler with absolute counts of animals from buried trays (section *a.* above) showed that it caught only about a quarter of the population. The exact proportion will vary from site to site, but it is obvious that the Surber sampler cannot be used for absolute population estimates from a shallow stream without a careful test of its efficiency to determine what correction factor should be applied.

c. Cylinders and boxes for delimiting an area

As pointed out above, when a box or cylinder is lowered into flowing water, as it approaches the bottom it is likely to cause this to be scoured. This problem is least serious with the Hess circular square-foot sampler (Hess, 1941) (fig. 42a), which is made of a fairly coarse mesh and may be rapidly turned so as to sink a little way into the bottom. The smaller organisms may be lost through the coarse grid. If a finer grid is used scouring becomes progressively more serious, but on the other hand drifting animals may pass through a coarse net and add cumulatively to the sample. Therefore Waters & Knapp (1961) designed a circular sampler with fine-mesh ('Nitex') screening; the emptying of the collecting bag was facilitated by attaching it to the sleeve with a zip-fastener. The use of these samplers is restricted to streams, as a current is necessary to carry the organisms into the collecting bag. The Wilding sampler (Wilding, 1940; see also Welch, 1948) may be used in still or

moving water. It consists of two cylinders; the outer cylinder has finely perforated sides and a band of saw teeth along the lower edge to aid penetration
into the bed of the stream or lake (these are not essential). This cylinder de-
limits the area and the larger organisms, rocks and other debris are removed;
then the whole is stirred and the inner cylinder (of slightly smaller diameter)
lowered inside. The inner cylinder has a rotary valve at the bottom through
which virtually all the water in the outer cylinder enters it (fig. 42*b* and *c*).

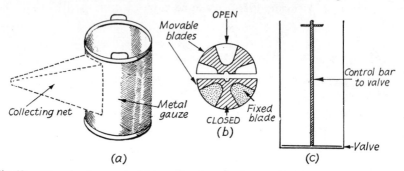

Fig. 42. *a*. Hess circular square-foot sampler. *b*. and *c*. Inner cylinder of the Wilding sampler
(simplified): *b*. diagram of rotary valve: upper half, open position; lower half, closed
position; *c*. section of cylinder.

When it is resting on the bottom the rotary valve is closed and the inner
cylinder, containing all the water and smaller animals, removed. Its contents
can be passed through a nest of sieves by opening the valve slowly.

The Gerking sampler and cages described above (p. 161) may also be used
for delimiting an area of bed for sampling, and simple metal frames and
cylinders were used for this purpose by Scott (1958) and Dunn (1961). Neill's
(1938) sampler is intermediate in design between the Hess and Wilding
models.

d. Movable nets – drags

The use of the Surber sampler and the various sampling cylinders is limited to
shallow waters (i.e. of depth of an arm's length or less); in deeper waters either
a moving net (drag, scoop, shovel) or a metal sampling box (dredge, grab,
etc. – see below) must be used. Several movable nets have been described (see
Welch, 1948; Macan, 1958; Albrecht, 1959); they may be pushed or pulled –
because they are themselves moved they are not dependent on a current in the
water. One of the most robust models is that devised by Usinger & Needham
(1954, 1956) (fig. 43) for sampling stone or gravel bottoms (none of these
movable nets are really suitable for soft mud). The tines on the mouth disturb
the substrate, but prevent large stones and debris from entering the bag, and
the weights and the heavy steel frame ensure that the tines really scour the
bottom. The bag is attached by means of a brass zip-fastener and protected
from tearing by a canvas sleeve. It is probable that a bag of one of the recent

synthetic materials, e.g. 'Tygan' or 'Nitex', would be more resistant to tearing than the nylon or silk originally used. Usinger & Needham (1954) found that,

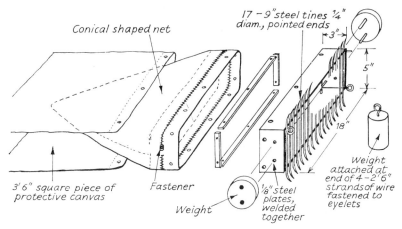

Fig. 43. Usinger & Needham's drag (after Usinger & Needham, 1956).

under the conditions they were working, this drag caught about one-quarter of the animals from the area it traversed. Therefore, unless standardized this is only a relative method.

e. Dredges and other devices for removing portions of the substrate
A wide variety of devices have been described for sampling a portion of the bed of a river or lake and bringing this to the surface (table 10). The variety has been due to the different emphasis placed by those primarily interested in physico-chemical investigations of the substrate from those working on benthic organisms; Cummins (1962) pleads for the combination of the two approaches. Further variation is due to the nature of the bottom and the depth of water in which the sampler must work (see table 10).
i. Dredges and grabs. These all take a comparatively shallow sample, which is more or less disturbed by the time it has reached the surface. Therefore they are not suitable for studies on stratification. One of the earliest pieces of equipment in this category is the Ekman dredge (Ekman, 1911), which is still widely used for sampling soft bottoms (fig. 44). It should be lowered gently into the water and, as it is lowered, the lid flaps will rise allowing it to settle into the mud without too much scouring. When the dredge has reached the bottom and settled, the messenger is dropped down the rope, and when this impacts on the spring mechanism above the box the two chains holding the jaws are released; the jaws are shut by the spring on their side. The dredge is then hauled to the surface. It is clear from the mode of operation that it relies on its own weight to sink and on the comparatively weak spring to close the jaws, therefore this dredge is limited to finely divided muddy or peaty bottoms; large bivalves or sticks will interfere with the closing of the jaws.

Table 10. Summary of some of the types of equipment for sampling portions of the benthic substrate – dredges, grabs, piston samplers, etc. Those in italics give undisturbed samples for the study of stratification

Substrate texture		May be used in water up to about 2 m deep	May be used in water of 'any' depth
Very soft ↓	Finely divided ↓		*Shapiro core-freezer* *Elgmork's sampler* *Brown's piston sampler* Ekman dredge
		Dendy inverting sampler	Hayward orange-peel bucket Petersen grab
		Allan grab	
Hard	Contains large particles – rocks, thick sticks		Smith & McIntyre sampler

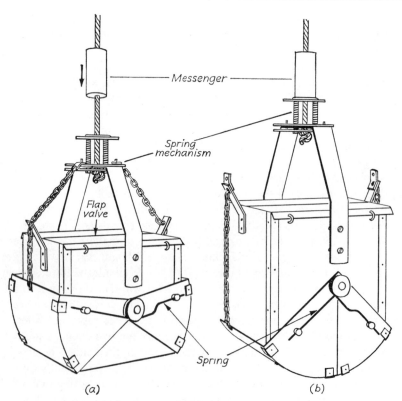

Fig. 44. Ekman dredge: *a*. open position while being lowered; *b*. closed after messenger has released jaws.

Slightly less homogeneous substrates, i.e. those containing fine gravel or small sticks, may be sampled by the Dendy (1944) inverting sampler (fig. 45). This apparatus consists of a brass cylinder of about 8 cm diameter, its top is covered with a piece of brass gauze. The cylinder is on the end of a long handle (this limits the depth of operation), which is used to drive it into the substrate; the pull cord is then tugged, the cylinder inverted and lifted to the surface. Only material that can pass out through the gauze is lost in the ascent (apart

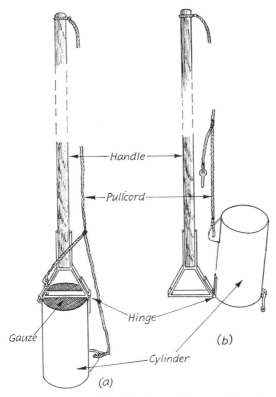

Fig. 45. Dendy inverting sampler (after Dendy, 1944): *a.* position when entering mud; *b.* inverted, ready to raise to surface.

from a small amount from the very bottom of the sample). The small size of this sampler relative to the Ekman dredge may indicate its use in preference to the latter from cost and sampling pattern considerations (see p. 18).

The commercially manufactured 'Hayward orange-peel bucket' may be used for bottom sampling of harder substrates in deep waters. Reish (1959) describes a simple modification whereby the use of a dropping messenger or second cable for closure is obviated. Its main disadvantages are that both very soft and rocky bottoms interfere with the closing mechanism.

The Petersen grab (Petersen, 1911) is a veteran piece of equipment that

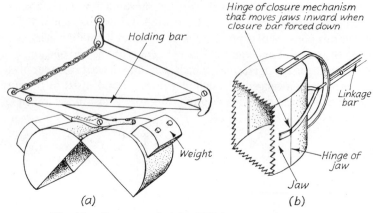

Fig. 46. *a*. Petersen grab (after Welch, 1948). *b*. Allan grab.

works in sand, gravel or marl (fig. 46*a*). It is lowered to the bottom on a cable and when it reaches the bottom the release of tension frees the holding bar so that the jaws start to 'bite' into the substrate under its own weight (about 35 lb); when the dredge is hoisted, leverage forcing the closure of the jaws aids the bite. The main disadvantage of this dredge is its weight and the hoisting apparatus necessary for its use. A modification has been described by Lisitsyn & Udintsev (1955) in which the messenger is replaced by a counterpoised weight (fig. 47).

In relatively shallow water samples may be taken from stony or vegetation-clothed bottoms by the Allan (1952) grab (fig. 46*b*), which, like the Dendy

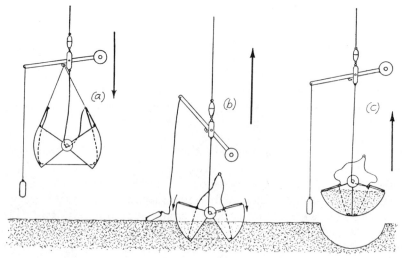

Fig. 47. A method of closing the Petersen grab using a counterpoised weight (after Lisitsyn & Udintsev, 1955).

sampler, is attached to the end of a long handle (tubular steel); this has a double advantage. The operator may exert direct force, through the linkage bar, on the closure mechanism, and will be aware when a large rock or piece of wood has jammed the jaws; secondly the dredge is held rigidly and so will enter the substrate vertically whatever the water current (rope-suspended dredges may be deflected).

No dredge is suitable for sampling really rocky beds; one of the most powerful is that designed by Smith & McIntyre (1954); its jaws are closed by strong springs.

ii. Piston-type samplers. These enable a vertical core to be taken from the bottom and are ideal for the study of stratification of micro-organisms and for the assessment of the physical and chemical properties of the various layers. One of the earliest was the Jenkin surface mud sampler (Jenkin & Mortimer, 1938; Mortimer, 1942).

Elgmork (1962) modified the Freidinger water sampler to take samples of soft mud; after sampling a piston was inserted and the sample slowly pushed out. The stratification of *Chaoborus punctipennis* was studied with this apparatus.

Livingstone (1955) described a piston sampler particularly well adapted for obtaining the lower layers of sediment from a muddy bottom; Vallentyne (1955) and Rowley & Dahl (1956) introduced modifications that made the construction simpler and less costly, and Brown (1956) has modified it to sample the mud–water interface as well and by the use of a clear plastic tube to allow the inspection of the intact core.

A different approach is that of Shapiro (1958), who surrounded the sampling tube (corer) with a tapered jacket. Just before lowering the jacket is filled with crushed solid carbon dioxide and *n*-butyl alcohol. It is lowered quickly through the water, allowed to settle, left for about five minutes and retrieved. The freezing mixture is replaced with water; the frozen core may soon be slid out and divided and handled in the solid state.

REFERENCES

ALBRECHT, M.-L., 1959. Die quantitative Untersuchung der Bodenfauna fliessender Gewässer (Untersuchungsmethoden und Arbeitsergebnisse). *Z. Fisch.* (N.F.) **8**, 481–550.

ALLAN, I. R. H., 1952. A hand-operated quantitative grab for sampling river beds. *J. anim. Ecol.* **21**, 159–60.

BATES, M., 1941. Field studies of the anopheline mosquitoes of Albania. *Proc. ent. Soc. Wash.* **43**, 37–58.

BRITT, N. W., 1955. New methods of collecting bottom fauna from shoals or rubble bottoms of lakes and streams. *Ecology* **36**, 524–5.

BROWN, S. R., 1956. A piston sampler for surface sediments of lake deposits. *Ecology* **37**, 611–13.

CHRISTIE, M., 1954. A method for the numerical study of larval populations of *Anopheles gambiae* and other pool-breeding mosquitoes. *Ann. trop. Med. Parasit., Liverpool* **48**, 271–6.

CLARKE, G. L. and BUMPUS, D. F., 1940. The Plankton sampler – an instrument for quantitative plankton investigations. *Limnol. Soc. Amer. Spec. Publ.* **5**, 1–8.

CUMMINS, K. W., 1962. An evaluation of some techniques for the collection and analysis of benthic samples with special emphasis on lotic waters. *Amer. Midl. Nat.* **67**, 477–503.

DENDY, J. S., 1944. The fate of animals in streamdrift when carried into lakes. *Ecol. Monogr.* **14**, 333–57.

DUNN, D. R., 1961. The bottom fauna of Llyn Tegid (Lake Bala), Merionethshire. *J. anim. Ecol.* **31**, 267–81.

EKMAN, S., 1911. Die Bodenfauna des Vättern, qualitativ und quantitativ untersucht. *Int. Revue ges. Hydrobiol. Hydrogr.* **7**, 146–204.

ELGMORK, K., 1962. A bottom sampler for soft mud. *Hydrobiologia* **20**, 167–72.

FORD, J. B., 1962. The vertical distribution of larvae Chironomidae (Dipt.) in the mud of a stream. *Hydrobiologia* **19**, 262–72.

FUJITA, H., 1956. The collection efficiency of a plankton net. *Res. Popul. Ecol.* **3**, 8–15.

GERKING, S. D., 1957. A method of sampling the littoral macrofauna and its application. *Ecology* **38**, 219–26.

GOODEY, J. B., 1957. Laboratory methods for work with plant and soil nematodes. *Tech. Bull. Min. Agric., Lond.* **2** (3rd ed.). H.M.S.O.

GOODWIN, M. H. and EYLES, D. E., 1942. Measurements of larval populations of *Anopheles quadrimaculatus*, Say *Ecology* **23**, 376.

GRIFFITH, R. E., 1957. A portable. apparatus for collecting horizontal plankton samples. *Ecology* **38**, 538–40.

HESS, A. D., 1941. New limnological sampling equipment. *Limnol. Soc. Amer. Spec. Publ.* **6**, 1–15.

JAMES, H. G. and NICHOLLS, C. F., 1961. A sampling cage for aquatic insects. *Canad. Ent.* **93**, 1053–5.

JENKIN, B. M. and MORTIMER, C. H., 1938. Sampling lake deposits. *Nature, Lond.* **142**, 834.

KAJAK, Z., 1963. Analysis of quantitative benthic methods. *Ekol. Polska A* **11**, 1–56.

LISITSYN, A. P. and UDINTSEV, G. B., 1955. New model dredges. [In Russian.] *Trudy vses. gidrobiol. Obsch.* **6**, 217–22.

LIVINGSTONE, D. A., 1955. A lightweight piston sampler for lake deposits. *Ecology* **36**, 137–9.

LONGHURST, A. R., 1959. The sampling problem in benthic ecology. *Proc. N.Z. ecol. Soc.* **6**, 8–12.

MACAN, T. T., 1958. Methods of sampling the bottom fauna in stony streams. *Mitt. int. Verein. theor. angew. Limnol.* **8**, 1–21.

MOON, H. P., 1935. Methods and apparatus suitable for an investigation of the littoral region of Oligotrophic Lakes. *Int. Revue ges. Hydrobiol. Hydrogr.* **32**, 319–33.

MORTIMER, C. H., 1942. The exchange of dissolved substances between mud and water in lakes. III and IV. *J. Ecol.* **30**, 147–201.

MUNDIE, J. H., 1956. A bottom sampler for inclined rock surfaces in lakes. *J. anim. Ecol.* **25**, 429–32.

NEEDHAM, P. R. and USINGER, R. L., 1956. Variability in macrofauna of a single riffle in Prosser creek, California, as indicated by the Surber sampler. *Hilgardia* **24** (14), 383–409.

NEILL, R. M., 1938. The food and feeding of the brown trout (*Salmot rutta* L.) in relation to the organic environment. *Trans. R. Soc. Edinb.* **59**, 481–520.

PETERSEN, C. G. J., 1911. Valuation of the sea. I. *Rep. Dan. biol. Stn* **20**, 1–76.

REISH, D. J., 1959. Modification of the Hayward orange peel bucket for bottom sampling. *Ecology* **40**, 502–3.

RICKER, W. E., 1938. On adequate quantitative sampling of the pelagic net plankton of a lake. *J. Fish. Res. Bd Can.* **4,** 19–32.

ROWLEY, J. R. and DAHL, A., 1956. Modifications in design and use of the Livingstone piston sampler. *Ecology* **37,** 849–51.

SCOTT, D., 1958. Ecological studies on the Trichoptera of the River Dean, Cheshire. *Arch. Hydrobiol.* **54,** 340–92.

SCOTT, D. and RUSHFORTH, J. M., 1959. Cover on river bottoms. *Nature, Lond.* **183,** 836–7.

SHAPIRO, J., 1958. The core-freezer – a new sampler for lake sediments. *Ecology* **39,** 758.

SMITH, W. and MCINTYRE, A. D., 1954. A spring-loaded bottom-sampler. *J. mar. biol. Ass. U.K.* **33,** 257–64.

SURBER, E. W., 1936. Rainbow trout and bottom fauna production in one mile of stream. *Trans. Amer. Fish. Soc.* **66,** 193–202.

USINGER, R. L. and NEEDHAM, P. R., 1954. *A plan for the biological phases of the periodic stream sampling program* (mimeographed). *Final Rep. to Calif. St. Wat. Pollution Cont. Bd.* 59 pp.

USINGER, R. L. and NEEDHAM, P. R., 1956. A drag-type riffle-bottom sampler. *Progve Fish. Cult.* **18,** 42–44.

VALLENTYNE, J. R., 1955. A modification of the Livingstone piston sampler for lake deposits. *Ecology* **36,** 139–41.

WATERS, T. F. and KNAPP, R. J., 1961. An improved stream bottom fauna sampler. *Trans. Amer. Fish. Soc.* **90,** 225–6.

WELCH, H. E. and JAMES, H. G., 1960. The Belleville trap for quantitative samples of mosquito larvae. *Mosq. News* **20,** 23–6.

WELCH, P. S., 1948. *Limnological methods.* Philadelphia, 381 pp.

WENE, G. and WICKLIFF, E. L., 1940. 'Basket' method of bottom sampling. *Canad. Ent.* **72,** 131–5

WICKSTEAD, J., 1953. A new apparatus for the collection of bottom plankton. *J. mar. biol. Ass. U.K.* **32,** 347–55.

WILDING, J. L., 1940. A new square-foot aquatic sampler. *Limnol. Soc. Amer. Spec. Publ.* **4,** 1–4.

WILLIAMS, T. R. and OBENG, L., 1962. A comparison of two methods of estimating changes in *Simulium* larval populations, with a description of a new method. *Ann. trop. Med. Parasit., Liverpool* **56,** 359–61.

WOLCOTT, R. H., 1901. A modification of the Birge collecting net. *J. appl. Microsc. Lab. Meth.* **4,** (8), 1407–9.

WOLFE, L. S. and PETERSON, D. G., 1958. A new method to estimate levels of infestations of black-fly larvae (Diptera: Simulidae). *Canad. J. Zool.* **36,** 863–7.

CHAPTER 7

Relative Methods of Population Measurement and the Derivation of Absolute Estimates

Most of these relative methods require only comparatively simple equipment and, as they often serve to concentrate the animals, they provide impressive collections of data from situations where few animals will be found by absolute methods. From entirely statistical considerations the plentiful data from relative methods is preferable to the hard-won, often scanty, information from unit area sampling. Most traps will collect specimens continuously, providing a relatively large return for the amount of time spent working with them; i.e. the cost (see p. 18) of the data is low. With all these apparent advantages it is hardly surprising that these methods have been extensively used and developed; there are probably more accounts of their design and use in the literature than references to all the other topics in this book (therefore the list at the end of this chapter is highly selective).

FACTORS AFFECTING THE SIZE OF RELATIVE ESTIMATES

The biological interpretation of relative population estimates (p. 3) is extremely difficult. Their size is influenced by the majority or all of the following factors:

(1) Changes in actual numbers – population changes.
(2) Changes in the numbers of animals in a particular 'phase'.
(3) Changes in activity.
(4) Changes in efficiency of the traps or the searching method.
(5) The responsiveness of that particular sex and species to the trap stimulus.

It is clear, therefore, that the estimation of absolute population by relative methods is difficult; what one is really estimating is the proportion of those members of the population that were in the 'phase' to respond to the trap and that did so under the prevailing climatic conditions and the current level of efficiency of the trap. The influence of factors 2–5 on these relative methods must be considered further.

The 'phase' of the animal

The susceptibility of an animal to being caught or observed may alter with age, because the behavioural attributes and responses of an animal vary from age to age. Many relative methods rely to some extent on the movement of the insect; insect movements are basically of two types: migratory and trivial (Southwood, 1962), and there is evidence from many species that migratory movements occur mainly early in adult life or between reproductive periods (Johnson, 1960, 1963; Kennedy, 1961). Trivial movements, during which the insect will be especially responsive to bait, may occur mostly in later life. The effects of these phenomena on trap catches had in fact been recorded before they themselves were recognized: Geier (1960) showed with the codling moth that the majority of the females taken in light-traps were in the pre-reproductive phase, whilst bait-trap catches were predominantly mature (i.e. egg-laying) or post-reproductive females. Another example is the fall-off in numbers of *Culicoides* midges caught on sticky traps which occurs before the actual population starts to decline (Nielsen, 1963).

The activity of the animal

The level of activity of an insect will be governed by its diurnal cycle, some insects flying by day, others at night (Lewis & Taylor, 1965), and the expression of this activity will be conditioned by the prevailing climatic conditions. The separation of changes in trap catch due to climate from those reflecting population change has long exercised entomologists. Williams (1940) approached the problem by taking running-means of the catches; the variation in these running-means (i.e. the long-term variation) reflected population changes and the departures of the actual catch from them reflected the influence of climate. Working with groups of species, such as the larger Lepidoptera, Williams was able to demonstrate both the long-term effects of climate through population change and the short-term effects on activity. When studying the populations of airborne aphids, Johnson (1952) found that the running-means reflected current climatic conditions and the deviations population trends; this was due to the relatively short period of time any given aphid spends in the air.

Thus the running-mean technique is unsafe on biological grounds, being influenced by the relative frequency of population and climatic change; furthermore its use places severe restrictions on the number of degrees of freedom available for the calculation of significance levels. Even if no attempt is made to separate population trend and activity and the regression of the actual catch of a group of animals on temperature is calculated, highly significant results are obtained, thereby emphasizing the role of temperature in the determination of catch size (e.g. Williams, 1940; Southwood, 1960).

Although it is occasionally possible to obtain a significant regression of

E M—G

catch size on temperature for a single species (e.g. Southwood, 1960), in general the relationship does not hold at the species level and Taylor (1963) has propounded and demonstrated the idea that there are upper and lower thresholds for flight. When the temperature is above the lower threshold (and below the upper threshold) the insect will be flying, when below (or above the upper threshold) it will be inactive. The thresholds may be determined by classifying each trapping period as either 1, one or more insects of the particular species were caught or 0, none were caught. Then the trapping periods are grouped according to the prevailing temperature and the percentage of occasions with flight plotted against temperature (fig. 48). For example if there were twenty-five trapping periods when the temperature was 16°C and one or more specimens were collected on ten occasions, a point would be entered at the 40% flight occurrence (fig. 48). Thresholds for light and other physical conditions may be determined in the same way. The transition from 0% flight occurrence to 100% is not sharp, presumably because of the variation in the

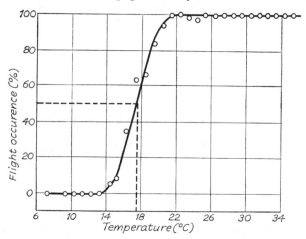

Fig. 48. The graphical determination of the flight threshold of a species (after Taylor, 1963).

individual animals and the microclimate of the sites from which they have flown. Taylor (1963) found that the mouse moth (*Amphipyra tragopoginis*) appeared to have two lower thresholds for temperature; but his data could also be interpreted as showing a steady increase in % flight occurrence to a maximum. Both interpretations are so contrary to the findings with other insects that this and any similar cases should be viewed with suspicion until further data has been obtained.

The influence of activity may therefore be expressed in terms of the various thresholds; once these have been determined fluctuations in numbers between the lower and upper thresholds for flight may be considered as due to other causes.

Taylor (1963) demonstrates elegantly that, when mixed populations of several species are considered, the series of thresholds will lead to an apparent regression of activity on temperature of the type demonstrated by Williams and others, therefore he concludes that regression analysis as a means of interpreting the effect of temperature on insect flight should be limited to multi-specific problems.

The efficiency of the trap or searching method

The efficiency of a method of population estimation is the percentage of the animals actually present that are recorded. The efficiency of a searching method will clearly depend on the skill of the observer and also on the habitat; for example, any observer is likely to see tiger beetles (Cicindellidae) far more easily on lacustrine mud flats than on grass-covered downlands.

Several types of traps – sticky, water and flight – catch insects that are carried into or on to them by the wind, and Johnson (1950) and Taylor (1962) have shown that the efficiency of such traps varies with wind speed and the size of the insect (table 11). Thus such traps may give widely different counts for the same aerial population if the wind speeds on the sampling occasions differ, and the results of Juillet (1963) are almost certainly an example of this. Taylor (1962) has, however, shown that it is possible to correct the catches from these traps if the wind speed is known (see p. 180).

It has long been known that light-traps take fewer insects on nights of full moon; this is due to a fall in the efficiency of the traps (Williams, Singh & El Ziady, 1956). (In actual fact there is evidence that populations of flying mosquitoes may be greater on moonlight nights (Bidlingmayer, 1964)). The efficiency of baits varies from many causes: the ageing and fermentation of artificial or non-living baits (Kawai & Suenaga, 1960) affecting their 'attractiveness', whilst living baits may differ in unexplained ways – Saunders (1964) found that two apparently identical black zebu oxen trapped different numbers of tsetse flies. The effectiveness of a given bait may vary from habitat to habitat (Starr & Shaw, 1944).

The efficiency of the various traps will be discussed further for each type, but the examples already given are sufficient to indicate that variation in efficiency provides a very real limitation on the value of relative estimates even for comparative purposes.

Variation in the responsiveness of different sexes and species to trap stimuli

In many groups significantly more of one sex or the other are caught in light-traps (Williams, 1939; Masaki, 1959). Take for example the Miridae; males make up the majority of light-trap catches and there is some evidence that male mirids do engage in significantly more trivial movement, 'flits', than females (Southwood, 1960; Waloff & Bakker, 1963), but the excess of male Miridae is greater in ultra-violet than in tungsten filament light-traps (Southwood, 1960), so that at least a proportion of this predominance must be due to a selective effect of the traps between the sexes, rather than a real difference in flight activity.

An interesting case of a difference between sexes is the large number of male relative to female tsetse flies usually taken on 'fly rounds' (Glasgow & Duffy, 1961); the biological interpretation of this seems to be that newly emerged female flies usually feed on moving prey and the early pairing, desirable in this species, is achieved by numbers of males following moving bait (Bursell, 1961).

With such marked differences between the sexes it is hardly surprising that different species respond very differently. Eastop (1955) and Heathcote (1957a) have compared the ratios of the numbers of different species of aphids caught in yellow sticky traps to the numbers caught in suction traps, presumably the true population. Eastop, for example, found ratios varying from 31 to 0·5 and even within a genus (*Macrosiphum*) they ranged from 14·7 to 0·8. Analogous observations on the relative numbers of different species of mosquitoes caught in light-traps compared with the results from a rotary trap have been made by Love & Smith (1957), and they found ratios (that they called the 'index of attraction') from over 7 down to 0·24.

THE USES OF RELATIVE METHODS

It is apparent from the above section that the actual data from relative methods should be used and interpreted with far more caution than has often been shown. Comparisons of different species and different habitats are particularly fraught with dangers.

Measures of the availability

This is the most direct approach; the availability of the population of an animal is the result of the response to the stimuli, the activity and the abundance; that is the product of factors 1–3 and 5 in the list above (p. 174); it may be defined as the ratio of total catch to total effort. Thus, assuming the efficiency of the trap or search does not change, the raw data of catch per unit time or effort will provide a measure of availability, but this assumption is by no means always justified (e.g. Vanderplank, 1960).

True availability is meaningful in many contexts: it is most easily interpreted with natural 'baits', e.g. the availability of bloodsucking insects to their normal prey (in a bait trap) is a measure of their 'biting level', and the availability of flying insects to colonize or oviposit on a trap host plant is a measure of these parameters. Extrapolations from more artificial situations can only be made in the light of additional biological knowledge. The availability of codling moth females to a light-trap gives a convenient indication of the magnitude and phenology of emergence and oviposition, and this may be used to time the application of control measures. But the peak of availability of the females to the bait traps indicates that the main wave of oviposition has passed (Geier, 1960), and therefore in warm climates, where the eggs will hatch quickly, this information may be too late for effective control measures.

In general, measures of availability may be used for the immediate assessment of the 'attacking' or colonization potential of a population and its phenology. Over a long period of time the changes in the species composition of the catches of the same trap in the same position may be used to indicate changes in the diversity of the fauna (see p. 332).

Indices of absolute population

When the efficiency of the trap and the responsiveness of the animal to it can be regarded as constant and if the effects of activity can be corrected for, then the resulting value is an index of the size of the population in that particular phase. The effects of activity due to temperature or other physical factors on the catch size of sticky, flight, pitfall and similar traps may be eliminated by the determination of the thresholds using Taylor's (1963) method (see above). With net catches the regression technique of Hughes (1955) serves the same purpose (p. 190). The animals' diel periodicity cycle may need to be known before these corrections can be made and the index derived. Such an index may be used in place of actual absolute population in damage assessment and in studies on the efficiency of pest control measures. The value of independent estimates of population size has been stressed (p. 4) and a series of such indices may be compared with actual population estimates: if the ratio of one to the other is more or less constant the reliability of the estimates has been confirmed. Indeed these indices may be used in place of absolute population estimates for any comparative purpose, but are of course of no value in life-table construction.

Estimates of absolute population

It is possible to derive estimates of absolute population from what are essentially relative methods by two approaches, each of which subdivides: the correction of the data, by 'calibration' with absolute estimates or by measurement of the efficiency, and its extension to determine density from the frequency of encounters (line transect theory) or from the rate by which trapping reduces the sizes of successive samples (removal trapping).

1. 'Calibration' by comparison with absolute estimates
When a series of indices of absolute population have been obtained simultaneously with estimates of absolute population by another method, the regression

of the index on absolute population may be calculated. This can then be used to give estimates of population directly from the indices, but such 'corrections' should only be made under the same conditions that held during the initial series of comparisons.

2. Correcting the catch to allow for variations in trap efficiency
This approach is really a refinement of that above; trap catches and absolute estimates are made simultaneously under a variety of conditions that are known to affect trap efficiency. A table of the correction terms for each condition can then be drawn up and will give much greater precision than a regression coefficient for all conditions (as in 1 above). A valuable approach along these lines has been made by Taylor (1962), who used the data from Johnson's (1950) comparison of sticky trap and tow-net with a suction trap to determine the efficiency of the two former. The efficiency of the suction trap had already been determined by him (see p. 130) and this gave a direct measure of the absolute density of the aerial population. Taylor was therefore able to construct a table of correction terms (table 11); they are of course only applicable to the particular traps Johnson used and it is important to note that

Table 11. The efficiency of a cylindrical sticky trap for different insects at different wind speeds (after Taylor, 1962)

	Wind speed (m.p.h.)				
	1	2	6	10	20
Small aphid (*Jacksonia*)	20	45	64	66	68
Small fly (*Drosophila*)	35	58	72	73	74
House fly (*Musca*)	45	64	76	76	76
Bumble bee (*Bombus*)	52	68	78	78	78

the sticky trap was white, not yellow. Taylor also computed the expected fall in efficiency of the traps allowing for the different volumes of air passing at different winds and the effect of this on the impaction of the insects on the sticky trap, assuming that they behave as inert particles; he found that a large part of the fall in efficiency at low wind speeds could be accounted for by these factors.

3. Line transects
The basic method of the line transect is that an observer walks at a constant speed through a habitat and records the number of animals he sees. This number will be a reflection of the density of the animals, their speed of move-

ment, the distance over which the observer perceives them and the observer's speed of movement. If the other factors are known the density can be arrived at. The method is developed in detail later (p. 187); it may perhaps be regarded as the mobile analogue of the nearest neighbour and other spacing methods (p. 39).

4. Removal trapping or collecting

The principle of removal trapping or collecting is that a known number of animals are removed from habitat on each trapping occasion, thus affecting subsequent catches. The rate at which trap catches fall off will be directly related to the size of the total population (unknown) and the number removed (known). Although Le Pelley (1935) first demonstrated that this fall of catch is geometric in observations on the hand-picking of the coffee bug, *Antestiopsis*, the method has been developed by mammalologists, starting with the work of Leslie & Davis (1939). They demonstrated the theory underlying this approach, which, like that of the line transect, is borrowed from physical chemistry and concerns the chances of collision of gas molecules.

For the application of the method the following conditions must be satisfied (Moran, 1951):

(1) The catching or trapping procedure must not lower (or increase) the probability of an animal being caught. For example, the method will not be applicable if the insects are being caught by the sweep net and after the first collection the insects drop from the tops of the vegetation and remain around the bases of the plants, or if the animals are being searched for and, as is likely, the most conspicuous ones are removed first (Kono, 1953).

(2) The population must remain stable during the trapping or catching period; there must not be any significant natality, mortality (other than by the trapping) or migration. The experimental procedure must not disturb the animals so that they flee from the area. As Glasgow (1953) has shown, if the trapping is extended over a period of time, immigration is likely to become progressively more significant as the population falls.

(3) The population must not be so large that the catching of one member interferes with the catching of another. This is seldom likely to be a problem with insects where each trap can take many individuals, but may be a significance in vertebrate populations where one trap can only catch one animal.

(4) The chance of being caught must be equal for all animals. This is the most serious limitation in practice. Some individuals of a population, perhaps those of a certain age, may never visit the tops of the vegetation and so will not be exposed to collection by a sweep net. In vertebrates 'trap-shyness' may be exhibited by part of the population.

Zippin (1956, 1958) has considered some of the specific effects of failures in the above assumptions. If the probability of capture falls off with time the population will be underestimated, but if the animals become progressively more susceptible to capture the population will be overestimated. Changes in susceptibility to capture will arise not only from the effect of the experiment on the animal, but also from changes in behaviour associated with weather conditions or a diel periodicity cycle.

The practice of the method is not dissimilar to that of Kelker's selective removal method when both sexes are hunted (p. 89); the approaches differ mainly in the method of analysis: in Kelker's method the total population is estimated from changes in the ratios of the different constituents of the population.

There are three different approaches to the analysis of removal trapping data. The simplest is the regression method (fig. 49). The number caught on the ith occasion are plotted against the previous total catch and the line may be fitted by eye (Hayne, 1949) or the regression line calculated (De Lury,

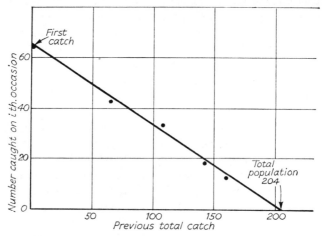

Fig. 49. The estimation of population by removal trapping – the fitting of the regression line by eye.

1947; Zippin, 1956; Kemp-Turnbull, 1960; Wada, 1962). Fitting by eye is acceptable only when the points lie fairly close to a straight line. Fitting by the regression equation is not really acceptable as the two values are not independent.

Working with the same basic approach, but apparently unaware of earlier work, Emsley (1957) estimated the total population by plotting accumulated catch against the trapping occasion; this describes a curve the asymptote of which indicates the level of the total population. As Menhinick (1963) points out, this will be something of an underestimate. Emsley, however, found that for a certain species in a given habitat the percentage of the total population obtained in the first catch was more or less constant, so that this single catch (actually made with a sweep net) could be taken as a fixed percentage of the total population. This is the calibration of a relative method (see above).

The second method, also simple but approximate, is that of Kono (1953) and was referred to by him as 'time–unit' collecting. He postulated that the exponential relationship between the number collected and time, which is the basis of all methods, may be discovered by the consideration of the catches at just three time points (t_1, t_2 and t_3), such that $\frac{1}{2}(t_1+t_2)=t_3$. Under these conditions:

$$P = \frac{n_3{}^2 - n_1 n_2}{2n_3 - (n_1 + n_2)}$$

where n_1, n_2 and n_3 = the accumulated catches at times t_1, t_2 and t_3 as defined above. Kono showed that it was important that the collectors are familiar with the animal before the start, so that the collecting efficiency does not improve during the estimation and that the greater the value of t_2, i.e. the closer n_2 approximates towards P, the more accurate the estimation of P.

Taking our previous example (fig. 49) with successive catches of 65, 43, 34, 18 and 12 at equal time intervals, then the accumulated catches are 65, 108, 142, 160 and 172. If $t_1=1$ and $t_2=5$, then $t_3=(1+5)/2=3$, hence $n_1=65$, $n_2=172$ and $n_3=142$ and therefore:

$$P = \frac{142^2 - 65 \times 172}{2 \times 142 - (65 + 172)} = 191$$

The third and most accurate method, which also provides an estimate of the standard error, is that based on maximum likelihood. First developed by Moran (1951), its application has been considerably simplified by Zippin (1956, 1958). Zippin's procedure will be illustrated with the previous example.

The total catch T is calculated

$$T = 65+43+34+18+12 = 172$$

Then the value of $\sum\limits_{i=1}^{k}(i-1)y_i$ is found, where k = the number of occasions (unrelated to 'k' elsewhere in this book) and y_i = the catch on the ith occasion.

Therefore

$$\sum_{i=1}^{k}(i-1)y_i = (1-1)65+(2-1)43+(3-1)34+(4-1)18+(5-1)12$$

$$= 0+43+68+54+48$$
$$\doteqdot 213$$

Next the ratio R is determined:

$$R = \frac{\sum\limits_{i=1}^{k}(i-1)y_i}{T}$$

Therefore

$$R = \frac{213}{172} = 1\cdot238$$

Now

$$R = \frac{q}{p} - \frac{kq^k}{(1-q^k)}$$

where p = the probability of capture on a single occasion and

$$q = 1-p$$

and the estimate of the total population is given by the equation:

$$P = \frac{T}{(1-q^k)}$$

The mathematics of these last steps may be circumvented for $k=3, 4, 5$ or 7 by the use of Zippin's charts (figs. 50 and 51).

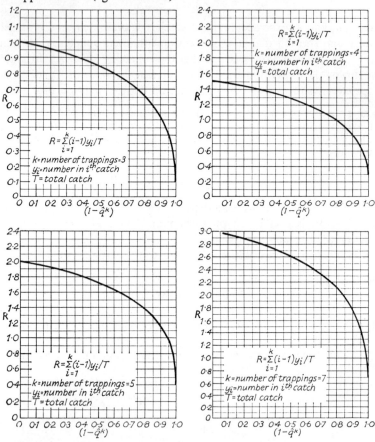

Fig. 50. Graphs for the estimation of $(1-q^k)$ from ratio R in removal trapping (after Zippin, 1956).

Therefore in the present example for $k=5$ and $R=1.24$ the value of $(1-q^k)$ is read off fig. 50 as 0.85, so that:

$$P = 172 \div 0.85 = 202$$

The standard error of P is given by

$$\text{S.E. of } P = \sqrt{\frac{P(P-T)T}{T^2 - P(P-T)[(kp)^2/(1-p)]}}$$

where the notation is as above and p is read from fig. 51.

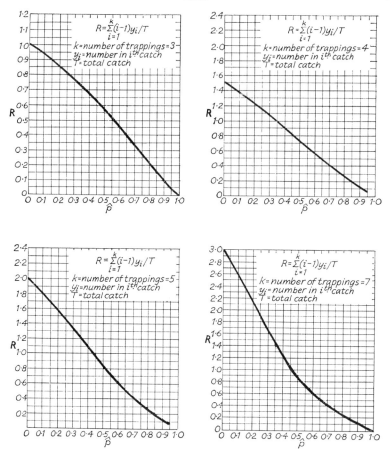

Fig. 51. Graphs for the estimation of p from ratio R in removal trapping (after Zippin, 1956).

In our example

$$\text{S.E. of } P = \sqrt{\frac{202(202-172)172}{172^2 - 202(202-172)[(5 \times 0{\cdot}33)^2/(1-0{\cdot}33)]}}$$

$$= 15$$

Therefore the 95% confidence limits of the estimate are:

$$202 \pm 2 \times 15$$

$$= 202 \pm 30$$

It will be noted that the estimate of P, obtained in fig. 49 by the visual fitting of the line and that obtained by Kono's method lie within these limits.

It has been shown by Zippin (1956, 1958) that a comparatively large proportion of the population must be caught to obtain reasonably precise estimates. His conclusions are presented in table 12, from which it may be seen

Relative Population Estimates

that, to obtain a coefficient of variation (c.v. = Estimate/Standard error × 100) of 30%, more than half the animals would have to be removed from a popula-

Table 12. Proportion of total population required to be trapped for specified coefficient of variation of $\hat{P}$ (after Zippin, 1956)

P	30%	20%	10%	5%
	Coefficient of variation			
	Proportion (to nearest ·05) of population to be captured (in 100 or fewer trappings)			
200	·55	·60	·75	·90
300	·50	·60	·75	·85
500	·45	·55	·70	·80
1,000	·40	·45	·60	·75
10,000	·20	·25	·35	·50
100,000	·10	·15	·20	·30

tion of less than 200. For this reason Turner (1962) found it impractical for estimating populations of insects caught in pitfall traps; the proportion of the population caught was too low. It is clearly desirable that, where this approach is used in life-table studies, the method of catching does not involve killing the animals, so that they may be kept captive and then released at the end of the estimation.

Collecting

Relative methods may be used as collecting methods, e.g. for animals for mark and recapture and for age determination in the construction of time-specific life-tables, provided the chances of all age and sex groups being captured are equal.

RELATIVE METHODS – CATCH PER UNIT EFFORT

Methods grouped here are those in which the movement or action that results in the capture or observation of the insect is made by the observer.

Visual observation

This is the simplest approach; the observer collects or counts *in situ* all the animals he can see in a fixed time or area. Because the efficiency of search is bound to differ in different habitats, contrary to the views of Mann (1955), fixed-time collecting is not very satisfactory for the comparison of faunas of different habitats (see also van der Drift, 1951). Within a given habitat it may give estimates that approach the measurement of absolute population and has been used widely, for example by Macan (1958) in stony streams, by Barnes & Barnes (1954) in a study of the spiders of drift lines and by Murray (1963) for mosquitoes; the last named author found this method more reliable than light-traps. The aspirator or 'pooter' (fig. 52) is convenient for the rapid collection of small insects in fixed-time estimations (e.g. Jepson & Southwood, 1958).

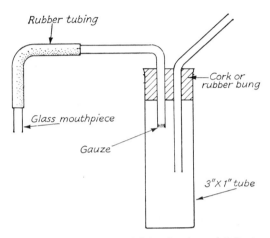

Fig. 52. The aspirator or 'pooter' (after Southwood & Leston, 1959).

Searching a fixed area, if completely efficient, provides an absolute estimate by a direct count (p. 108). However, methods that seem promising in this respect, for example Yeo & Foster's (1958) for the estimation of the coreid, *Pseudotheraptus wayi*, on coconut palms, may prove to be unreliable owing to variations in availability under different weather conditions and at different times of the day (Vanderplank, 1960). But the search is seldom as biased as the trap and sampling by searching the resting sites has provided valuable information in tsetse fly studies (Isherwood, 1957; Glasgow & Duffy, 1961).

Absolute population from the line transect
As indicated above searching may provide estimates, or at least indices, of absolute population directly; Yapp (1956) has devised another approach. If the observer walks in a straight line at a constant speed the number of animals he sees will depend on their average speed, his speed, the distance over which he can recognize them (the effective radius of the animal) and the density of the animal. The relationship between these variables can be expressed by the following equation (based on the kinetic theory of gases):

$$D = \frac{Z}{2RV} \tag{1}$$

where D = density of the population

$\quad\quad Z$ = number of encounters/unit time

$\quad\quad R$ = effective radius – the radial distance within which the animal must approach the observer to effect an encounter

$\quad\quad V$ = average velocity of the organism relative to the observer, which is given by:

$$V^2 = \bar{u}^2 + \bar{w}^2 \tag{2}$$

where $\bar{u}$ = average velocity of the observer and $\bar{w}$ = average velocity of the animal.

The applicability of this approach has been investigated by Skellam (1958), who concluded that the first formula was valid, but that the derivation of V contained an approximation the effect of which would be most serious when the speed of the observer and the animal were equal and almost negligible when the two were very dissimilar; Skellam also showed that equation 2 could be regarded as a Poisson variable provided the animals did not move back on their tracks or move in groups; under these conditions the variance would equal the mean. Aggregation will increase the variance.

The major practical difficulty in the application of this method – for the estimation of populations of butterflies, dragonflies, birds and other animals for which it would seem to be appropriate – is the determination of the average speed of the animal. Care must of course be taken with the units: if Z is expressed as the number of encounters/hour and R in metres, the speed, must be expressed in metres/hour.

Flushing

The observer moves through the habitat and records the number of animals that fly up ahead of him. If the width of the strip from which he will flush animals and the percentage of those within this strip that will be disturbed by him are known, then the total population can be estimated. If these are not known, but there is reason to suppose that the percentage flushed is a constant, then an index of absolute population is obtained. If the efficiency of flushing varies, only a relative measure of availability is given.

This method has been used for the assessment of populations of the red locust (*Nomadacris septemfasciata*) in its outbreak areas. The observer moved across the area in a motor vehicle (Land Rover) and counted the insects disturbed ahead (Scheepers & Gunn, 1958). Although the response of a locust to flushing depends on its condition (Nickerson, 1963), this method appears to have a fairly constant efficiency, about 75% of the locusts within the path of the vehicle rising (Symmons, Dean & Stortenbeker, 1963). In an attempt to cover a larger area more readily, flushing by a low-flying aircraft was tried, but the efficiency of flushing, even when increased by spraying a noxious chemical, was low in sparse populations; it was suggested that a siren might be used to disturb a higher proportion of locusts (Symmons *et al.*, 1963).

Collecting with a net or similar device

A number of approaches are included under this heading: in aquatic habitats dipping with a net or strainer is a widely practised relative method (Sheman-chuk, 1959; Zimmerman, 1960); animals on terrestrial vegetation may be collected with a sweep net or, for those on trees, a beating tray. The latter approaches an absolute method and is discussed in chapter 4 (p. 113). Anderson & Poorbaugh (1964) have obtained indices of the populations of dung-frequenting Diptera by collecting over a known area with a Dietrick suction sampler (p. 115).

Aerial insects may be collected by random strokes through the air with a light net (Parker, 1949; Linsley *et al.*, 1952; Nielsen, 1963) or with net or gauze cones on a car (Stage *et al.*, 1952), ship (Yoshimoto & Gressitt, 1959; Yoshimoto *et al.*, 1962), or an aeroplane (Glick, 1939; Odintsov, 1960; Gressitt *et al.*, 1961); because of the impedance to airflow due to the gauze, which becomes more severe at higher speeds, it is difficult – but not im-possible – to obtain direct measure of aerial density from such sampling cones.

The sweep net is perhaps the most widely used piece of equipment for sampling insects from vegetation; its advantages are its simplicity and speed – a high return for a small cost – and it will collect comparatively sparsely dis-persed species. However, only those individuals on the top of the vegetation that do not fall off or fly away on the approach of the collector are caught. The influence of these behavioural patterns on the efficiency of the method has been investigated by the comparison of sweep net samples with those from cylinders or suction apparatus (p. 115) (Beall, 1935; Romney, 1945; Johnson, Southwood & Entwistle, 1957; Race, 1960; Heikinheimo & Raatikainen, 1962), or by a long series of sweeps in the same habitat (Hughes, 1955; Fewkes, 1961). Changes in efficiency may be due to:

(1) different habitat or changes in the habitat
(2) different species
(3) changes in the vertical distribution of the species being studied
(4) variation in the weather conditions
(5) the influence of the diel cycle of vertical movements

A sweep net cannot be used on very short vegetation. Once plants become more than about 30 cm tall further increases in height mean that the net will be sampling progressively smaller proportions of any insect whose vertical distribution is more or less random.

Even related species may differ in their availability for sweeping (Johnson *et al.*, 1957; Heikinheimo & Raatikainen, 1962) and therefore the method is unsuitable for synecological work; these same workers also showed with a nabid bug and a leafhopper that the vertical distribution of the various larval instars and the adults differed (fig. 53). Within the adult stage the vertical distribution in vegetation may alter with age; ovipositing females of the grass mirid, *Leptopterna dolabrata*, are relatively unavailable to the sweep net (Southwood, unpub.); the same appears to be true of mature healthy males and females of the leafhopper, *Javesella* (= *Calligypona*) *pellucida*, in cereals, although parasitized individuals do not change their behaviour with age and so the percentage of parasitism would be overestimated by sweeping (Heikinheimo & Raatikainen, 1962).

Weather factors profoundly affect the vertical distribution and hence the availability to the sweep net and have been studied by Romney (1945) and Hughes (1955). The last named author found with the chloropid fly, *Meromyza*,

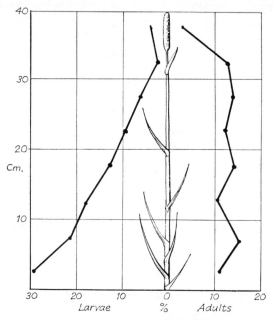

Fig. 53. The vertical distribution of larval instars IV and V and adults of *Javesella pellucida* on Timothy grass (after Heikinheimo & Raatikainen, 1962).

that the regressions of numbers swept against the various factors gave the following coefficients: wind speed −0·1774, time since saturation −0·0815, air temperature +0·0048, radiation intensity +0·0010 and radiation penetration −0·0367. Thus the major influences on the catches of this fly are the first two factors listed, maximum efficiency being achieved at low wind speeds and immediately after a shower. Fewkes (1961) confirmed Romney's (1945) observation that some insects move up and down the grass periodically every 24 hours, the maximum number being on the upper parts a few hours after sunset.

The bags of sweep nets are usually made of linen, thick cotton or some synthetic fibre; the mouth is most often round; a square-mouthed net does not give more consistent results (Beall, 1935), but a D-shaped mouth is useful for collecting from short vegetation, especially young crops. There may be considerable variation in the efficiency of different collectors; usually the more rapidly the net is moved through the vegetation the larger the catch (Balogh & Loksa, 1956).

The number of sweeps necessary to obtain a mean that is within 25% of the true value has been investigated by Gray & Treloar (1933) for collections from lucerne (alfalfa), and found to vary from taxa to taxa, with an average of 26 units each of 25 sweeps. These authors suggested that this high level of variability was due to heterogeneity in the insect's spatial distribution and much of this may have been attributable to the diurnal periodicity demonstrated by Fewkes (1961). In contrast Luczak & Wierzbowska (1959) considered 10 units of 25 sweeps adequate for grassland spiders and Banks & Brown (1962) found that sweep net catches of the shield bug, *Eurygaster integriceps*, on wheat had sampling errors of only 10% and reflected absolute population differences determined by other methods.

RELATIVE METHODS – TRAPPING

The methods described in this section, in contrast to the last, are those in which it is the animal rather than the observer that makes the action that leads to its enumeration. Basically traps may be divided into those that catch animals randomly and those that attract them in some way. (The word 'attract' is used in its widest sense without any connotation of desire: the studies of Verheijen (1960), for example, have shown that animals are trapped by artificial light through interference with the normal photic orientation and not strictly because of attraction.) It is important to distinguish between these two types as those that are based on attraction allow the possibility of a further source of error. But a strict division is impossible as some traps, more particularly water and sticky traps, are intermediate in position.

Interception traps

These are traps that intercept the animals, more or less randomly as they move through the habitat: air, water or land. Indices of absolute population may theoretically be obtained more easily from this type of trap than from others, as there is no variation due to attraction.

1. Air – flight traps

Here we are concerned with stationary flight traps that are not believed to attract the insects; those that have some measure of attraction are discussed below (p. 196); others described elsewhere are moving (rotary) nets which may give absolute samples (p. 102) or, if the quantity of air they filter is uncertain, they are regarded as aerial sweeps (p. 189).

One of the simplest type is the suspended cone net as used by Johnson (1950); this may have a wind vane attachment to ensure that it swivels around to face into the wind; Taylor (1962) has shown that its efficiency at different wind speeds may be calculated (p. 180). Nets are particularly useful for weak flyers such as aphids (Davis & Landis, 1949) or at heights or in situations where the wind speed is always fairly high (Gressitt *et al.*, 1960) so that the insects cannot crawl out after capture. Similar traps have been used on moving ships (p. 189).

The Malaise trap is more elaborate; it consists basically of an open-fronted tent of cotton or nylon net, black or green in colour; the 'roof' slopes

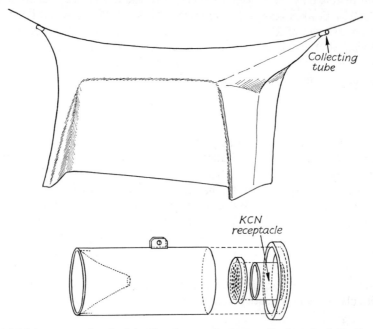

Fig. 54. Malaise trap: *a.* sketch of the Gressitt type; *b.* plastic collecting tube (after Gressitt & Gressitt, 1962).

upwards to the innermost corner at which there is an aperture leading to a trap. It was developed by Malaise (1937) as a collector's tool; modified designs have been described by Gressitt & Gressitt (1962), Townes (1962) and Butler (1965), and a basically similar trap by Leech (1955). Gressitt's (fig. 54) and Butler's models are much simpler to construct and transport than Townes. Gressitt's is large (7 m long and 3·6 m high). Butler's is smaller, being made from a bed-mosquito-net by cutting out part of one side and a hole in the roof into which the collecting trap, a metal cylinder and a polythene bag, is placed. Townes (1962) gives very full instructions for the construction of his model, which is more durable and traps insects from all directions. When maximum catches are desired (for collecting) Malaise traps should be placed across 'flight paths' such as woodland paths, but in windy situations they cannot be used. The studies of Juillet (1963), who compared a Malaise trap with others including the rotary which is believed to give unbiased catches, suggest that for the larger Hymenoptera and some Diptera this trap is unbiased, but it is unsatisfactory for Coleoptera and Hemiptera. Further tests are clearly needed to determine the potential of this trap for ecological work.

Flying Coleoptera and other insects that fall on hitting an obstacle during flight may be sampled with a window trap, which is basically a large sheet of glass held vertically with a trough, containing water with a wetting agent and a little preservative below it (Chapman & Kinghorn, 1955) (fig. 55).

One of the most important uses of stationary flight traps is to determine the direction of flight (see p. 268). Nielsen (1960) has observed that migratory

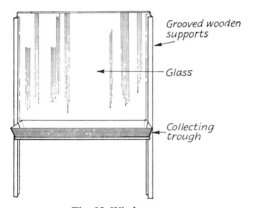

Grooved wooden supports

Glass

Collecting trough

Fig. 55. Window trap.

butterflies will enter stationary nets and remain trapped, whereas those engaging in trivial movement will fly out again. The direction of migration can be determined by a number of stationary flight traps arranged so as to sample from four fixed directions. Stationary nets may be used (Nielsen, 1960), a Malaise trap modified to collect the insects from each side separately (Roos, 1957) or a window or water trap in which the baffle is used to divide the collecting trough, so separating the catches from either side (see fig. 57). A more extensive trap is the 'robot observer' which was used in work on blowflies and consisted of a zigzag wall of net, with 10 V-shaped bays each with a 2m square aperture and ending in a fly trap; the catches from the 10 opposing bays on each side are directly comparable (J. Macleod, pers. comm.).

Special traps have been designed to collect and distinguish between the insects entering and leaving the 'homes' of vertebrates, principally burrows and houses (Myers, 1956; Service, 1963; Muirhead-Thomson, 1963). Exit-traps are usually net cones that are inverted above the exit hole; entrance-traps have to be inconspicuous from the outside and a metal gauze cylinder with a dark canvas 'skirt' that could be spread out to prevent passage round it was used in rabbit burrows by Myers, who concluded, however, that the entrance-trap did not sample as randomly as the exit-trap. In houses, ingress and egress may be measured by identical traps, but Service's (1963) results show that in this habitat the former is measured less efficiently. The traps consist of a net cone leading into a net or net and 'Perspex' box; Saliternik (1960) trapped the mosquitoes leaving cesspits with a similar trap. This could be a measure of emergence.

2. Water – aquatic traps

There are two types depending on whether they are used to collect animals drifting in stream currents or to trap animals swimming about in comparatively still water. Waters (1962) studied the drift of stream animals by placing 3-ft-long tapered nets of 'Nitex' (a synthetic fabric), with their mouths facing upstream, on boards. These boards had previously been sunk flush with the stream bottom and thus provided a flat substrate; the board and net were held in position with vertical metal rods driven into the stream bed (fig. 56*a*).

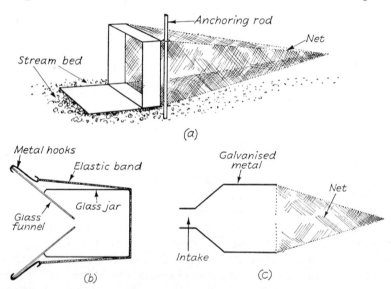

Fig. 56. Aquatic interception traps: *a*. Waters type for stream drift animals; *b*. Pieczynski type trap for water mites; *c*. Cushing type trap for stream drift animals.

A heavier trap has been described by Cushing (1964) (fig. 56*c*); the narrow inlet prevents backflow and increases filtration, an important attribute as drift nets often quickly become clogged with algae or other plant material.

Pieczynski (1961) has found that what is in effect an unbaited glass lobster-pot (fig. 56*b*) will trap numbers of water mites and other free swimming animals. Usinger & Kellen (1955) used a similar trap constructed of plastic screen rather than glass and caught large numbers of aquatic insects; their trap is figured in Usinger (1963; p. 55). These traps are the aquatic equivalents of the pitfall trap.

3. Land – pitfall and other traps

Like the lobster-pot the pitfall trap was an adaptation by the ecologist of the technique of the hunter; basically it consists of a glass jar or metal can sunk into the soil so that the mouth is level with the soil surface. Many apterous animals that walk about on the soil surface fall into the trap and are unable to escape. Pifall traps may be emptied with a hand-operated or mechanical suction apparatus (p. 115), thereby avoiding the disturbance to the surroundings that would result from continued removal and re-sinking.

Pitfall traps have been used extensively for studies on surface dwellers such as spiders, Collembola, centipedes and beetles, especially Carabidae (e.g. Barber, 1931; Tretzel, 1955; Boyd, 1957; Grüm, 1959; Doane, 1961; Duffey, 1962; Kaczmarek, 1963). More elaborate traps have been designed to facilitate emptying (Rivard, 1962), with rain-guards (Fichter, 1941; Steiner *et al.*, 1963) or timing devices that allow the catch from each time period to be segregated (Williams, 1958). Artificial baits (Stammer, 1949) or natural baits (Barber, 1931; Walsh, 1933) can be used in pitfall traps, but this may introduce a further source of error. Baited pitfall traps have been found useful for collecting beetles from vertebrates' burrows (Welch, 1964), but Greenslade (1964) found baits had no effect on the catch of Carabidae.

Critical studies of the efficiency of pitfall trapping have recently been made by Grüm (1959), Briggs (1961), Mitchell (1963) and Greenslade (1964). These studies show that pitfall traps are of little value for the direct estimation of populations or for the comparison of communities: Briggs concluded 'it is evident that the size of the population plays at most a minor role in determining the numbers trapped'; Greenslade that 'pitfall trapping cannot properly be used for the quantitative assessment of the Carabid fauna of any habitat, nor should it be employed to compare the numbers of one species in different habitats'. Although these studies were restricted to Carabidae it seems unlikely that the traps will be found more useful for other animals; indeed, with many of these the errors are likely to be greater. Pitfall traps are of course still useful as a collecting device and with caution may be used to study the daily rhythm of activity, seasonal incidence and the dispersion of a single species in one type of vegetation.

Pitfall traps are influenced by the changes in activity due to prevailing weather conditions (Grüm, 1959) and by variation in the 'phase' of the animal, discussed above. In Carabidae, activity is also influenced by the food supply (Briggs, 1961), the general habitat surrounding the trap (Mitchell, 1963) and the amount of moisture in the soil (Mitchell, 1963). The trap's efficiency varies from species to species, as those active during the day seem to avoid capture (van der Drift, 1951; Greenslade, 1964), from habitat to habitat and according to the precise placement of the trap. Greenslade (1964) found that both the level of the mouth of the trap, whether flush with the surface of the soil or the surface of the litter, and the amount of vegetation-free ground around the trap, affected the catch qualitatively and quantitatively. Large species may damage or even devour smaller ones before the traps are emptied, but the use of preservatives such as alcohol has usually been avoided because of their possible repellent effect; an aqueous solution of picric acid might well be a suitable non-repellent preservative (see p. 148).

Walking animals may also be caught on sticky traps, bands placed round tree trunks (see also p. 246) and glass plates lain on the ground. Mellanby (1962) found that the latter caught numbers of springtails and other animals; he suggested a gauze roof over the trap to prevent flying insects being caught. Details of the design of sticky traps are given below.

Flight traps combining interception and attraction

The distinction between water and sticky traps and those flight traps described above (p. 191) should not be regarded as rigorous for, as Taylor (1962) has shown, a white sticky trap catches insects almost as if they are inert particles, whereas a net may sample selectively. The two approaches may be combined in the sticky net described by Provost (1960). However, many aphids are particularly attracted to yellow (Broadbent, 1948; Moericke, 1950; Hottes, 1951), ceratopogonid midges to black (Hill, 1947); flower-dwelling thrips to white (Lewis, 1959), frit flies to blue (Mayer, 1961) and bark beetles to red (Entwistle, 1963); therefore the quality and magnitude of water and sticky trap catches will be greatly influenced by the colour of the trap and this will be an additional source of variation in the efficiency of these traps. It is probable that the attraction of different colours to a given species may vary with both age and sex.

1. Sticky traps

These are an extension of the 'fly-paper'; the animal settles or impacts on the adhesive surface and is retained. A variety of adhesives may be utilized; those resins developed for trapping moths ascending fruit trees have proved particularly useful (e.g. 'Eclipse fruit-tree banding gum', 'Tanglefoot', 'Ostico', 'Stickem', 'Stop moth' and 'Deadline'). Greases may also be used (e.g. cup grease (Close, 1959), 'Dow Corning' high vacuum grease (Staples & Allington, 1959)) or a mixture of grease, oil and spirit (Provost, 1960). The insects are separated from most fruit-tree banding resins by warming and then scraping the resin plus insects into hot paraffin from which they can be filtered, but 'Ostico' may be dissolved by trichlorethylene. The separation from the greases is easier; a mixture of benzene and isopropyl alcohol rapidly dissolves the adhesive. Thus, when possible, a grease will be used in preference to a resin, but only weak insects will be trapped by a grease – mosquitoes (Provost,

1960), mites (Staples & Aĺlington, 1959) and aphids (Close, 1959). For these a grease may be more efficient, as the effective area of the trap is not reduced by the numbers of large insects that are also trapped if a powerful adhesive is used (Close, 1959). Greases may become too fluid at high temperatures.

Sticky traps are of several basic designs: Até strands, an African birdlime, were used by Golding (1941, 1946) in warehouses, and Provost (1960) used sticky nets, but most traps have been either large screens or small cylinders, boxes or plates. Large screens consisting of a wooden lattice or series of boards have been used to measure movement at a range of heights of aphids and beetles (Dud'. ?, Searles & Weed, 1928; Moreland, 1954; Prescott & Newton, 1963; Taɪ & Jernigan, 1964). Individual boards, white and yellow in colour, were used by Roesler (1953) and Wilde (1962) for studies of various flies and psyllids.

Ibbotson (1958) introduced the idea of glass plates for sticky traps. These were 8 in. square, the upper surface coated with the adhesive and the under painted yellow (or as desired). Glass has the advantage that the adhesive is easily scraped off with a knife or the whole plate immersed in a solvent. Ibbotson used his trap for the frit fly; Staples & Allington (1959) used grease-coated microscope slides for trapping mites; Wakerley (1963) found Ibbotson's trap suitable for the carrot fly, *Psila rosae*, and Maxwell (1965) a similar trap for the apple maggot fly, *Rhagoletis*. These plates may be exposed either vertically or horizontally; the exposure will affect the catch (table 13);

Table 13. The catches of some species of aphid on three types of trap expressed as a ratio of the number caught by a suction trap (after Heathcote, 1957*a*)

	Water	Cylindrical sticky	Flat sticky
Aphis fabae group	2·28	1·92	0·84
Tuberculoides			
annulatus	3·91	0·45	0·18
Cavariella aegopodii	0·36	2·00	0·27
Myzus persicae	1·34	0·34	0·78
Hyalopterus pruni	0·33	1·50	0·40
Drepanosiphum			
platanoidis	1·29	0·25	0·01
Brevicoryne brassicae	0·47	0·06	0·07
Sitobion spp.	0·08	0·17	0·06

(Heathcote, 1957a); the influence of colour is less with vertical plates where most insects are caught by wind impaction, i.e. the catches are less biased. However, fixed vertical plate traps will sample a different proportion of the passing air depending upon the wind direction, and eddies will develop at the sides of the plates and around sticky boxes (Fröhlich, 1956). Small glass plates may be mounted at right angles to a windvane and so present a constant exposure to the wind.

A good design, sampling at random from the passing air, is the cylinder sticky trap of Broadbent *et al.* (1948) (fig. 57*a*), which consists basically of a piece of plastic material covering a length of stove-pipe. Taylor (1962) showed that if the wind speed was known the catches of small insects on a white sticky trap of this type could be converted to a measure of aerial density (see table 11, p. 180); however, as Broadbent (1948) found, yellow traps catch more aphids than white ones, and these catch more than black. Care should therefore be exercised in applying these corrections to a species whose reaction

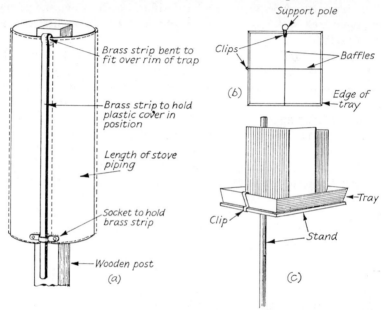

Fig. 57. *a*. Cylindrical sticky trap (after Broadbent *et al.*, 1948). *b*. and *c*. Water trap with baffle (Coon & Rinicks' design): *b* plan from above; *c*. general view.

to the colour of the trap is unknown. Colour will presumably have the greatest effect at low wind speeds. Cylindrical sticky traps have been utilized in studies on the cacao mealy bug (Cornwell, 1960) and small ones of 1-in. diameter were used by Lewis (1959) for trapping thrips.

The relation of the size of the sticky trap to the catch has been investigated by Heathcote (1957*b*) and Staples & Allington (1959), who found that although catch usually increases with size, it is not proportional to size so that the smallest trap catches the largest number per unit area (table 14).

2. Water traps

These are simply glass, plastic or metal bowls or trays filled with water to which a small quantity of detergent and a preservative (usually a little for-

Table 14. The effect of trap size on the catch of black cylindrical sticky traps
(after Heathcote, 1957*b*)

	Trap diameter		
	3 cm	6 cm	12 cm
Total catch	837	1473	2017
Catch/unit area (3-cm trap = 1)	837	736·5	504·2

malin) have been added. Omission of the detergent will more than halve the catch (Harper & Story, 1962). The traps may be transparent or painted various colours and placed at any height. Yellow bowls were used by Moericke (1951) and others for trapping aphids and by Fröhlich (1956) and Fritzsche (1956) for a weevil; white trays were used by Southwood *et al.* (1961) for the frit fly. A variety of colours were tested by Harper and Story (1962) for the sugar beet fly, *Tetanops myopaeformis*: the total numbers taken in the different coloured traps were as follows: yellow 330, white 264, black 202, red 107, blue 64, green 53.

Sticky traps would be chosen in preference to water traps because the relationship between wind speed and the catch of the water trap is likely to prove less simple than that for the sticky trap investigated by Taylor (1962) and because water traps must be frequently attended, or they overflow in heavy rain or dry out in the sun. On the other hand water traps have certain advantages: the insects that are caught are in good condition for identification, as the catch is easily separated by straining or individual insects picked out with a pipette or forceps. Furthermore, when the population is sparse a water trap will, with aphids at least, make catches when a sticky trap of a manageable size would not (Heathcote, 1957*a*). The 'catching power' of a water trap can be further increased by standing two upright baffles of aluminium sheeting at right angles to each other to form a cross in the tray (Coon & Rinicks, 1962), (fig. 57*b* and *c*). These divisions enable one to separate the insect according to the quadrant in which it has been captured; this is related to the direction of flight at the time of capture (see also pp. 193, 268). The results of Coon & Rinicks show that the effect of the baffle varies from species to species; in the four cereal aphids that they studied it increased the catch of *Rhopalosiphum maidis* tenfold, nearly doubled the very low catch of *Schizaphis agrostis* (=*Toxoptera graminum*) but had no effect on those of the two others, *Macrosiphum granarium* and *Rhopalosiphum fitchii*.

A floating water trap that collected the insects settling on the surface of ponds was devised by Grigarick (1959*a*), the animals being drowned through the action of the detergent. The tray of his trap was surrounded by a wooden frame, therefore it would seem that the contrast presented by this surround might bias the catch and a more transparent float (e.g. an air-filled polythene tube) would be preferable.

Light and other visual traps

1. Mode of action and limitations

Light-traps are probably the most widely used insect traps and there are several hundred references to them. Originally, paraffin and acetylene lamps were used by collectors (Frost, 1952); later the tungsten filament electric light and, after its development by Robinson & Robinson (1950), the ultra-violet trap became widely used. The detailed studies of Verheijen (1960) have shown that these traps catch insects because the high illumination of trap relative to the surroundings interferes with the normal photic orientation; this results in the insects moving towards the light source. Thus anything that reduces this contrast, e.g. the illumination from surrounding houses or street lamps or moonlight, will have the effect of reducing the catch. In the arctic few mosquitoes are caught in light-traps during the twilight summer nights, therefore Haufe & Burgess (1960) increased the contrast by using a white and black cylinder below the trap and eventually discarded the lamp. This principle has also been used by Bracken *et al.* (1962), who have been able to trap numbers of tabanids with visual traps. It is possible that the Morris tsetse trap (see p. 212) is also a visual trap.

The uses of light-traps in ecology are subject to all the general limitations of relative methods outlined above (pp. 174–8); but the variation in efficiency of the trap from insect to insect, from night to night and from site to site is more serious than in almost every other type of trap because light-traps are entirely artificial, relying on the disturbance of normal behaviour for their functioning. It is not justified to claim on *a priori* grounds, as Mulhern (1953) has done, that, being mechanical, light-traps are more reliable than hand collection per unit of habitat.

Furthermore in the discussion of the pros and cons of the many models of light-trap it is often implied that the bigger the catch, the 'better' the trap: although it is true that the larger figures are often more acceptable for statistical analysis it is unwise to assume that they are biologically more valuable.

Light-traps have been used in attempts to control insects by extensive trapping, but these have been unsuccessful (e.g Stahl, 1954; Stanley & Dominick, 1957); indeed there is evidence that the previous night's trapping has little effect (Williams *et al.*, 1955). They may be used to survey or make phenological observations on species that are caught by them, e.g. Bogush (1958), Geier (1960). Although light-traps are unlikely to reflect the exact relative abundance of different species they may be used for general or long-term studies on the diversity of a fauna of a particular group (Williams, 1950; Southwood, 1960). The extent to which the relative abundance in light-trap catches reflects the actual populations may be determined by comparison with other methods: such studies have often shown considerable discrepancies (e.g. Love & Smith, 1957; Breyev, 1963).

2. The effects of trap design on catch

From Verheijen's (1960) important study and earlier work we can conclude that the extent to which a light-trap catches those insects that see it will depend on:

(1) The extent to which the angular light distribution departs from the normal, which is equivalent to the amount of contrast between the light source and surroundings. The greater the contrast, the greater the trapping effect, for the contrast leads to the disturbance of the animal's normal photic orientation causing an enforced drift towards the lamp.

(2) Most animals will have a tendency to withdraw from the high light intensity immediately adjacent to the lamp.

(3) The extent to which an animal may be able to change from approach to avoidance will depend on its flight speed; the faster, heavier flyers are unable to stop and change course quickly.

The effect of the illumination of the environment on the catch was utilized by Common (1959), who designed a transparent light-trap for Lepidoptera. The main advantage of this over the Robinson trap, of which it is a modification, is that the number of Coleoptera (especially Scarabaeidae) caught is greatly reduced; large numbers of beetles will damage many of the moths in a catch.

An increase in the intensity of the lamp, frequently brought about by the substitution of an ultra-violet lamp for an incandescent one, usually leads to an increased catch (e.g. Williams, 1951; Williams *et al.*, 1955; Barr *et al.*, 1963; Belton & Kempster, 1963; Breyev, 1963). Because of the role of intensity in the mechanism of trapping, the actual size of the light source is of less importance (Belton & Kempster, 1963) and a small trap may often be substituted for a larger one without the catch being reduced in proportion to the change in light output (Smith *et al.*, 1959).

Many workers (e.g. Gui *et al.*, 1942) have considered that the differences in quality of the light, from incandescent lamps, from mercury-quartz lamps emitting ultra-violet and visible light, and from black (or 'blue') lamps emitting only or mainly ultra-violet, affect the catch; but Verheijen's study would seem to indicate that this is unlikely and must be due to a combination of factors 1–3 above. Whatever the mechanism, there are considerable differences; for example, many Diptera and Miridae are taken in the largest numbers in traps with incandescent (tungsten filament) lamps; Corixidae, many Lepidoptera (especially noctuids) are more abundant in 'UV traps' and are even better represented in 'black-light traps', as are Trichoptera (Frost, 1953; Williams *et al.*, 1955; Breyev, 1958; Southwood, 1960; Tshernyshev, 1961).

Some of these differences are explained by the increased intensity of the ultra-violet traps leading to the repulsion of the insect when close to the lamp; slow flyers such as many Diptera Nematocera and geometrid and pyralid moths stop their approach before they enter the trap, whilst the heavier, faster flyers, like noctuid and sphingid moths, pass straight into the trap. Suction fans have therefore been incorporated in light-traps to catch those insects that avoid capture at the 'last moment' (e.g. Glick *et al.*, 1956; Downey, 1962). The same phenomenon was demonstrated in the opposite way by Hollingsworth *et al.* (1961), who found that a suitably placed wind-break could increase the catch of trap: in the exposed situation many species would avoid trapping by being blown off course, but in the lee of the wind-break this would not occur and the larger moths would be caught particularly efficiently. The addition of baffles to the trap also serves to catch those insects whose repulsion by the high intensity close to the lamp would otherwise cause them to escape; Frost (1958*a*) almost doubled the numbers caught by a trap by adding four intersecting baffles to it.

When differences due to flight speed and momentum have been eliminated, other specific differences in susceptibility to trapping remain: e.g. amongst the mosquitoes, *Aedes* seem especially susceptible to trapping (Love & Smith, 1957; Loomis, 1959*b*). Males are often taken in much greater numbers than females at light-traps (e.g. Southwood, 1960).

Although strictly speaking it is not a feature of design, the height above the vegetation at which the trap is exposed will influence the catch. As the aerial density of most insects decreases with height, in general the higher the trap the smaller the catch (Frost, 1958*c*). There are a few exceptions; Taylor & Carter (1961) have shown that some Lepidoptera may occur at a maximum density at as much as 30 ft above the ground and many ornithophilic mosquitoes and blackflies also have maxima some distance above the ground.

3. Techniques and types of trap

Many light-traps retain the insects alive; Merzheevskaya & Gerastevich (1962) did this by covering the collecting funnel of a Pennsylvania type trap with a cloth bag and inserting another shallow cone in the neck. The Robinson trap retains the insects in the drum of the trap; but Belton & Kempster (1963) showed that unless the opening was under $\frac{1}{2}$ in. in diameter, many small moths, like geometrids, would leave the trap in the morning, more especially if the sun shone on it; however, such a small cone opening will restrict the entry of other species.

A large number of killing agents have been used in light-traps; some of the chlorinated hydrocarbons such as tetrachlorethylene, trichlorethylene and tetrachlorethane are particularly useful. They may be poured on to a block of plaster of Paris at the bottom of the killing bottle, where their heavy vapours will be slowly evolved and remain relatively concentrated (Williams, 1948; Haddow & Corbet, 1960). Excessive inhalation of their vapours over a long period may be dangerous to man. Delicate insects such as Ephemeroptera or

Psocoptera may be collected straight into alcohol and chafer beetles into kerosene (Frost, 1964). Potassium and sodium cyanides are traditional, but dangerous poisons; the last named is more suitable in moist climates (Frost, 1964).

White (1964) has designed a killing tin to preserve the light-trap catch in good condition (fig. 58). It has the further advantage that only specimens too large to pass through the screen across the top of the funnel are retained; the

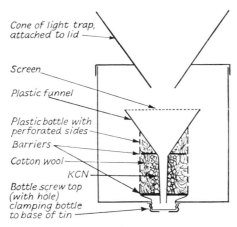

Cone of light trap,
attached to lid
Screen
Plastic funnel
Plastic bottle with
perforated sides
Barriers
Cotton wool
KCN
Bottle screw top
(with hole)
clamping bottle
to base of tin

Fig. 58. White's light-trap killing tin.

mesh of this screen may be so fine as to retain the whole catch or, for example, it may be of such a size that the unwanted Diptera and small Trichoptera escape (White, pers. comm.). When only the smaller species are required, the larger ones may be excluded and so prevented from damaging the catch by covering the entrance to the trap with a coarse screen (e.g. Downey, 1962). If all specimens are to be captured a series of graded screens in the killing bottle will tend to separate the insects by size and aid in the subsequent sorting (Frost, 1964). In connection with the latter operation the sorting tray described by Gray (1955) may be useful.

a. The Rothamsted trap (fig. 59a)
Originally used by C. B. Williams as a research tool for studying the influence of climate on the numbers of flying insects, this trap takes moderate numbers of most groups, including nematocerous flies and the larger moths; it would seem to be less selective than most other light-traps and is useful in studies on the diversity of restricted groups. It is described in detail by Williams (1948): it has a roof, that allows its operation in all weathers but reduces the catch. The collections from different periods of the night may be separated by an automatic device (Williams, 1935). A simple transportable non-ultra-violet trap has been developed by Jalas (1960).

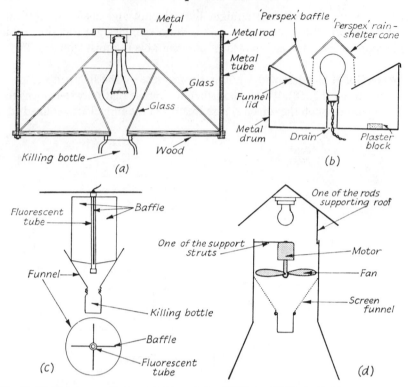

Fig. 59. Light-traps: *a.* Rothamsted trap (after Williams, 1948); *b.* Robinson type trap; *c.* Pennsylvanian trap (sectional view and plan); *d.* New Jersey trap.

b. The Robinson trap (fig. 59*b*)

This was the first trap using ultra-violet light and was designed by Robinson & Robinson (1950) to make maximum catches of the larger Lepidoptera. The trap is without a roof and although the bulb is protected by a celluloid cone and there is a drainage hole in the bottom, it cannot be used in all weathers. The drum is partly filled with egg boxes or similar pieces of cardboard in which the insects can shelter. The catch may be retained alive or killed by placing blocks of plaster of Paris saturated with a killing agent on the floor. Large numbers of fast-flying nocturnal insects (e.g. Noctuidae, Sphingidae, Corixidae, Scarabaeidae) are trapped (Williams, 1951; Williams *et al.*, 1955); but fewer beetles are caught in Common's (1959) transparent trap.

c. The Pennsylvanian and Texas traps (fig. 59*c*)

These traps are basically similar, consisting of a central fluorescent tube surrounded by four baffles; below the trap is a metal funnel and a collecting jar (Frost, 1957; Hollingsworth *et al.*, 1963). The Pennsylvanian trap has a circular roof to prevent the entry of rain into the killing bottle and it is presumably a reflection of the climates of the two States that the Texas trap is roofless.

Frost's (1958*b*) experiments suggest that the largest catches would be obtained with a 15-W black-light fluorescent tube; Graham *et al.* (1961) used three argon-glow lamps in the Texas trap in survey work on the pink bollworm, *Platyedra gossypiella*, and found moths were trapped over a radius of 200 ft from the lamp. Fluorescent tubes may be run for many hours from batteries (Sartor & Oertel, 1963) and King *et al.* (1965) have devised a mechanism for separating the catches from different time periods, by changing the killing bottle at fixed intervals.

The Minnesota light-trap is basically similar to the Pennsylvanian model, but the roof is cone-shaped rather than flat and this appears to reduce the catch (Frost, 1952, 1958*b*).

d. The New Jersey trap (fig. 59*d*)
Developed by T. J. Headlee this is primarily a trap for sampling mosquitoes; it combines light and suction – the lamp causes the insects to come into the vicinity of the trap and they are drawn in by the suction of the fan (Mulhern, 1942). The trap is therefore particularly useful for weak flyers that may fail to be caught by the conventional light-trap, as when close to the lamp they are repelled by its high intensity. Fitted with an ultra-violet lamp the New Jersey trap has been used to collect other groups of Nematocera, as well as mosquitoes (Zhogolev, 1959). Kovrov & Monchadskii (1963) found that if the trap was modified to emit polarized light many insects, but not mosquitoes, were caught in larger numbers. Like the Rothamsted and Pennsylvanian traps, this trap may be fitted with an automatic interval collector; one is described by Bast (1960). A miniature battery-operated model has been developed (Sudia & Chamberlain, 1962). For comparative studies using different traps it is important to standardize the airflow (Loomis, 1959*a*), although, as has been pointed out several times, relative trapping methods, and especially light-traps, may sample different proportions of the population in different areas even when the traps are identical.

e. The Haufe–Burgess visual trap (fig. 60*a*)
As Verheijen's (1960) studies have shown that the trapping effect of light depends on the degree of contrast between the lamp and the surroundings, it is not surprising that light-traps are ineffective in the twilight nights of the arctic, and Haufe & Burgess (1960) designed the present trap for mosquitoes; it has been found to catch other groups as well. Basically the trap is an exposed cone type of suction trap on the outside of which is a revolving cylinder painted with $1\frac{5}{8}$-in. wide black and white stripes. A horizontal disc extends out at the top of the cylinder and the insects are drawn through slits at the junction between the cylinder and the disc. Harwood (1961) retained the light-bulb above the trap (as in the New Jersey light-trap) and exposed various animal baits below the trap, but the combination of so many attractants makes the interpretation of the results very difficult.

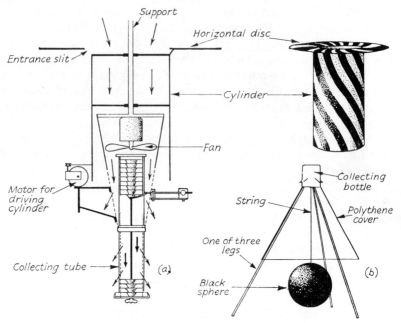

Fig. 60. Visual traps: *a*. Haufe–Burgess mosquito trap, sectional view (after Haufe & Burgess, 1960) and external view of the attraction cylinder; *b*. Manitoba horse fly trap.

f. The Manitoba horse fly trap (fig. 60*b*)

Tabanidae are attracted to the highlights of a black or red sphere (Bracken, Hanec & Thorsteinson, 1962) and large numbers may be collected by suspending a sphere of these colours (e.g. a balloon) beneath a polythene collecting cone (Thorsteinson, Bracken & Hanec, 1965).

g. Aquatic light-traps

There are two types: floating and submerged. Baylor & Smith (1953) have described an ingenious floating trap, principally for Cladocera, which utilizes their 'attraction' to yellow to get them into the trap and their 'repulsion' to blue to drive them into the collecting net (fig. 61*b*). It is important that the blue light is not visible laterally; thus the level of the blue 'Cellophane' must not extend above the lip of the funnel. Baylor & Smith suggest that the trap could be improved with refinements, such as the polarization of the yellow light that would increase the 'fishing area' without increasing the intensity (see also Kovrov & Monchadskii, 1963).

A subaquatic light-trap was designed by Hungerford, Spangler & Walker (1955). The body of the trap is a length of wide galvanized piping and the light source a torch, held inside a glass fruit-preserving jar (fig. 61*a*). When the trap is hauled to the surface, the water is drained out through the 'well traps' and the animals retained in these. The well traps are pieces of metal pipe with gauze at one end and flange at the other.

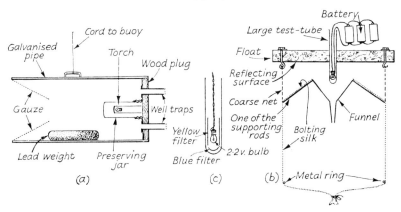

Fig. 61. Aquatic light-traps: *a.* Hungerford's subaquatic light-trap; *b.* and *c.* Baylor & Smith's floating trap: section (after Baylor & Smith, 1953); *c.* detail of test tube and light source.

Traps that attract the animal by some natural stimulus or a substitute

When these traps are entirely natural they have the advantage over artificial ones in that the variations in efficiency reflect real changes in the properties of the population: the changes in the numbers of a phytophagous insect colonizing a plant or of a bloodsucking species biting the host may not reflect population changes, but they do reflect accurately changes in the colonizing or feeding rates of the species. That is, with the possible exception of artificial bait traps, these traps give measures of availability that are biologically meaningful.

1. Shelter traps

Cubical boxes (1 cu ft in volume) with one open side and painted red have been used in mosquito surveys; they are often termed 'artificial resting units' (Goodwin, 1942; Goodwin & Love, 1957; Burbutis & Jobbins, 1958). As might be expected only certain mosquitoes settle in these shelters, particularly species of *Culex*, *Culiseta* and *Anopheles*. Loomis & Sherman (1959) found that visual counts of the resting mosquitoes with a torch were accurate to within 10% of the true value. Dales (1953) found that large numbers of *Tipula* would shelter in and be unable to escape from small metal truncated cones (15 cm aperture at top, 25 cm high and 28 cm at base).

Ground dwellers such as woodlice, centipedes and carabids that shelter beneath logs and stones (Cryptozoa), may be trapped by placing flat boards in the habitat. The 'cryptozoa boards' can be placed systematically in the habitat and used to study the dispersion of the animals (Cole, 1946); however, the proportion of the population that shelters beneath them will vary with soil moisture and other factors (Paris, 1965).

E M—H

Many insects shelter in cracks or under bark scales on tree trunks, for over-wintering or as a mode of life. Artificial shelters consisting of several grooved boards bolted together have been placed in trees to trap earwigs (Chant & McLeod, 1952), in the field to trap over-wintering *Bryobia* mites (Morgan & Anderson, 1958) and screwed on to the tree bark beside a fungus to trap the beetle, *Tetratoma fungorum* (Paviour-Smith, 1964).

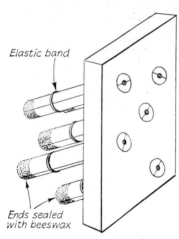

Elastic band

Ends sealed
with beeswax

Fig. 62. Levin's trap nests for solitary Hymenoptera.

Trap nests, made by drilling holes in woody stems (e.g. sumac) or in pieces of dowelling which are split and then bound together, will be colonized by solitary Hymenoptera if the open ends are exposed in a board (fig. 62); the binding may be removed and the nest contents easily exposed (Medler & Fye, 1956; Levin, 1957; Medler, 1964).

2. Trap host plants

Insect-free potted host plants exposed in a habitat may be colonized by insects; these can be removed and counted and their numbers will be directly proportional to the colonization potential of the population in that habitat. Trap host plants are therefore most useful for measuring emergence and colonization (Fritzsche, 1956; Grigarick, 1959*b*; Smith, 1962; Waloff & Bakker, 1963) and susceptible logs will record the same phenomena in bark beetles (Chapman, 1962). The actual adult insects may be counted or the resulting eggs or larvae. Michelbacher & Middlekauff (1954) studied population changes in *Drosophila* in tomato fields by placing as 'traps' ripe tomatoes that had been slit vertically on the sides and squeezed slightly; the number of eggs laid in the flesh on either side of the cuts could be easily ascertained in the laboratory. It is of course important to ensure that the plants, fruit or logs remain in the condition where they are attractive to the insects.

3. The use of vertebrate hosts or substitutes as bait

The methods described in this section are used principally to determine the biting rate of intermittent ectoparasites under various conditions, the host range and the relative importance of different hosts and vectors and other measurements of significance in epidemiological studies. Some give unbiased indices of these behavioural characteristics, but in others the presence of the trap may repel some insects or attract others independently of the presence of the host. Dyce & Lee (1962) found that the presence of the drop-cone trap about 1 ft above the rabbit would deter certain species of mosquito, but not others, from biting it. In contrast, Colless (1959) showed that from one-third to half the catch of a Malayan trap is independent of the presence of the host. As there is often a marked diurnal periodicity in biting rate (Haddow, 1954) it is important that assessments should be made throughout the 24 hours.

These methods therefore give measures of availability and when 'attractiveness' is constant indices of absolute population (i.e. relative abundance). Under certain circumstances they might be used to measure absolute population density by the removal technique.

Reference should also be made to the Manitoba horse fly trap (p. 206), the carbon dioxide trap (p. 214) and perhaps even the Haufe–Burgess mosquito trap (p. 205) which could have been included here on the grounds that they are substitutes for vertebrate hosts.

a. Moving baits
As ectoparasite incidence is often low and non-random, and as landing rate may vary in relation to the time of exposure in one spot (fig. 63), a moving bait may give more extensive data than one stationary over a long period. The 'fly-round' first developed by W. H. Potts has been used extensively in

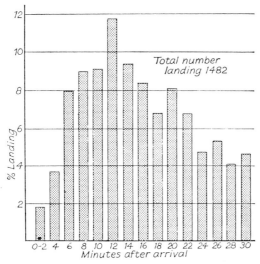

Fig. 63. The variation in landing rate of *Culicoides* with time after arrival of human bait (after Jamnback & Watthews, 1963).

work on the ecology of the tsetse fly. In this the catching party consisting of the human bait and the collectors would walk through the habitat, making a number of stops at which flies were caught. Ford *et al.* (1959) proposed a transect fly-round that followed arbitrary straight lines with equidistantly placed halting sites. These transect rounds have advantages in the statistical analysis necessary for the determination of dispersion, but the catches are still variable and Glasgow (1961) concluded that a 7500-yd fly-round done once a week could not detect less than a fivefold change in the mean catch (i.e. in the index of absolute population). More males than females are usually (Glasgow & Duffy, 1961), but not always (Morris, 1960), caught on fly-rounds. This appears to be due to the fact that only teneral females feed on moving hosts, mature females are therefore seldom taken; furthermore the males follow the moving objects (even vehicles) not so much to feed (except those that are teneral) as to be in the vicinity to pair with the young females (Bursell, 1961). Oxen and other animals may be used instead of man as the bait on fly-rounds; the species of *Glossina* taken will be influenced by the bait animal (Jordan, 1962). Studying the biting habits of *Chrysops*, Duke (1955) found that biting rate per individual of a group of human baits was greater than that for a single individual working on his own. Single human baits were used by Murray (1963) in studies on *Aedes* and found to give a better picture of seasonal variation than light-traps.

Ticks and fleas sit on grass and other vegetation and attach themselves to their hosts as they pass by. Rothschild (1961) and Bates (1962) sampled fleas with what they termed artificial rabbits and birds: a skin with an internal heating device (a hot-water bottle) that was pulled across the ground. Ticks have been sampled by dragging blankets and pieces of cloth over the vegetation; Wilkinson (1961) has compared various methods and concludes that the 'hinged-flag sampler' a modification of Blagoveschenskii's (1957) technique, was most efficient and gave a good correlation with counts on cattle in the same enclosure. This sampler consists of a piece of plywood (50 cm square), covered with cloth and with a handle strongly hinged to the centre of one side. The sampler is held as rigidly as possible with the lower edge making contact with the grass. In very rough country this cannot be used and cloth-covered leggings are the only available method. Ticks may be removed from these samplers, retained and stored on transparent adhesive tape (e.g. 'Sellotape').

b. Stationary baits

The most natural situation is achieved when the host is freely exposed in the normal habit; when man is the host this is of course possible, and it may be feasible for one individual to act as both bait and collector. In order to obtain a complete collection the bait may need to enclose himself periodically in a cage. Klock & Bidlingmayer (1953) devised one that was essentially an umbrella with blinds that could be released and would rapidly drop to the ground. Blagoveschenskii *et al.* (1943) dropped a bell-shaped cover over their human bait at intervals and Myers (1956) extended this principle to the rabbit with the 'drop-cone trap': a muslin cone is suspended by a rope over a pulley about 1 ft above a tethered bait (fig. 64a); it may be quickly lowered by an observer some distance away. But as Dyce & Lee (1962) showed, the presence of the drop-cone trap just above the bait may affect the behaviour of some species. These authors also suggest that the effect of man handling the traps in

which other species are exposed may invalidate comparisons between the
biting rate on man and these other animals.

Blackflies (Simuliidae) are less easily disturbed when feeding on their hosts,
and Anderson & Defoliart (1961) investigated their host preferences by exposing various birds and mammals in net or wire cages for 15 minutes, and

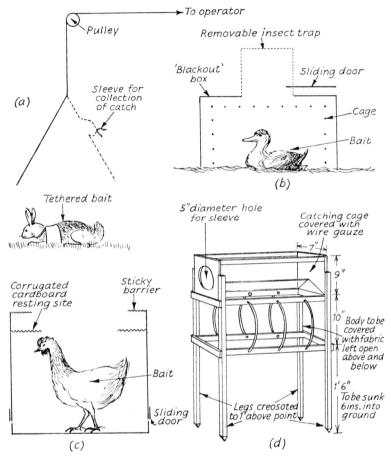

Fig. 64. *a*. The Myers drop-cone trap. *b*. Anderson & Defoliart's method for trapping
blackflies. *c*. Harrison's trap for poultry mites. *d*. The Morris trap.

then covering these with a blackout box with removable insect trap on top
(fig. 64*b*). The flies would soon be attracted to the light and move into the
muslin trap. The blackout box was conveniently made of a strong cardboard
box strengthened with wood.

Apart from any influence due to the trap, the catches at a bait may be influenced by the length of time it has been present (fig. 63) (Jamnback &
Watthews, 1963) and there are considerable local variations due to site (e.g.

Saunders, 1964). Selection due to the influence of the trap itself will be greater with those methods where the animal is more or less enclosed; four types of trap for flying ectoparasite do this. They are:

(1) The stable trap originally designed by E. H. Magoon and W. C. Earle
(2) Cage traps for small animals
(3) The Malayan trap originally designed by B. A. R. Gater
(4) The Lumsden trap developed by W. H. R. Lumsden

The stable trap design has been modified by Bates (1944) to retain a large proportion of the mosquitoes that had fed on the donkey, mule or other bait, and in a modified form has been used with night-herons as bait and hoisted into trees by Flemings (1959). Basically the stable trap consists of a portable sectional wood and screen shed into which mosquitoes may enter by a horizontal slit in the lower part of the walls; most are then trapped, as only a few fly downwards after feeding and so manage to escape. Small animals may be exposed in cage traps that are covered with fine netting above and open below (Worth & Jonkers, 1962) or in traps resembling the carbon dioxide trap (fig. 65).

The Malayan human bait trap consists of a mosquito-net cage, the flaps of which can be dropped by pulling a string (this is usually done every hour). Wharton *et al.* (1963) used a similar cage for exposing monkeys to mosquitoes. It has some resemblance both to Klock & Bidlingmayer's (1953) umbrella with blinds and to a Malaise trap (p. 192); in view of its similarity to the latter it is not surprising that an unbaited trap catches up to half as many mosquitoes as a baited one (Colless, 1959).

Lumsden's trap (Lumsden, 1958) is constructed of a 'Perspex'* hood leading to a suction fan, a gauze funnel and a collecting tube ('an inverted suction trap'). A bait animal is tethered, or placed in a cage, below the hood. The fan is switched on periodically and the resulting air current carries the insects feeding on the bait into the collecting tube. Portable, battery- or generator-operated, versions have been developed by Snow *et al.* (1960) and Minter (1961); these catch large numbers of *Culicoides* and *Phlebotomus*, but the air-flow seems insufficient to retain many of the mosquitoes.

A special trap has been constructed by Harrison (1963) for studying the poultry red mite, *Dermanyssus*. It consists of a box containing the bait chicken with a number of holes near the base (fig. 64c); these may be closed with a time switch or hand-operated barrier. The trap could be used for other ectoparasites that leave the host after feeding (e.g. Cimicidae).

R. H. T. P. Harris devised a trap that apparently attracted and retained tsetse flies; his design was considerably modified and improved by Morris & Morris (1949) and this trap is now generally known as the 'Morris trap' (fig. 64d). A portable folding version has been described by Morris (1961). The flies enter the traps from below and only a few seem able to escape; however,

* 'Plexiglass' is a similar plastic material.

if the traps were emptied less than once every 24 hours losses of trapped flies occurred due to predation by ants (Smith & Rennison, 1961, part IV). A high proportion of the flies caught in the Morris trap are females and this is their great advantage compared with the fly-round; however, the dispersion pattern suggested by trap catches does not coincide with that found by fly-rounds or searching the resting sites (Glasgow & Duffy, 1961). Thus their value as an

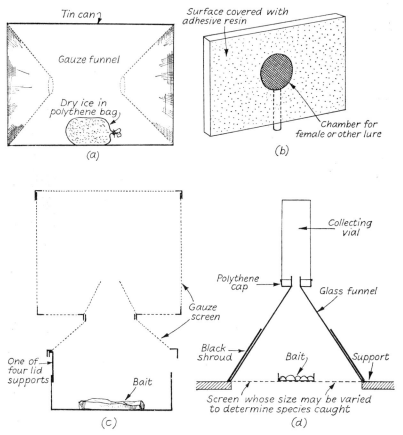

Fig. 65. *a.* Carbon dioxide mosquito trap. *b* Sticky cage for exposing female or other lure (Coppel, Casida & Dauterman's type, 1960). *c.* MacLeod's carrion bait trap. *d.* Bait trap (Citrus Experimental Station type).

index of absolute population must be doubted and the time of day of maximum catch in the Morris trap seems to differ from that at oxen (Smith & Rennison, 1961, part II). Several species of *Glossina* and many tabanids are caught by Morris traps, but others are not taken even when they attack tethered oxen in the vicinity (Morris, 1960, 1961; Jordan, 1962). Black-coloured cloth on the trap seemed to attract more tabanids (Morris, 1961) and, in the wet season, more tsetse flies, than did brown hessian (Morris,

1960). Fredeen (1961) used basically similar traps (termed silhouette traps) to collect Simuliidae, which, as Wenk & Schlörer (1963) have shown, are attracted to the silhouette of their hosts.

4. Bait traps utilizing non-living materials

Animals are attracted to these traps by a 'scent', either of their food, mate or a substitute for it; the scent may be a simple chemical, like carbon dioxide, or a complex mixture, like the odour of decaying fish. The relative performance of different trap designs and baits for flying insects may be tested in the field by arranging them on a slowly revolving wooden turntable (Dow, 1959; Mulla, Dorner, Georghiou & Garber, 1960); such rotary tests may be set up in the form of a Latin square. Besides being used to study populations bait traps are often used in attempts at control, when an insecticide or chemo-sterilant is incorporated into the lure.

a. Carbon dioxide and 'scents' of animals

Many bloodsucking insects are attracted to carbon dioxide. Mosquitoes may be trapped using dry ice in a polythene bag; the bag is closed with a rubber band and the carbon dioxide is slowly released (fig. 65a). The catch of such a trap may drop from several hundred to less than ten if it is moved a few metres (Bellamy & Reeves, 1952; Dow, 1959). Carbon dioxide has also been used as an attractant for trapping ticks (Garcia, 1962), tsetse flies (Rennison & Robertson, 1959) and blackflies (Fallis & Smith, 1964). The last named authors have also attracted certain simuliids to ether extracts of their hosts.

b. Carrion and dung

Various flies, especially blowflies, have been extensively studied using traps baited with carrion (fig. 65c) (Dodge & Seago, 1954; Judd, 1956); the fresh-ness of the bait and the precise position of the trap will affect the results (MacLeod & Donnelly, 1956, 1963; Fukuda, 1960; Kawai & Suenaga, 1960).

The work of Cragg & Ramage (1945) showed that trapped blowflies tend to attract other blowflies; thus the attractiveness of a trap would increase slowly at first but once a number of flies had been caught, its attractiveness would in-crease rapidly, exaggerating the difference between one trap and another. To minimize this effect MacLeod & Donnelly (1956) suggested that the lures should not be too attractive so that only a few flies would be caught in any one trapping occasion. If traps are being used to study the dispersion of a popu-lation, it is important to know if the presence of the trap is attracting flies into the area over a great distance; MacLeod & Donnelly's (1963) studies suggest that the range of attraction of a trap, baited with about 100 g of meat, was about 25 metres.

Baits placed in pitfall traps may aid in the collection of Coleoptera (p. 195), and Boyd (1957) trapped earthworms in artificial dung pats.

c. *Fruits and other attractants*

The great economic importance of Trypetidae, together with studies on *Drosophila* species and other insects, has led to a tremendous number of publications in this specialized field. Fermenting fruits were used by Sevastopulo (1963) in his 'butterfly' trap (consisting of a wide net cylinder, closed above and open below, in which the fruit is suspended) and in early work on fruit flies (Ripley & Hepburn, 1929). Bananas mixed with yeast or yeasts alone will attract *Drosophila* species; contamination with other insects may be reduced by exposing the lures only in the early morning or late afternoon (the peaks of *Drosophila* flight) (Da Cunha *et al.*, 1951; Cooper & Dobzhansky, 1956). Vinegar–yeast–sugar solutions will also serve as bait for *Drosophila* (Mason, 1963), and many insects are attracted to mixtures of honey, treacle or molasses and beer used by lepidopterists (Miles, 1954). The addition of oil of geranium (geraniol) or other aromatic compound increases the attractiveness of the lure (Steiner, 1929), or these substances may be used on their own. Terpinyl acetate will attract the males of several species of fruit fly (Ripley & Hepburn, 1935), the methyl ester of linoleic acid attracts the pine weevil *Hylobius abietis* (Hesse *et al.*, 1955) and ethyl proprionate attracts elaterid beetles (Steiner, 1929). Angelica seed or root oil is a lure for some fruit flies (Steiner *et al.*, 1957; Šimunic, 1961). Too strong a concentration of some of these attractants can act as a repellent.

McPhail (1939) found that hydrolysed proteins would act as lures for fruit flies; he used crude mixtures such as casein or cow hide with sodium hydroxide, and many other workers have subsequently confirmed this: e.g. Boyce & Bartlett (1941) used mixtures of glycerine (2%) and conc. sodium hydroxide (3%) for *Rhagoletis completa*, Neilson (1960) found enzymatic protein hydrolysates most effective for *Rhagoletis pomonella* and Ruffinelli *et al.* (1962) found *Ceratitis capitata* and *Anastrepha* attracted to diammonium phosphate solution. Proteinaceous materials are also attractive to eye gnats, *Hippelates* (Mulla, Georghiou & Dorner, 1960).

Pure chemicals also serve as lures: Cragg & Ramage (1945) found that blowflies were attracted to ammonium carbonate, hydrogen sulphide and indole mixtures. Only males come to other baits. The cupesid beetle, *Priacma serrata*, is attracted to the chlorine from bleaching agents (Atkins, 1957); the oriental fruit fly (*Dacus dorsalis*) to methyl euginol (Steiner, 1957), the mediterranean fruit fly (*Ceratitus capitata*) to sec-butyl 6-methyl-3-cyclohexene-1-carboxylate (Gertler *et al.*, 1958; Ruffinelli *et al.*, 1962) and to sec-butyl trans-4-chloro-2-methyl cyclohexane-carboxylate, which is more attractive and is sold under the name 'Medlure' (Beroza *et al.*, 1961). A synthetic sex attractant has been developed for the gypsy moth (*Lymantria dispar*); it is known as 'Gyplure' and is, chemically, 10-acetaxy-cis-7-hexadecen-1-ol (Jacobson *et al.*, 1961); however, unlike the natural lure, this will not attract males of *Lymantria monacha* (Adlung, 1964). Francke-Grosmann

(1963) has reviewed these and other examples of the use of attractants in forest entomology.

Virgin females themselves may be exposed in a sticky cage (fig. 65*b*) (Coppel, Casida & Dauterman, 1960) or an extract of them used to lure males (Ouye & Butt, 1962). Bark beetles are apparently attracted to freshly invaded logs and Vité & Gara (1962) (and Gara & Vité, 1962) exposed these in traps in which a current of air is passed over the log and out through the collecting funnel and baffle; they referred to these as 'field olfactometers'.

A great variety of bait traps have been designed; naturally the purpose influences the design and when it is desired to retain and kill the insects, in an attempt to control the population, the inside of the trap can be coated with a sticky resin (Holbrook *et al.*, 1960) or a board coated with Tanglefoot or a similar resin (see p. 196) placed behind the vent of the trap (Still, 1960) or around the bait (fig. 65*b*).

In ecological work some type of 'lobster-pot' trap is most useful; modifications of the carbon dioxide and blowfly traps (figs. 65*a* and *c*) may be used, or a smaller one (fig. 65*d*). For *Drosophila* Mason (1963) simply placed the bait on a dental roll in small plastic vials with a 2-mm diameter entrance hole bored in the cap. Maksimović (1960) has shown how the collections of gypsy moths in a sex-attractant trap may be used to give an index of absolute population that is directly related to subsequent egg density.

5. Sound traps

Recent studies have shown that mosquitoes and probably other insects may be attracted by certain sounds (Belton, 1962); these could be used as the attractant in a trap.

REFERENCES

ADLUNG, K. G., 1964. Field tests on the attraction of male nun moths(*Lymantria monacha* L.) and gipsy moths (*Lymantria dispar* L.) to Gyplure, a synthetic sex attractant. *Z. angew. Ent.* **54**, 304–9.

ANDERSON, J. R. and DEFOLIART, G. R., 1961. Feeding behaviour and host preferences of some black flies (Diptera: Simulidae). *Ann. ent. Soc. Amer.* **54**, 716–29.

ANDERSON, J. R. and POORBAUGH, J. H., 1964. Observations on the ethology and ecology of various Diptera associated with northern California poultry ranches. *J. med. Ent.* **1**, 131–47.

ATKINS, M. D., 1957. An interesting attractant for *Priacma serrata* (Lec.) (Cupesidae: Coleoptera). *Canad. Ent.* **89**, 214–19.

BALOGH, J. and LOKSA, I., 1956. Untersuchungen über die Zoozönose des Luzernenfeldes. *Acta Zool. Acad. Sci. Hung.* **2** (1–3), 17–114.

BANKS, C. J. and BROWN, E. S., 1962. A comparison of methods of estimating population density of adult Sunn Pest, *Eurygaster integriceps* Put. (Hemiptera: Scutelleridae) in wheat fields. *Ent. exp. appl.* **5**, 255–60.

BARBER, H., 1931. Traps for cave-inhabiting insects. *J. Elisha Mitchell sci. Soc.* **46**, 259–66.

BARNES, B. M. and BARNES, R. D., 1954. The ecology of the spiders of maritime drift lines. *Ecology* **35**, 25–35.

BARR, A. R., SMITH, T. A., BOREHAM, M. M. and WHITE, K. E., 1963. Evaluation of some factors affecting the efficiency of light traps in collecting mosquitoes. *J. econ. Ent.* **56**, 123–7.

BAST, T. F., 1960. An automatic interval collector for the New Jersey light trap. *Proc. N.J. Mosq. Exter. Ass.* **47**, 95–104.

BATES, J. K., 1962. Field studies on the behaviour of bird fleas. 1. Behaviour of the adults of three species of bird flea in the field. *Parasitology* **52**, 113–32.

BATES, M., 1944. Notes on the construction and use of stable traps for mosquito studies. *J. Nat. Malaria Soc.* **3**, 135–45.

BAYLOR, E. R. and SMITH, F. E., 1953. A physiological light trap. *Ecology* **34**, 223–4.

BEALL, G., 1935. Study of arthropod populations by the method of sweeping. *Ecology* **16**, 216–25.

BELLAMY, R. E. and REEVES, W. C., 1952. A portable mosquito bait trap. *Mosq. News* **12**, 256–8.

BELTON, P., 1962. Effects of sound on insect behaviour. *Proc. ent. Soc. Manitoba* **18**, 1–9.

BELTON, P. and KEMPSTER, R. H., 1963. Some factors affecting the catches of Lepidoptera in light traps. *Canad. Ent.* **95**, 832–7.

BEROZA, M., GREEN, N., GERTLER, S. I., STEINER, L. F. and MIYASHITA, D. H., 1961. New attractants for the Mediterranean fruit fly. *J. agric. Fd Chem.* **9**, 361–5.

BIDLINGMAYER, W. L., 1964. The effect of moonlight on the flight activity of mosquitoes. *Ecology* **45**, 87–94.

BLAGOVESCHENSKII, D. I., 1957. Biological principles of the control of ixodid ticks. [In Russian.] *Ent. Obozr.* **36**, 125–33.

BLAGOVESCHENSKII, D. I., SREGETOVA, N. G. and MONCHADSKII, A. S., 1943. Activity in mosquito attacks under natural conditions and its diurnal periodicity. [In Russian.] *Zool. Zhur.* **22**, 138–53.

BOGUSH, P. P., 1958. Some results of collecting click-beetles (Coleoptera, Elateridae) with light-traps in Central Asia. [In Russian.] *Ent. Obozr.* **31**, 347–57 (transl. *Ent. Rev.* **37**, 291–9).

BOYCE, A. M. and BARTLETT, B. R., 1941. Lures for the walnut husk fly. *J. econ. Ent.* **34**, 318.

BOYD, J. M., 1957. Comparative aspects of the ecology of Lumbricidae on grazed and ungrazed natural maritime grassland. *Oikos* **8**, 107–21.

BRACKEN, G. K., HANEC, W. and THORSTEINSON, A. J., 1962. The orientation of horseflies and deer flies (Tabanidae: Diptera). II. *Canad. J. Zool.* **40** (5), 685–95.

BREYEV, K. A., 1958. On the use of ultra violet light-traps for determining the specific composition and numbers of mosquito populations. [In Russian.] *Parazit. Sborn.* **18**, 219–38 (abs. *Rev. appl. Ent. B* **50**, 88).

BREYEV, K. A., 1963. The effect of various light sources on the numbers and species of blood-sucking mosquitoes (Diptera: Culicidae) collected in light traps. [In Russian.] *Ent. Obozr.* **42**, 280–303 (transl. *Ent. Rev.* **42**, 155–68).

BRIGGS, J. B., 1961. A comparison of pitfall trapping and soil sampling in assessing populations of two species of ground beetles (Col.: Carabidae). *Rep. E. Malling Res. Sta.* **1960**, 108–12.

BROADBENT, L., 1948. Aphis migration and the efficiency of the trapping method. *Ann. appl. Biol.* **35**, 379–94.

BROADBENT, L., DONCASTER, J., HULL, R. and WATSON, M., 1948. Equipment used for trapping and identifying alate aphids. *Proc. R. ent. Soc. Lond. A* **23**, 57–8.

BURRUTIS, P. P. and JOBBINS, D. M., 1958. Studies on the use of a diurnal resting box for the collection of *Culiseta melanura* (Coquillet). *Bull. Brooklyn ent. Soc. (N.S.).* **53**, 53–8.

BURSELL, E., 1961. The behaviour of tsetse flies (*Glossina swynnestoni* Austen) in relation to problems of sampling. *Proc. R. ent. Soc. Lond. A* **36**, 9–20.

BUTLER, G. D., 1965. A modified Malaise insect trap. *Pan. Pacif. Ent.* **41** (1), 51–3.

CHANT, D. A. and MCLEOD, J. H., 1952. Effects of certain climatic factors on the daily abundance of the European earwig, *Forficula auricularia* L. (Dermaptera: Forficulidae), in Vancouver, British Columbia. *Canad. Ent.* **84**, 174–80.

CHAPMAN, J. A., 1962. Field studies on attack flight and log selection by the Ambrosia beetle, *Trypodendron lineatum* (Oliv.) (Coleoptera: Scolytidae). *Canad. Ent.* **94**, 74–92.

CHAPMAN, J. A. and KINGHORN, J. M., 1955. Window-trap for flying insects. *Canad. Ent.* **82**, 46–7.

CLOSE, R., 1959. Sticky traps for winged Aphids. *N.Z. J. agric. Res.* **2**, 375–9.

COLE, L. C., 1946. A study of the Cryptozoa of an Illinois woodland. *Ecol. Monogr.* **16**, 49–86.

COLLESS, D. H., 1959. Notes on the culicine mosquitoes of Singapore. VI. Observations on catches made with baited and unbaited trap-nets. *Ann. Trop. Med. Parasit., Liverpool* **53**, 251–8.

COMMON, I. F. B., 1959. A transparent light trap for the field collection of Lepidoptera. *J. Lepid. Soc.* **13**, 57–61.

COON, B. F. and RINICKS, H. B., 1962. Cereal aphid capture in yellow baffle trays. *J. econ. ent.* **55**, 407–8.

COOPER, D. M. and DOBZHANSKY, T., 1956. Studies on the ecology of *Drosophila* in the Yosemite region of California. 1. The occurrence of species of *Drosophila* in different life zones and at different seasons. *Ecology* **37**, 526–33.

COPPEL, H. C., CASIDA, J. E. and DAUTERMAN, W. C., 1960. Evidence for a potent sex attractant in the introduced pine sawfly, *Diprion similis* (Hymenoptera: Diprionidae). *Ann. ent. Soc. Amer.* **53**, 510–12.

CORNWELL, P. B., 1960. Movements of the vectors of virus diseases of cacao in Ghana. II. *Bull. ent. Res.* **51**, 175–201.

CRAGG, J. B. and RAMAGE, G. R., 1945. Chemotropic studies on the blowflies, *Lucilla sericata* Mg. and *Lucilla caesar* L. *Parasitology* **36**, 168–75.

CUSHING, C. E., 1964. An apparatus for sampling drifting organisms in streams. *J. Wildl. Mgmt* **28**, 592–4.

DA CUNHA, A. B., DOBZHANSKY, T. and SOKOLOFF, A., 1951. On food preferences of sympatric species of *Drosophila*. *Evolution* **5**, 97–101.

DALES, R. P., 1953. A simple trap for Tipulids (Dipt.). *Ent. mon. Mag.* **89**, 304.

DAVIS, E. W. and LANDIS, B. J., 1949. An improved trap for collecting aphids. *U.S.D.A. Bur. Ent. Pl. Quar. E.T.* **278**, 3 pp.

DE LURY, D. B., 1947. On the estimation of biological populations. *Biometrics* **3** (4), 145–67.

DOANE, J. F., 1961. Movement on the soil surface, of adult *Ctenicera aeripennis destructor* (Brown) and *Hypolithus bicolor* Esch. (Coleoptera: Elateridae), as indicated by funnel pitfall traps, with notes on captures of other arthropods. *Canad. Ent.* **93**, 636–44.

DODGE, H. R. and SEAGO, J. M., 1954. Sarcophagidae and other Diptera taken by trap and net on Georgia mountain summits in 1952. *Ecology* **35**, 50–9.

DOW, R. P., 1959. A method of testing insect traps and attractants, and its application to studies of *Hippelates pusio* and *Culex tarsalis*. *J. econ. Ent.* **52**, 496–503.

DOWNEY, J. E., 1962. Mosquito catches in New Jersey Mosquito traps and ultra-violet light traps. *Bull. Brooklyn ent. Soc.* **57**, 61–3.

DRIFT, J. VAN DER, 1951. Analysis of the animal community in a beech forest floor. *Tijdschr. Ent.* **94**, 1–168.

DUDLEY, J. E., SEARLES, E. M. and WEED, A., 1928. Pea aphid investigations. *Trans. IV int. Congr. Ent.* **2**, 608–21.

DUFFEY, E. (A. G.), 1962. A population study of spiders in limestone grassland. Description of study area, sampling methods and population characteristics. *J. anim. Ecol.* **31**, 571–599.

DUKE, B. O. L., 1955. Studies on the biting habits of *Chrysops*. III. *Ann. Trop. Med. Parasit. Liverpool* **49** (4), 362–7.

DYCE, A. L. and LEE, D. J., 1962. Blood-sucking flies (Diptera) and myxomatosis transmission in a mountain environment in New South Wales. II. Comparison of the use of man and rabbit as bait animals in evaluating vectors of myxomatosis. *Aust. J. Zool.* **10**, 84–94.

EASTOP, V., 1955. Selection of aphid species by different kinds of insect traps. *Nature, Lond.* **176**, 936.

EMSLEY, M. G., 1957. A coarse method of estimating mirid populations in the field. *Emp. Cotton Grow. Rev.* **34**, 191–5.

ENTWISTLE, P. F., 1963. Some evidence for a colour sensitive phase in the flight period of Scolytidae and Platypodidae. *Ent. exp. appl.* **6**, 143–8.

FALLIS, A. M. and SMITH, S. M., 1964. Ether extracts from birds and CO_2 as attractants for some ornithophilic simuliids. *Canad. J. Zool.* **42**, 723–30.

FEWKES, D. W., 1961. Diel vertical movements in some grassland Nabidae (Heteroptera). *Ent. mon. Mag.* **97**, 128–30.

FICHTER, E., 1941. Apparatus for the comparison of soil surface arthropod populations. *Ecology* **22**, 338–9.

FLEMINGS, M. B., 1959. An altitude biting study of *Culex tritaeniorhynchus* (Giles) and other associated mosquitoes in Japan. *J. econ. Ent.* **52**, 490–2.

FORD, J., GLASGOW, J. P., JOHNS, D. L. and WELCH, J. R., 1959. Transect fly-rounds in field studies of Glossina. *Bull. ent. Res.* **50**, 275–85.

FRANCKE-GROSMANN, H., 1963. Some new aspects in forest entomology. *A. Rev. Ent.* **8**, 415–38.

FREDEEN, F. J. H., 1961. A trap for studying the attacking behaviour of black flies *Simulium arcticum* Mall. *Canad. Ent.* **93**, 73–8.

FRITZSCHE, R., 1956. Untersuchungen zur Bekämpfung der Rapsschädlinge. IV. Beiträge zur Ökologie und Bekämpfung des Grossen Rapsstengelrüsslers (*Ceuthorrhynchus napi* Gyll.). *NachrBl. dtsch. PflSchDienst, Berlin* **10** (5), 97–105.

FRÖHLICH, G., 1956. Methoden zur Bestimmung der Befalls-bzw. Bekämpfungstermine verschiedener Rapsschädlinge, insbesondere des Rapsstengelrüsslers (*Ceuthorrhynchus napi* Gyll.). *NachrBl. dtsch. PflSchDienst, Berlin* **10**, 48–53.

FROST, S. W., 1952. Light traps for insect collection, survey and control. *Bull. Pa agric. Exp. Sta.* **550**, 32 pp.

FROST, S. W., 1953. Response of insects to black and white light. *J. econ. Ent.* **46** (2), 376–7.

FROST, S. W., 1957. The Pennsylvania insect light trap. *J. econ. Ent.* **50**, 287–92.

FROST, S. W., 1958a. Insects captured in light traps with and without baffles. *Canad. Ent.* **90**, 566–7.

FROST, S. W., 1958b. Traps and lights to catch night-flying insects. *Proc. X int. Congr. Ent.* **2**, 583–7.

FROST, S. W., 1958c. Insects attracted to light traps placed at different heights. *J. econ. Ent.* **51**, 550–1.

FROST, S. W., 1964. Killing agents and containers for use with insect light traps. *Ent. News* **75**, 163–6.

FUKUDA, M., 1960. On the effect of physical condition of setting place upon the number of flies collected by fish baited traps. *Endemic Dis. Bull. Nagasaki Univ.* **2** (3), 222–8.

GARA, R. I. and VITÉ, J. P., 1962. Studies on the flight patterns of bark beetles (Coleoptera, Scolytidae) in second growth Ponderosa pine forest. *Contrib. Boyce Thompson Inst.* **21**: 275–90.

GARCIA, R., 1962. Carbon dioxide as an attractant for certain ticks (Acarina: Argasidae and Ixodidae). *Ann. ent. Soc. Amer.* **55**, 605–6.

GEIER, P. W., 1960. Physiological age of codling moth females (*Cydia pomonella* L.) caught in bait and light traps. *Nature, Lond.* **185**, 709.

GERTLER, S. I., STEINER, L. F., MITCHELL, W. C. and BARTHEL, W. F., 1958. Esters of 6-methyl-3-cyclohexene-1-carboxylic acid as attractants for the Mediterranean fruit fly. *J. agric. Fd Chem.* **6**, 592–4.

GLASGOW, J. P., 1953. The extermination of animal populations by artificial predation and the estimation of populations. *J. anim. Ecol.* **22**, 32–46.

GLASGOW, J. P., 1961. The variability of fly-round catches in field studies of *Glossina*. *Bull. ent. Res.* **51**, 781–8.

GLASGOW, J. P. and DUFFY, B. J., 1961. Traps in field studies of *Glossina pallidipes* Austen. *Bull. ent. Res.* **52**, 795–814.

GLICK, P. A., 1939. The distribution of insects, spiders and mites in the air. *U.S.D.A. Tech. Bull.* **673**, 150 pp.

GLICK, P. A., HOLLINGSWORTH, J. P. and EITEL, W. J., 1956. Further studies on the attraction of pink bollworm moths to ultra-violet and visible radiation. *J. econ. Ent.* **49**, 158–61.

GOLDING, F. D., 1941. Two new methods of trapping the cacao moth (*Ephestia cautella*). *Bull. ent. Res.* **32**, 123–32.

GOLDING, F. D., 1946. A new method of trapping flies. *Bull. ent. Res.* **37**, 143–54.

GOODWIN, M. H., 1942. Studies on artificial resting places of *Anopheles quadrimaculatus* Say. *J. Nat. Mal. Soc.* **1**, 93–9.

GOODWIN, M. H. and LOVE, G. J., 1957. Factors influencing variations in populations of *Anopheles quadrimaculatus* in southwestern Georgia. *Ecology* **38**, 561–70.

GRAHAM, H. M., GLICK, P. A. and HOLLINGSWORTH, J. P., 1961. Effective range of argon glow lamp survey traps for pink bollworm adults. *J. econ. Ent.* **54**, 788–9.

GRAY, H. and TRELOAR, A., 1933. On the enumeration of insect populations by the method of net collection. *Ecology* **14**, 356–67.

GRAY, P. H. H., 1955. An apparatus for the rapid sorting of small insects. *Entomologist* **88**, 92–3.

GREENSLADE, P. J. M., 1964. Pitfall trapping as a method for studying populations of Carabidae (Coleoptera). *J. anim. Ecol.* **33**, 301–10.

GRESSITT, J. L., LEECH, R. E. and O'BRIEN, C. W., 1960. Trapping of air-borne insects in the antarctic area. *Pacific Insects* **2**, 245–50.

GRESSITT, J. L., SEDLACEK, J., WISE, K. A. J. and YOSHIMOTO, C. M., 1961. A high speed airplane trap for air-borne organisms. *Pacific Insects* **3**, 549–55.

GRESSITT, J. L. and GRESSITT, M. K., 1962. An improved Malaise trap. *Pacific Insects* **4**, 87–90.

GRIGARICK, A. A., 1959*a*. A floating pan trap for insects associated with the water surface. *J. econ. Ent.* **52**, 348–9.

GRIGARICK, A. A., 1959*b*. Bionomics of the rice leaf miner, *Hydrellia griseola* (Fallen.), in California (Diptera: Ephydridae). *Hilgardia* **29** (1), 80 pp.

GRÜM, L., 1959. Sezonowe zmiany aktywności biegaczowatych (Carabidae). *Ekol. Polska A* **7** (9), 255–68.

GUI, H. L., PORTER, L. C. and PRIDEAUX, G. F., 1942. Response of insects to colour intensity and distribution of light. *Agricul. Engin.* **23**, 51–8.

HADDOW, A. J., 1954. Studies on the biting habits of African mosquitoes. An appraisal of methods employed, with special reference to the twenty-four-hour catch. *Bull. ent. Res.* **45**, 199–242.

HADDOW, A. J. and CORBET, P. S., 1960. Observations on nocturnal activity in some African Tabanidae (Diptera). *Proc. R. ent. Soc. Lond. A* **35**, 1–5.

HARPER, A. M. and STORY, T. P., 1962. Reliability of trapping in determining the emergence period and sex ratio of the sugar-beet root maggot *Tetanops myopaeformis* Röder) (Diptera: Otitidae). *Canad. Ent.* **94**, 268–71.

HARRISON, I. R., 1963. Population studies on the poultry red mite *Dermanyssus gallinae* (Deg.). *Bull. ent. Res.* **53**, 657–64.

HARWOOD, R. F., 1961. A mobile trap for studying the behaviour of flying bloodsucking insects. *Mosq. News* **21**, 35–9.

HAUFE, W. O. and BURGESS, L., 1960. Design and efficiency of mosquito traps based on visual response to patterns. *Canad. Ent.* **92**, 124–40.

HAYNE, D. W., 1949. Two methods of estimating populations from trapping records. *J. Mammal.* **30** (4), 399–411.

HEATHCOTE, G. D., 1957a. The comparison of yellow cylindrical, flat and water traps and of Johnson suction traps, for sampling aphids. *Ann. appl. Biol.* **45**, 133–9.

HEATHCOTE, G. D., 1957b. The optimum size of sticky aphid traps. *Plant Path.* **6**, 104–7.

HEIKINHEIMO, O. and RAATIKAINEN, M., 1962. Comparison of suction and netting methods in population investigations concerning the fauna of grass leys and cereal fields, particularly in those concerning the leafhopper, *Calligypona pellucida* (F.). *Valt. Maatalourk. Julk., Helsingfors*, **191**, 31 pp.

HESSE, G., KAUTH, H. and WÄCHTER, R.,1955. Frasslockstoffe beim Fichtenrüsselkäfer *Hylobius abietis. Z. angew. Ent.* **37**, 239–44.

HILL, M. A., 1947. The life-cycle and habits of *Culicoides impunctatus* Goet. and *C. obsoletus* Mg., together with some observations on the life-cycle of *Culicoides odibilis* Aust., *Culicoides pallidicornis* Kief., *Culicoides cubitalis* Edw. and *Culicoides chiopterus* Mg. *Ann. Trop. Med. Parasit.* **41**, 55–115.

HOLBROOK, R. F., BEROZA, M. and BURGESS, E. D., 1960. Gypsy moth (*Porthetria dispar*). Detection with the natural female sex lure. *J. econ. Ent.* **53**, 751–6.

HOLLINGSWORTH, J. P., BRIGGS, C. P., GLICK, P. A. and GRAHAM, H. M., 1961. Some factors influencing light trap collections. *J. econ. Ent.* **54**, 305–8.

HOLLINGSWORTH, J. P., HARTSOCK, J. G. and STANLEY, J. M., 1963. Electrical insect traps for survey purposes. *U.S.D.A. Agric. Res. Serv.* (*ARS*) 42–3–1, 10 pp.

HOTTES, F. C., 1951. A method for taking aphids in flight. *Pan-Pacif. Ent.* **27**, 190.

HUGHES, R. D., 1955. The influence of the prevailing weather conditions on the numbers of *Meromyza variegata* Meigen (Diptera: Chloropidae) caught with a sweep net. *J. anim. Ecol.* **24**, 324–35.

HUNGERFORD, H. B., SPANGLER, P. J. and WALKER, N. A., 1955. Sub-aquatic light traps for insects and other animal organisms. *Trans. Kanas Acad. Sci.* **58**, 387–407.

IBBOTSON, A., 1958. The behaviour of frit fly in Northumberland. *Ann. appl. Biol.* **46**, 474–9.

ISHERWOOD, F., 1957. The resting sites of *Glossina swynnertoni* Aust. in the wet season. *Bull. ent. Res.* **48**, 601–6.

JACOBSON, M., BEROZA, M. and JONES, W. A., 1961. Insect sex attractants. 1. The isolation, identification, and synthesis of the sex attractant of the gypsy moth. *J. Amer. chem. Soc.* **83**, 4819–24.

JALAS, I., 1960. Eine leichtgebaute, leichttransportable Lichtreuse zum Fangen von Schmetterlingen. *Suom. hyönt. Aikak.* (*Ann. ent. Fenn.*) **26**, 44–50.

JAMNBACK, H. and WATTHEWS, T., 1963. Studies of populations of adult and immature *Culicoides sanguisuga* (Diptera: Ceratopogonidae). *Ann. ent. Soc. Amer.* **56**, 728–32.

JEPSON, W. F. and SOUTHWOOD, T. R. E., 1958. Population studies on *Oscinella frit* L. *Ann. appl. Biol.* **46**, 465–74.

JOHNSON, C. G., 1950. The comparison of suction trap, sticky trap and tow-net for the quantitative sampling of small airborne insects. *Ann. appl. Biol.* **37**, 268–85.

JOHNSON, C. G., 1952. The role of population level, flight periodicity and climate in the dispersal of aphids. *Trans. IX int. Congr. Ent.* **1**, 429–31.

JOHNSON, C. G., 1960. A basis for a general system of insect migration and dispersal flight. *Nature, Lond.* **186**, 348–50.

JOHNSON, C. G., 1963. Physiological factors in insect migration by flight. *Nature, Lond.* **198**, 423–7.

JOHNSON, C. G., SOUTHWOOD, T. R. E. and ENTWISTLE, H. M., 1957. A new method of extracting arthropods and molluscs from grassland and herbage with a suction apparatus. *Bull. ent. Res.* **48**, 211–18.

JORDAN, A. M., 1962. The ecology of the *fusca* group of tsetse flies (*Glossina*) in Southern Nigeria. *Bull. ent. Res.* **53**, 355–85.

JUDD, W. W., 1956. Results of a survey of Calypterate flies of medical importance conducted at London, Ontario, during 1953. *Amer. Midl. Nat.* **56**, 388–405.

JUILLET, J. A., 1963. A comparison of four types of traps used for capturing flying insects. *Canad. J. Zool.* **41**, 219–23.

KACZMAREK, W., 1963. An analysis of interspecific competition in communities of the soil macrofauna of some habitats in the Kampinos National Park. *Ekol. Polska A* **11** (17), 421–83.

KAWAI, S. and SUENAGA, O., 1960. Studies of the methods of collecting flies. III. On the effect of putrefaction of baits (fish). [In Japanese, Eng. summary.] *Endemic Dis. Bull. Nagasaki Univ.* **2**, 61–6.

KEMP-TURNBULL, P. ST J., 1960. Quantitative estimations of populations of the river crab *Potamon* (*Potamonautes*) *perlatus* (M. Edw.) in Rhodesian trout streams. *Nature, Lond.* **185**, 481.

KENNEDY, J. S., 1961. A turning point in the study of insect migration. *Nature, Lond.* **189**, 785–91.

KING, E. W., PLESS, C. D. and REED, J. K., 1965. An automatic sample-changing device for light-trap collecting. *J. econ. Ent.* **58**, 170–2.

KLOCK, J. W. and BIDLINGMAYER, W. L., 1953. An adult mosquito sampler. *Mosq. News* **13**, 157–9.

KONO, T., 1953. On the estimation of insect population by time unit collecting. [In Japanese.] *Res. Popul. Ecol.* **2**, 85–94.

KOVROV, B. G. and MONCHADSKII, A. S., 1963. The possibility of using polarized light to attract insects. [In Russian.] *Ent. Obozr.* **42**, 49–55 (transl. *Ent. Rev.* **42**, 25–8).

LEECH, H. B., 1955. Cheesecloth flight trap for insects. *Canad. Ent.* **85**, 200.

LE PELLEY, R. H., 1935. Observations on the control of insects by hand-collection. *Bull. ent. Res.* **26**, 533–41.

LESLIE, P. H. and DAVIS, D. H. S., 1939. An attempt to determine the absolute numbers of rats on a given area. *J. anim. Ecol.* **8**, 94–113.

LEVIN, M. D., 1957. Artificial nesting burrows for *Osmia lignaria* Say. *J. econ. Ent.* **50**, 506–7.

LEWIS, T., 1959. A comparison of water traps, cylindrical sticky traps and suction traps for sampling Thysanopteran populations at different levels. *Ent. exp. appl.* **2**, 204–15.

LEWIS, T. and TAYLOR, L. R., 1965. Diurnal periodicity of flight by insects. *Trans. R. ent. Soc. Lond.* **116**, 393–469.

LINSLEY, E. G., MACSWAIN, J. W. and SMITH, R. F., 1952. Outline for ecological life histories of solitary and semi-social bees. *Ecology* **33**, 558–67.

LOOMIS, E. C., 1959a. A method for more accurate determination of air volume displacement of light traps. *J. econ. Ent.* **52**, 343–5.

LOOMIS, E. C., 1959b. Selective response of *Aedes nigromaculis* (Ludlow) to the Minnesota light trap. *Mosq. News* **19**, 260–3.

LOOMIS, E. C. and SHERMAN, E. J., 1959. Comparison of artificial shelter and light traps for measurements of *Culex tarsalis* and *Anopheles freeborni* populations. *Mosq. News* **19**, 232–7.

LOVE, G. J. and SMITH, W. W., 1957. Preliminary observations on the relation of light trap collections to mechanical sweep net collections in sampling mosquito populations. *Mosq. News* **17**, 9–14.

LUCZAK, J. and WIERZBOWSKA, T., 1959. Analysis of likelihood in relation to the length of a series in the sweep method. *Bull. Acad. pol. Sci., Ser. Sci. Biol.* **7**, 313–18.

LUMSDEN, W. H. R., 1958. A trap for insects biting small vertebrates. *Nature, Lond.* **181**, 819–20.

MACAN, T. T., 1958. Methods of sampling the bottom fauna in stony streams. *Mitt. int. Ver. Limnol.* **8**, 1–21.

MACLEOD, J. and DONNELLY, J., 1956. Methods for the study of Blowfly populations. I. Bait trapping. Significance of limits for comparative sampling. *Ann. appl. Biol.* **44**, 80–104.

MACLEOD, J. and DONNELLY, J., 1963. Dispersal and interspersal of blowfly populations. *J. anim. Ecol.* **32**, 1–33.

MAKSIMOVIĆ, M., 1960. Klopke-savremena metoda kontrole brojnosti populacije gubara. *Plant Prot.* **56**, 65–70.

MALAISE, R., 1937. A new insect-trap. *Ent. Tidskr.* **58**, 148–60.

MANN, K. H., 1955. The ecology of the British freshwater leeches. *J. anim. Ecol.* **24**, 98–119.

MASAKI, J., 1959. Studies on rice crane fly (*Tipula aino* Alexander, Tipulidae, Diptera) with special reference to the ecology and its protection. [In Japanese.] *J. Kanto-Tosan agric. Exp. Sta.* **13**, 195 pp.

MASON, H. C., 1963. Baited traps for sampling *Drosophila* populations in tomato field plots. *J. econ. Ent.* **56**, 897–8.

MAXWELL, C. W., 1965. Tanglefoot traps as indicators of apple maggot fly activities. *Canad. Ent.* **97**, 110.

MAYER, K., 1961. Untersuchungen über das Wahlverhalten der Fritfliege (*Oscinella frit* L.) beim Anflug von Kulturpflanzen im Feldversuch mit der Fangschalenmethode. *Mitt. biol. Bund. Anst. Ld- u. Forstw., Berlin* **106**, 1–47.

MCPHAIL, M., 1939. Protein lures for fruit flies. *J. econ. Ent.* **32**, 758–61.

MEDLER, J. T., 1964. Biology of *Rygchium foraminatum* in trap-nests in Wisconsin (Hymenoptera: Vespidae). *Ann. ent. Soc. Amer.* **57**, 56–60.

MEDLER, J. T. and FYE, R. E., 1956. Biology of *Ancistrocerus antilope* (Panzer) in trap nests in Wisconsin. *Ann. ent. Soc. Amer.* **49**, 97–102.

MELLANBY, K., 1962. Sticky traps for the study of animals inhabiting the soil surface. *In* Murphy, P. W. (ed.), *Progress in Soil. Zoology* 226–7.

MENHINICK, E. F., 1963. Estimation of insect population density in herbaceous vegetation with emphasis on removal sweeping. *Ecology* **44**, 617–21.

MERZHEEVSKAYA, O. I. and GERASTEVICH, E. A., 1962. A method of collecting living insects at light. [In Russian.] *Zool. Zhur.* **41**, 1741–3.

MICHELBACHER, A. E. and MIDDLEKAUFF, W. W., 1954. Vinegar fly investigations in Northern California. *J. econ. Ent.* **47**, 917–22.

MILES, P. M., 1954. A trap designed to collect insects attracted by 'sugar'. *Ent. mon. Mag.* **90**, 86–7.

MINTER, D. M., 1961. A modified Lumsden suction-trap for biting insects. *Bull. ent. Res.* **52**, 233–8.

MITCHELL, B., 1963. Ecology of two carabid beetles, *Bembidion lampros* (Herbst.) and *Trechus quadristriatus* (Schrank). II. *J. anim. Ecol.* **32**, 377–92.

MOERICKE, V., 1950. Über den Farbensinn der Pfirsichblattlaus *Myzodes persicae* Sulz. *Z. Tierpsychol.* **7**, 265–74.

MOERICKE, V., 1951. Eine Farbfalle zur kontrolle des Fluges von Blattläusen, insbesondere der Pfirsichblattlaus *Myzodes persicae* (Sulz.). *NachrBl. dtsch. PflSchDienst, Stuttgart* **3**, 23–4.

MORAN, P. A. P., 1951. A mathematical theory of animal trapping. *Biometrika* **38**, 307–11.

MORELAND, C., 1954. A wind frame for trapping insects in flight. *J. econ. Ent.* **47**, 944.

MORGAN, C. V. G. and ANDERSON, N. H., 1958. Techniques for biological studies of tetranychid mites, especially *Bryobia arborea* M. & A. and *B. praetiosa* Koch. (Acarina: Tetranychidae). *Canad. Ent.* **90**, 212–15.

MORRIS, K. R. S., 1960. Trapping as a means of studying the game tsetse, *Glossina pallidipes* Aust. *Bull. ent. Res.* **51**, 533–57.

MORRIS, K. R. S., 1961. Effectiveness of traps in tsetse surveys in the Liberian rain forest. *Amer. J. trop. Med. hyg.* **10**, 905–13.

MORRIS, K. R. S. and MORRIS, M. G., 1949. The use of traps against tsetse in West Africa. *Bull. ent. Res.* **39**, 491–523.

MUIRHEAD-THOMSON, R. C. (ed.), 1963. *Practical entomology in Malaria eradication.* WHO (MHO/PA/62.63) Part 1, Chapter 1 (mimeographed).

MULHERN, T. D., 1942. New Jersey mechanical trap for mosquito surveys. *N.J. Agric. Exp. Sta. Circ.* **421**, 1–8.

MULHERN, T. D., 1953. Better results with mosquito light traps through standardizing mechanical performance. *Mosq. News* **13**, 130–3.

MULLA, M. S., DORNER, R. W., GEORGHIOU, G. P. and GARBER, M. J., 1960. Olfactometer and procedure for testing baits and chemical attractants against *Hippelates* eye gnats. *Ann. ent. Soc. Amer.* **53**, 529–37.

MULLA, M. S., GEORGHIOU, G. P. and DORNER, R. W., 1960. Effect of ageing and concentration on the attractancy of proteinaceous materials to *Hippelates* gnats. *Ann. ent. Soc. Amer.* **53**, 835–41.

MURRAY, W. D., 1963. Measuring adult populations of the pasture mosquito, *Aedes migromaculis* (Ludlow). *Proc. 27th Conf. Calif. Mosq. Contr. Ass.* **1959**, 67–71.

MYERS, K., 1956. Methods of sampling winged insects feeding on the rabbit *Oryctolagus cuniculus* (L.). *Aust. C.S.I.R.O. Wildl. Res.* **1**, 45–58.

NEILSON, W. T. A., 1960. Field tests of some hydrolyzed proteins as lures for the apple maggot, *Rhagoletis pomonella* (Walsh). *Canad. Ent.* **92**, 464–7.

NICKERSON, B,, 1963. An experimental study of the effect of changing light intensity on the activity of adult locusts. *Ent. mon. Mag.* **99**, 139–40.

NIELSEN, B. OVERGAARD, 1963. The biting midges of *Lyngby aamose* (Culicoides: Ceratopogonidae). *Natura jutl.* **10**, 48 pp.

NIELSEN, E. T., 1960. A note on stationary nets. *Ecology* **41**, 375–6.

ODINTSOV, V. S., 1960. (Air catch of insects as a method of study upon entomofauna of vast territories.) [In Russian.] *Ent. Obozr.* **39**, 227–30.

OUYE, M. T. and BUTT, B. A., 1962. A natural sex lure extracted from female pink bollworms. *J. econ. Ent.* **55**, 419–21.

PARIS, O. H., 1965. The vagility of P^{32}-labelled Isopods in grassland. *Ecology* **46**, 635–48.

PARKER, A. H., 1949. Observations on the seasonal and daily incidence of certain biting midges (*Culicoides* Latreille – Diptera, Ceratopogonidae) in Scotland. *Trans. R. ent. Soc. Lond.* **100**, 179–90.

PAVIOUR-SMITH, K., 1964. The life history of *Tetratoma fungorum* F. (Col., Tetratomidae) in relation to habitat requirements, with an account of eggs and larval stages. *Ent. mon. Mag.* **100**, 118–34.

PIECZYNSKI, E., 1961. The trap method of capturing water mites (Hydracarina). *Ekol. Polska B* **7** (2), 111–15.

PRESCOTT, H. W. and NEWTON, R. C., 1963. Flight study of the clover root Curculio. *J. econ. Ent.* **56**, 368–70.

PROVOST, M. W., 1960. The dispersal of *Aedes taeniorhynchus*. III. Study methods for migratory exodus. *Mosq. News* **20**, 148–61.

RACE, S. R., 1960. A comparison of two sampling techniques for lygus bugs and stink bugs on cotton. *J. econ. Ent.* **53**, 689–90.

RENNISON, B. D. and ROBERTSON, D. H. H., 1959. The use of carbon dioxide as an attractant for catching tsetse. *Rep. E. Afr. Trypan. Res. Organ.* **1958**, 26.

RIPLEY, L. B. and HEPBURN, G. A., 1929. Studies on reactions of the Natal fruit-fly to fermenting baits. *S. Afr. Dept. Agric. Ent. Mem.* **1** (6), 19–53.

RIPLEY, L. B. and HEPBURN, G. A., 1935. Olfactory attractants for male fruit-flies. *S. Afr. Dept. Agric. Ent. Mem.* **1** (9), 3–17.

RIVARD, I., 1962. Un piège à fosse amélioré pour la capture d'insectes actifs à la surface du sol. *Canad. Ent.* **94,** 1270–1.

ROBINSON, H. S. and ROBINSON, P. J. M., 1950. Some notes on the observed behaviour of Lepidoptera in flight in the vicinity of light-sources together with a description of a light-trap designed to take entomological samples. *Ent. Gaz.* **1,** 3–15.

ROESLER, R., 1953. Über eine Methode zur Feststellung der Flugzeit schädlicher Fliegenarten (Kirschfliege, Kohlfliege, Zwiebelfliege). *Mitt. biol. Reichsanst.* (*ZentAnst.*) *Ld- u. Forstw.*, *Berlin* **75,** 97–9.

ROMNEY, V. E., 1945. The effect of physical factors upon catch of the beet leafhopper (*Eutettix tenellus* (Bak.)) by a cylinder and two sweep-net methods. *Ecology* **26,** 135–48.

ROOS, T., 1957. Studies on upstream migration in adult stream-dwelling insects. *Inst. Freshw. Res. Drottningholm Rep.* **38,** 167–93.

ROTHSCHILD, M., 1961. Observations and speculations concerning the flea vector of myxomatosis in Britain. *Ent. mon. Mag.* **96,** 106–9.

RUFFINELLI, A., ORLANDO, A. and BIGGI, E., 1962. Novos ensaios com substâncias atrativas para as 'môscas das frutas' – *Ceratitis capitata* (Wied.) e *Anastrepha mombinpraeoptans* Sein. *Arq. Inst. biol. Sâo Paulo* **27** (1960), 1–9.

SALITERNIK, Z., 1960. A mosquito light trap for use on cesspits. *Mosq. News* **20,** 295–6.

SARTOR, M. H. and OERTEL, J. C., 1963. Portable black-light trap: battery and AC operation. *J. econ. Ent.* **56,** 536.

SAUNDERS, D. S., 1964. The effect of site and sampling and method on the size and composition of catches of tsetse flies (*Glossina*) and Tabanidae (Diptera). *Bull. ent. Res.* **55,** 483.

SCHEEPERS, C. C. and GUNN, D. L., 1958. Enumerating populations of adults of the red locust, *Nomadacris septemfasciata* (Serville), in its outbreak areas in East and Central Africa. *Bull. ent. Res.* **49,** 273–85.

SERVICE, M. W., 1963. The ecology of the mosquitoes of the northern Guinea savannah of Nigeria. *Bull. ent. Res.* **54,** 601–32.

SEVASTOPULO, D. G., 1963. Field notes from East Africa – Part XI. *Entomologist* **96,** 162–5.

SHEMANCHUK, J. A., 1959. Mosquitoes (Diptera: Culicidae) in irrigated areas of southern Alberta and their seasonal changes in abundance and distribution. *Canad. J. Zool.* **37,** 899–912.

ŠIMUNIC, I., 1961. Comparative investigations of attractants for the fruit-fly. [In Serbo-Croat.] *Plant Prot.* **62,** 49–59 (*Rev. appl. Ent. A* **51,** 326).

SKELLAM, J. G., 1958. The mathematical foundations underlying the use of line transects in animal ecology. *Biometrics* **14,** 385–400.

SMITH, B. D., 1962. The behaviour and control of the blackcurrant gall mite *Phytoptus ribis* (Nal.). *Ann. appl. Biol.* **50,** 327–34.

SMITH, I. M. and RENNISON, B. D., 1961. Studies of the sampling of *Glossina pallidipes* Aust. I, II. *Bull. ent. Res.* **52,** 165–89; III and IV. *ibid.* **52,** 601–19.

SMITH, P. W., TAYLOR, J. G. and APPLE, J. W., 1959. A comparison of insect traps equipped with 6- and 15-watt black light lamps. *J. econ. Ent.* **52,** 1212–14.

SNOW, W. E., PICKARD, E. and SPARKMAN, R. E., 1960. A fan trap for collecting biting insects attacking avian hosts. *Mosq. News* **20,** 315–16.

SOUTHWOOD, T. R. E., 1960. The flight activity of Heteroptera. *Trans. R. ent. Soc. Lond.* **112** (8), 173–220.

SOUTHWOOD, T. R. E., 1962. Migration of terrestrial arthropods in relation to habitat. *Biol. Rev.* **37,** 171–214.

SOUTHWOOD, T. R. E., JEPSON, W. F. and VAN EMDEN, H. F., 1961. Studies on the behaviour of *Oscinella frit* L. (Diptera) adults of the panicle generation. *Ent. exp. appl.* **4**, 196–210.

STAGE, H. H., GJULLIN, C. M. and YATES, W. W., 1952. Mosquitoes of the Northwestern States. *U.S.D.A., Agric. Handbk* **46**, 95 pp.

STAHL, C., 1954. Trapping hornworm moths. *J. econ. Ent.* **47**, 879–82.

STAMMER, H. J., 1949. Die Bedeutung der Äthylenglycolfallen für tierökologische und phänologische Untersuchungen. *Verh. dtsch. Zoologen. Kiel* (**1948**), 387–91.

STANLEY, J. M. and DOMINICK, C. B., 1957. Response of tobacco and tomato hornworm moths to black light. *J. econ. Ent.* **51**, 78–80.

STAPLES, R. and ALLINGTON, W. B., 1959. The efficiency of sticky traps in sampling epidemic populations of the Eriophyid mite *Aceria tulipae* (K.), vector of wheat streak mosaic virus. *Ann. ent. Soc. Amer.* **52**, 159–64.

STARR, D. F. and SHAW, J. G., 1944. Pyridine as an attractant for the Mexican fruit fly. *J. econ. Ent.* **37**, 760–3.

STEINER, L. F., 1929. Codling moth bait trap studies. *J. econ. Ent.* **22**, 636–48.

STEINER, L. F., 1957. Low-cost plastic fruit fly trap. *J. econ. Ent.* **50**, 508.

STEINER, L. F., MIYASHITA, D. H. and CHRISTENSON, L. D., 1957. Angelica oils as mediterranean fruit fly lures. *J. econ. Ent.* **50**, 505.

STEINER, P., WENZEL, F. and BAUMERT, D., 1963. Zur Beeinflussung der Arthropodenfauna nordwestdeutscher Kartoffelfelder durch die Anwendung synthetischer Kontaktinsektizide. *Mitt. biol. BundAnst. Ld- u. Forstw.*, Berlin **109**, 38 pp.

STILL, G. W., 1960. An improved trap for deciduous tree fruit flies. *J. econ. Ent.* **53**, 967.

SUDIA, W. D. and CHAMBERLAIN, R. W., 1962. Battery-operated light trap, an improved model. *Mosq. News.* **22**, 126–9.

SYMMONS, P. M., DEAN, G. J. W. and STORTENBEKER, C. W., 1963. The assessment of the size of populations of adults of the red locust, *Nomadacris septemfasciata* (Serville), in an outbreak area. *Bull. ent. Res.* **54**, 549–69.

TAFT, H. M. and JERNIGAN, C. E., 1964. Elevated screens for collecting boll weevils flying between hibernation sites and cottonfields. *J. econ. Ent.* **57**, 773–5.

TAYLOR, L. R., 1962. The efficiency of cylindrical sticky insect traps and suspended nets. *Ann. appl. Biol.* **50**, 681–5.

TAYLOR, L. R., 1963. Analysis of the effect of temperature on insects in flight. *J. anim. Ecol.* **32**, 99–112.

TAYLOR, L. R. and CARTER, C. I., 1961. The analysis of numbers and distribution in an aerial population of Macrolepidoptera. *Trans. R. ent. Soc. Lond.* **113**, 369–86.

THORSTEINSON, A. J., BRACKEN, G. K. and HANEC, W., 1965. The orientation behaviour of horse flies and deer flies (Tabanidae, Diptera). III. The use of traps in the study of orientation of Tabanids in the field. *Ent. exp. appl.* **8**, 189–92.

TOWNES, H., 1962. Design for a Malaise trap. *Proc. ent. Soc. Wash.* **64**, 253–62.

TRETZEL, E., 1955. Technik und Bedeutung des Fallenfanges für ökologische Untersuchungen. *Zool. Anz.* **155**, 276–87.

TSHERNYSHEV, W. B., 1961. (Comparison of field responses of insects to the light of a mercury-quartz lamp and clear ultra-violet radiation of the same lamp.) [In Russian.] *Ent. Obozr.* **40**, 568–70 (transl. *Ent. Rev.* **40**, 308–9).

TURNER, F. B., 1962. Some sampling characteristics of plants and arthropods of the Arizona desert. *Ecology* **43**, 567–71.

USINGER, R. L. (ed.), 1963. *Aquatic insects of California.* Berkeley and Los Angeles, 508 pp.

USINGER, R. L. and KELLEN, W. R., 1955. The role of insects in sewage disposal beds. *Hilgardia* **23**, 263–321.

VANDERPLANK, F. L., 1960. The availability of the coconut bug, *Pseudotheraptus wayi* Brown (Coreidae). *Bull. ent. Res.* **51**, 57–60.

VERHEIJEN, F. J., 1960. The mechanisms of the trapping effect of artificial light sources upon animals. *Arch. Néerland. Zool.* **13**, 1–107.

VITÉ, J. P. and GARA, R. I., 1962. Volatile attractants from Ponderosa pine attacked by bark beetles (Coleoptera: Scolytidae). *Contr. Boyce Thompson Inst.* **21**, 251–73.

WADA, Y., 1962. Studies on the population estimation for insects of medical importance. I. A method of estimating the population size of mosquito larvae in a fertilizer pit. *Endemic Dis. Bull. Nagasaki Univ.* **4**, 22–30. II. A method of estimating the population size of larvae of *Aedes togoi* in the tide-water rock pool. *ibid.* **4**, 141–56.

WAKERLEY, S. B., 1963. Weather and behaviour in carrot fly (*Psila rosae* Fab. Dipt. Psilidae) with particular reference to oviposition. *Ent. exp. appl.* **6**, 268–78.

WALOFF, N. and BAKKER, K., 1963. The flight activity of Miridae (Heteroptera) living on broom, *Sarothamnus scoparius* (L.) Wimm. *J. anim. Ecol.* **32**, 461–80.

WALSH, G. B., 1933. Studies in the British necrophagous Coleoptera. II. The attractive powers of various natural baits. *Ent. mon. Mag.* **69**, 28–32.

WATERS, T. F., 1962. Diurnal periodicity in the drift of stream invertebrates. *Ecology* **43**, 316–20.

WELCH, R. C., 1964. A simple method of collecting insects from rabbit burrows. *Ent. mon. Mag.* **100**, 99–100.

WENK, P. and SCHLÖRER, G., 1963. Wirtsorientierung und Kopulation bei blutsaugenden Simuliiden (Diptera). *Zeit. Trop. Med. Parasit.* **14**, 177–91.

WHARTON, R. H., EYLES, D. E. and WARREN, MCW., 1963. The development of methods for trapping the vectors of Monkey Malaria. *Ann. Trop. Med. Parasit., Liverpool* **57**, 32–46.

WHITE, E. G., 1964. A design for the effective killing of insects caught in light traps. *N.Z. Entomologist* **3**, 25–7.

WILDE, W. H. A., 1962. Bionomics of the pear psylla, *Psylla pyricola* Foerster in pear orchards of the Kootenay valley of British Columbia, 1960. *Canad. Ent.* **94**, 845–9.

WILKINSON, P. R., 1961. The use of sampling methods in studies of the distribution of larvae of *Boophilus microplus* on pastures. *Austr. J. Zool.* **9**, 752–83.

WILLIAMS, C. B., 1935. The times of activity of certain nocturnal insects, chiefly Lepidoptera as indicated by a light-trap. *Trans. R. ent. Soc. Lond.* **83**, 523–55.

WILLIAMS, C. B., 1939. An analysis of four years captures of insects in a light trap. Part I. General survey; sex proportion; phenology and time of flight. *Trans. R. ent. Soc. Lond.* **89**, 79–132.

WILLIAMS, C. B., 1940. An analysis of four years captures of insects in a light trap. Part II. The effect of weather conditions on insect activity; and the estimation and forecasting of changes in the insect population. *Trans. R. ent. Soc. Lond.* **90**, 228–306.

WILLIAMS, C. B., 1948. The Rothamsted light trap. *Proc. R. ent. Soc. Lond. A* **23**, 80–5.

WILLIAMS, C. B., 1950. Diversity as a measurable character of an animal or plant population. *Ann. Biol.* **27**, 129–41.

WILLIAMS, C. B., 1951. Comparing the efficiency of insect traps. *Bull. ent. Res.* **42**, 513–17.

WILLIAMS, C. B., FRENCH, R. A. and HOSNI, M. M., 1955. A second experiment on testing the relative efficiency of insect traps. *Bull. ent. Res.* **46**, 193–204.

WILLIAMS, C. B., SINGH, B. P. and EL ZIADY, S., 1956. An investigation into the possible effects of moonlight on the activity of insects in the field. *Proc. R. ent. Soc. Lond. A* **31**, 135–44.

WILLIAMS, G., 1958. Mechanical time-sorting of pitfall captures. *J. anim. Ecol.* **27**, 27–35.

WORTH, C. B. and JONKERS, A. H., 1962. Two traps for mosquitoes attracted to small vertebrate animals. *Mosq. News* **22**, 18–21.

YAPP, W. B., 1956. The theory of line transects. *Bird Study* **3**, 93–104.

YEO, D. and FOSTER, R., 1958. Preliminary note on a method for the direct estimation of populations of *Pseudotheraptus wayi* Brown on coconut palms. *Bull. ent. Res.* **49**, 585–90.

YOSHIMOTO, C. M. and GRESSITT, J. L., 1959. Trapping of airborne insects on ships on the Pacific (Part II). *Proc. Hawaiian Ent. Soc.* **17** (1), 150–5.

YOSHIMOTO, C. M., GRESSITT, J. L. and WOLFF, T., 1962. Airborne insects from the Galathea expedition. *Pacific Insects* **4**, 269–91.

ZHOGOLEV, D. T., 1959. Light-traps as a method for collecting and studying the insect vectors of disease organisms. [In Russian.] *Ent. Obozr.* **38**, 766–73.

ZIMMERMAN, J. R., 1960. Seasonal population changes and habitat preferences in the genus *Laccophilus* (Coleoptera: Dytiscidae). *Ecology* **41**, 141–52.

ZIPPIN, C., 1956. An evaluation of the removal method of estimating animal populations. *Biometrics* **12**, 163–89.

ZIPPIN, C., 1958. The removal method of population estimation. *J. Wildl. Mgmt* **22**, 82–90.

CHAPTER 8

Estimates based on Products and Effects
of Insects

Measures of the size of populations based on the magnitude of their products or effects are often referred to as population indices. The relationship of these indices to the absolute population varies from equivalence, when the number of exuviae are counted, to no more than an approximate correlation, when the index is obtained from general measures of damage.

PRODUCTS

Exuviae

The larval or pupal exuviae of insects with aquatic larval stages are often left in conspicuous positions around the edges of water bodies, and where it is possible to gather these they will provide a measure of the emergence rate and of the absolute population of newly emerged adults. The method is most easily applied to large insects such as dragonflies (Corbet, 1957). The exuviae of the last immature, subterranean stage of some insects are also often conspicuous and with cicadas Strandine (1940) and Dybas & Lloyd (1962) found that the number of larval cases per unit area was correlated with the number of emergence holes and provided a useful index of population; different species could be recognized from the exuviae.

Paramonov (1959) drew attention to the possibility of obtaining an index of the population of arboreal insects from their exuviae, more particularly from the head capsules of lepidopterous larvae that may be collected in the same way as frass (see below). He found that the head capsules could be separated from the other debris by flotation. In most species the stage of the larva can be determined from the size of the capsule and if all the capsules could be collected an elegant measurement of absolute population would be obtained. However, a significant, and probably fluctuating, number fail to be recovered and this variable needs to be carefully investigated in a given situation before the method is employed to measure either absolute population or even an index of it.

Frass

The faeces of insects are generally referred to as frass; as this is based on the incorrect use of a German word, the term feculae has been suggested (Frost,

1928), but seldom used. (The German words *frass*=insect damage or food, whilst *kot*=faeces.) The frass-drop, the number of frass pellets falling to the ground, was first used as an index of both population and insect damage by a number of forest entomologists in Germany (Rhumbler, 1929; Gösswald

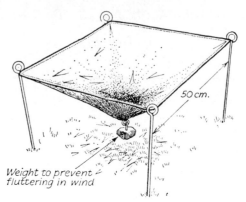

Fig. 66. Frass-collector, constructed of cloth (after Tinbergen, 1960).

1935). The falling frass is collected in cloth or wooden trays or funnels under the trees (fig. 66). In order for such collections to be of maximum value for population estimation one should be able to identify the species and the developmental stage, information is also required on the quantity of frass produced per individual per unit of time and the proportion of this that falls to the ground and is collected.

a. Identification

Although the frass of early instars of several species may be confused, in the later instars it is generally distinctive and keys for the identification of frass pellets have been prepared (Nolte, 1939; Morris, 1942; Weiss & Boyd, 1950, 1952; Hodson & Brooks, 1956). With the nun moth (*Lymantria monacha*) Eckstein (1938) concluded the frass size was a more reliable indicator of larval instar than the width of the head capsule; in the sawfly, *Diprion hercyniae* (Morris, 1949), and the armyworm (*Pseudaletia unipuncta*) (Pond, 1961) instar can easily be determined from pellet size. Water-soluble constituents are washed out when the pellets are exposed to rain and so pellet weight may fall by as much as 30%; however, in these species the volume is not affected. Bean (1959) considered that in the spruce budworm (*Choristoneura fumiferana*), the width of the pellet rather than its volume was closely correlated with larval instar; furthermore this author also found that larvae, feeding on pollen, ejected frass pellets that were considerably larger than those produced by the same instar larvae feeding on foliage.

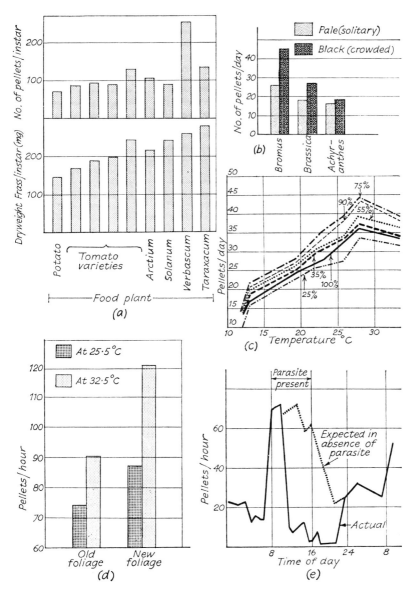

Fig. 67. Variations in frass-drop rate with different factors: *a.* the influence of food plant on the weight and number of pellets per instar from *Protoparce sexta* (Sphingidae) (data from Waldbauer, 1964); *b.* the influence of phase and foodplant on the number of pellets per day from *Leucania separata* (Noctuidae) (data from Iwao, 1962); *c.* the influence of temperature and humidity on the number of pellets per day from *Dendrolimus pini* (Lasiocampidae) (from Gösswald, 1935); *d.* the influence of temperature and condition of the foliage on the number of pellets per hour from 20 larvae of the sawfly, *Neodiprion lecontei* (Diprionidae) (data from Green & de Freitas, 1955); *e.* the influence of the presence of a dipterous parasite on the number of pellets per hour from 20 larvae of the sawfly, *N. lecontei* (modified from Green & de Freitas, 1955).

b. The rate of frass production
This can be measured in terms of dry weight or number of pellets, but the two may not vary in direct proportion (fig. 67a). Whatever units are used the rate of frass production is affected by many factors: the phase and generation (Fridén, 1958; Iwao, 1962), the temperature and humidity (Gösswald, 1935; Morris, 1949; Green & de Freitas, 1955; Pond, 1961), the available food, both the plant species and its condition (Morris; Green & de Freitas; Pond; Dadd, 1960; Waldbauer, 1964), the developmental rate as determined by the phenology of the season (Tinbergen, 1960) and the presence of adult parasites (Green & de Freitas) (fig. 67). Therefore it is not possible to assume that the number of pellets produced in different areas or different seasons reflects very precisely changes in the actual populations. Direct comparisons should be made with other measurements of population; such a comparison was made by Tinbergen (1960), who found that in six out of seven years frass-drop provided a reliable index of the absolute population. When a difference is indicated this must be investigated further to determine whether the absolute method has become inaccurate or if the frass-drop rate per individual has changed. The latter can be measured by the use of a coprometer, that collects the frass voided each hour into a separate compartment (Green & Henson, 1953; Green & de Freitas, 1955).

c. Efficiency of collection
Another variable is the proportion of the frass that actually reaches the ground and is collected. As Morris (1949) points out, a greater proportion of the frass will be retained, on the foliage, in calm weather than under more windy conditions, and where the young larvae produce webbing the frass will tend to be caught up with this and its fall delayed (Bean, 1959).

Most of the above work has referred to Lepidoptera and sawflies; the frass of Coleoptera may also be identified (Eckstein, 1939) and Campbell (1960) used frass-drop as an index of population in studies of stick insects, Phasmida.

It can be concluded that frass-drop measurements may with caution be used as a second method to check trends established by another technique (see p. 4); if comparisons are limited to a certain area where the insect has but a single host plant the chances that a good relative estimate will be obtained are maximal.

Other products

Populations of web-building spiders can be estimated by counting the number of webs and the visibility of the webs increased by dusting with lycopodium powder (Cherrett, 1964), or by spraying with a fine mist of water from a knapsack sprayer. I have found that the webs over a large area can be rapidly assessed using the latter method.

Indices of the populations of colonial nest-building caterpillars have been obtained by counting the number of nests, rather than the caterpillars; the great advantage of this approach lies in extensive work, as it enables the population level to be measured over many acres (Tothill, 1922; Legner & Oatman, 1962, Morris, 1964). Some mites also produce webbing and this may be used as an index (Newcomer, 1943).

EFFECTS

Effects due to an individual insect

These are of great value to the ecologist, as they are immediately convertible into absolute population. When, at a given stage of the life-cycle, each animal has some unique effect (for example, the commencement of a leaf mine), a count of these, after all the animals have passed this stage, will provide a precise measure of the total number passing through that stage, whilst the counts of the actual animals would need to be integrated to provide such a total (see p. 278). These effects are therefore measures of the number of animals entering a stage, and as such could be considered in the next chapter.

Cicada larvae construct conspicuous and distinctive turreted emergence holes which may be counted to measure the total emerging population (Dybas & Davis, 1962). Populations of solitary Hymenoptera can be assessed from the number of nest holes (Bohart & Lieberman, 1949); this will give the number of reproducing females, but in some species a female will construct more than one nest.

Measures of absolute population can be obtained for plant feeders when they enter the plant. Leaf-miners allow particularly elegant studies, as at the end of a generation it is possible to determine the number of larvae that commenced mining, the number that completed development and often some indication of the age and cause of death in those that failed. When the larva cuts characteristic cases at different ages even more information may be gathered (De Gryse, 1934).

Galls are easily counted, but many harbour a variable number of insects and it is usually impossible to determine externally whether these have been parasitized or not (Bess & Haramoto, 1959).

Some stem-borers cause the growing shoot to die; when multiple invasion is sufficiently rare to be overlooked estimates of these 'deadhearts' may be taken as equivalent to the total number of larvae invading, and the same approach can be applied to insects in grains or seeds (Jepson & Southwood, 1958).

General effects – damage

The effect of an insect population on a plant stand is the product of two opposing processes: the eating rate of the insects and the growing rate of the plant. The eating rate of the insects will depend on their age, the temperature conditions and the other factors that affect frass production (see above), as well as on population size. Measures of damage cannot therefore be used as anything other than very approximate indices of population size, but because of the intrinsic interest to the entomologist of damage *per se* it will be discussed further.

1. Criteria

a. Economic damage
This measure is the one least related to insect population and describes the effects of the insects in economic terms; it is of considerable importance to the agriculturalist and forester as it indicates the need for control measures, which become desirable once the economic threshold is reached. The economic threshold is defined by Stern *et al.* (1959) as 'the density at which control measures should be determined to prevent an increasing pest population from reaching the economic injury level'. Changing economic conditions will alter the economic injury level from season to season and its relation to the size of the insect population will vary greatly from species to species. Pests that cause blemishes to fruits (Graham, 1948) or destroy the leading shoots of growing trees cause damage whose economic level is very high relative to the amount of plant material destroyed.

b. Loss of Yield
This is a measure of the extent to which the weight, volume or number of the marketable parts of the plant is reduced. Although more of a biological measure than economic damage, variations in yield may be caused by many factors other than pest numbers (Möllerström, 1963). Furthermore, the same number of insects attacking a plant can have very different effects depending on the timing of the attack in relation to the growth stages of the plant. For example, the larva of the frit fly invades and kills a young shoot of the oat plant; early in the season the plant will have time to develop another tiller that will contribute towards the yield of grain, and so the latter is not affected. Later in the season any tillers destroyed would have contributed towards the crop, but there is insufficient growing time for the tillers that replace them to ripen grain; this is the time of the maximum effect of attack on yield. At a still later time any tillers that are young enough to be susceptible to the frit fly are so far behind the bulk of the crop that their contribution to the eventual yield would be insignificant. If the frit fly attacks such tillers yield will not be reduced; it might even be increased. Gough (1947) describes a similar

situation with the wheat bulb fly (*Leptohylemyia coarctata*). Prasad (1961) studied the reduction in weight of cabbage heads following the artificial colonization by newly emerged larvae of the small cabbage butterfly (*Pieris rapae*) at various dates after transplantation. It was found (fig. 68) that the

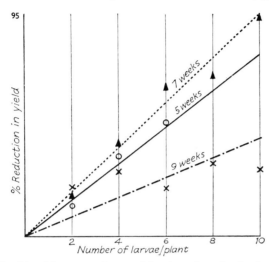

Fig. 68. The relationship of damage to the age of the plant; the reduction in yield of cabbage plants when infested with different numbers of *Pieris rapae* larvae 5, 7 and 9 weeks after transplantation (after Prasad, 1961).

greatest reduction in yield occurred when the larvae were introduced seven weeks after transplantation, as the leaves damaged at this time contribute to the head. On the other hand attacks soon after transplanting affect the growth of the plant.

c. The amount of plant consumed
This is perhaps the most meaningful biological measure and could be expressed precisely in kilocalories as the amount of the primary production consumed by the insect (see chapter 14).

Although studies have sometimes been made in which damage is assessed in terms of reduction of dry weight (e.g. Ortman & Painter, 1960), it is always easier to measure some index of the amount of plant destroyed rather than the actual quantity. For example, Coaker (1957) used various degrees of tattering of the leaf margin of cotton as an index of mirid damage, and Coombs (1963) assessed the level of damage in stored grain from the weight of fine dust present in a given volume of grain. In forest insects gross effects on the colour of the tree may be detected by aerial photography, thus allowing the survey of damage over large areas (Franz & Karafiat, 1958; Waters *et al.*, 1958; Aldrich *et al.*, 1959; Wear *et al.*, 1964).

Insect defoliation of trees affects the growth rate and is reflected in the annual growth rings (Mott *et al.*, 1957; Varley & Gradwell, 1962). Considering more particularly the effects of defoliators on trees, Henson & Stark (1959) proposed that insect populations could be defined:

(1) Tolerable – Populations that do not utilize the entire excess biological productivity of the host; that is the insect and the host plant populations could continue at this level indefinitely.

(2) Critical – 'Populations that utilize more than the excess biological productivity of the hosts, but less than the total productivity'. Such population levels cannot be continued indefinitely and Henson & Stark (1959) (fig. 69) and Churchill *et al.* (1964) show the long-term effects of insect attack on perennial hosts.

(3) Intolerable – 'Populations that are depleting the host at a rate greater than the current rate of production'.

The condition of the host tree (expressed as the number of leaf needles per branch tip) and the history of attack in previous years will interact with the intensity of larval population (larvae per tip) in the determination of the appropriate description of population in these terms (fig. 69).

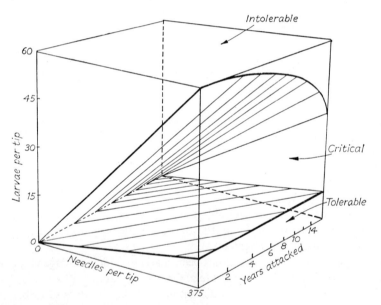

Fig. 69. The relationship of tree condition, insect population intensity and previous history to intolerable, critical and tolerable populations (after Henson & Stark, 1959).

2. Determining the relationship between damage and insect populations

As has been indicated above, the level of damage a plant suffers is influenced by many factors, such as soil, climate, age and health of the plant, as well as the size of the insect population. Therefore attempts to relate insect numbers to damage by the correlation of these two variables measured in different areas and seasons are seldom satisfactory (Lockwood, 1924; Strickland, 1956), although it may be possible to separate the roles of the different factors by a carefully planned sampling programme emphasizing the comparison of near-by fields (Sen & Chakrabarty, 1964). The comparisons will be even more exact if they are made in the same field, as then climatic and soil effects will be identical. Theoretically there are three techniques for making such comparisons:

(1) The introduction of a known number of animals on to pest-free plants (e.g. Neiswander & Herr, 1930; Bowling, 1963).

(2) The exclusion of the animals from certain plots by mechanical barriers.

(3) The exclusion of the animals or the reduction of their populations in some plots by the use of pesticides.

Methods 1 and 2 both suffer from the fact that the barriers erected to exclude or retain the animals will severely modify the climate and growth conditions of the plant; the exclusion technique is of course widely used in studies on the effects of grazing by vertebrates.

The third method has been used successfully by Strickland (1956), Dahms & Wood (1957) and Jepson (1959). Working on the frit fly (*Oscinella frit*) the last named author found that a detailed knowledge of the periods of oviposition of the pest allowed frequent 'blanket spraying' to be replaced by a limited number of timed sprays or granular applications (Jepson & Mathias, 1960).

REFERENCES

ALDRICH, R. C., BAILEY, W. F. and HELLER, R. C., 1959. Large scale 70 mm color photography techniques and equipment and their application to a forest sampling problem. *Photogrammetric Eng.* **25**, 747–54.

BEAN, J. L., 1959. Frass size as an indicator of spruce budworm larval instars. *Ann. ent. Soc. Amer.* **52**, 605–8.

BESS, H. A. and HARAMOTO, F. H., 1959. Biological control of Pamakani, *Eupatorium adenophorum*, in Hawaii by a tephritid gall fly, *Procecidochares utilis*. 2. Population studies of the weed, the fly and the parasites of the fly. *Ecology* **40**, 244–9.

BOHART, G. E. and LIEBERMAN, F. V., 1949. Effect of an experimental field application of DDT dust on *Nomia melanderi*. *J. econ. Ent.* **42**, 519–22.

BOWLING, C. C., 1963. Cage tests to evaluate stink bug damage to rice. *J. econ. Ent.* **56**, 197–200.

CAMPBELL, K. G., 1960. Preliminary studies on population estimation of two species of stick insects (Phasmatidae Phasmatodea) occurring in plague numbers in Highland Forest areas of south-eastern Australia. *Proc. Linn. Soc. N.S.W.* **85**, 121–37.

CHERRETT, J. M., 1964. The distribution of spiders on the Moor House National Nature Reserve, Westmorland. *J. anim. Ecol.* **33**, 27–48.

CHURCHILL, G. B., JOHN, H. H., DUNCAN, D. P. and HODSON, A. C., 1964. Long-term effects of defoliation of aspen by the forest tent caterpillar. *Ecology* **45**, 630–3.

COAKER, T. H., 1957. Studies of crop loss following insect attack on cotton in East Africa. II. Further experiments in Uganda. *Bull. ent. Res.* **48**, 851–66.

COOMBS, C. W., 1963. A method of assessing the physical condition of insect-damaged grain and its application to a faunistic survey. *Bull. ent. Res.* **54**, 23–35.

CORBET, P. S., 1957. The life-history of the Emperor dragonfly, *Anax imperator* Leach (Odonata: Aeshnidae). *J. anim. Ecol.* **26**, 1–69.

DADD, R. H., 1960. Observations on the palatability and utilisation of food by locusts, with particular reference to the interpretation of performances in growth trials using synthetic diets. *Ent. exp. Appl.* **3**, 283–304.

DAHMS, R. G. and WOOD, E. D., 1957. Evaluation of green bug damage to small grains. *J. econ. Ent.* **50**, 443–6.

DE GRYSE, J. J., 1934. Quantitative methods in the study of forest insects. *Sci. Agr.* **14**, 477–95.

DYBAS, H. S. and DAVIS, D. D., 1962. A population census of seventeen-year periodical Cicadas (Homoptera: Cicadidae: Magicicada). *Ecology* **43**, 432–44.

DYBAS, H. S. and LLOYD, M., 1962. Isolation by habitat in two synchronized species of periodical cicadas (Homoptera: Cicadidae: Magicicada). *Ecology* **43**, 444–59.

ECKSTEIN, K., 1938. Die Bewertung des Kotes der Nonnenraupe, *Psilura monacha* L., als Grundlage für die Festellung ihres Auftretens und der zu ergreifenden Massregeln. *Allgem. Forst. Jagdztg.* **114**, 132–48.

ECKSTEIN, K., 1939. Das Bohrmehl des Waldgärtners, *Myelophilus pimperda* L., nebst Bemerkungen über den 'Frass' der Borkenkäfer und anderen Insekten. *Arb. physiol. angew. Ent.* **6**, 32–41.

FRANZ, J. and KARAFIAT, H., 1958. Eigen sich Kartierung und Serienphotographie von Tannenläusen für Massenwechsel-studien? *Z. angew. Ent.* **43**, 100–12.

FRIDÉN, F., 1958. *Frass-drop frequency in Lepidoptera.* Uppsala (Almqvist & Wiksells Boktryckeri), 59 pp.

FROST, S. W., 1928. Insect scatology. *Ann. ent. Soc. Amer.* **21**, 35–46.

GÖSSWALD, K., 1935. Über die Frasstätigkeit von Forstschädlingen unter verschiedener Temperatur und Luftfeuch tigkeit und ihre praktische und physiologische Bedeutung. I. *Z. angew. Ent.* **21**, 183–7.

GOUGH, H. C., 1947. Studies on wheat bulb fly, *Leptohylemyia coarctata*, Fall. II. Numbers in relation to crop damage. *Bull. ent. Res.* **37**, 439–54.

GRAHAM, L. T., 1948. Criteria of effect used in determining codling moth injury. *J. econ. Ent.* **41**, 70–5.

GREEN, G. W. and DE FREITAS, A. S., 1955. Frass drop studies of larvae of *Neodiprion americanus banksianae*, Roh. and *Neodiprion lecontii*, Fitch. *Canad. Ent.* **87**, 427–40.

GREEN, G. W. and HENSON, W. R., 1953. A new type of coprometer for laboratory and field use. *Canad. Ent.* **85**, 227–30.

HENSON, W. R. and STARK, R. W., 1959. The description of insect numbers. *J. econ. Ent.* **52**, 847–50.

HODSON, A. C. and BROOKS, M. A., 1956. The frass of certain defoliators of forest trees in the north central United States and Canada. *Canad. Ent.* **88**, 62–8.

IWAO, S., 1962. Studies on the phase variation and related phenomena in some Lepidopterous insects. *Mem. Coll. Agric. Kyoto Univ.* (Ent. no. 12) **84**, 1–80.

JEPSON, W. F., 1959. The effects of spray treatments on the infestation of the oat crop by the frit fly (*Oscinella frit* L.). *Ann. appl. Biol.* **47**, 463–74.

JEPSON, W. F. and MATHIAS, P., 1960. The control of frit fly, *Oscinella frit* (L.) in sweet corn (*Zea mays*) by Thimet (*O,O*-Diethyl *S*-ethyethio-methyl phosphorodithioate). *Bull. ent. Res.* **51**, 427–33.

JEPSON, W. F. and SOUTHWOOD, T. R. E., 1958. Population studies on *Oscinella frit* L. *Ann. appl. Biol.* **46**, 465–74.

LEGNER, E. F. and OATMAN, E. R., 1962. Sampling and distribution of summer eye-spotted bud moth *Spilonota ocellana* (D. & S.), larvae and nests on apple trees. *Canad. Ent.* **94**, 1187–9.

LOCKWOOD, S., 1924. Estimating the abundance of, and damage done by grasshoppers. *J. econ. Ent.* **17**, 197–202.

MÖLLERSTRÖM, G., 1963. Different kinds of injury to leaves of the sugar beets and their effect on yield. *Medd. Växtskyddsanst.* **12**, 299–309.

MORRIS, R. F., 1942. The use of frass in the identification of forest insect damage. *Canad. Ent.* **74**, 164–7.

MORRIS, R. F., 1949. Frass-drop measurement in studies of the European spruce sawfly. *Univ. Michigan Sch. Forestry and Conserv. Bull.* **12**, 58 pp.

MORRIS, R. F., 1964. The value of historical data in population research, with particular reference to *Hyphantria cunea* Drury. *Canad. Ent.* **96**, 356–68.

MOTT, D. G., NAIRN, L. O. and COOK, J. F., 1957. Radial growth in forest trees and effects of insect defoliation. *For. Sci.* **3** (3), 286–304.

NEISWANDER, C. R. and HERR, E. A., 1930. Correlation of corn borer populations with degree of damage. *J. econ. Ent.* **23**, 938–45.

NEWCOMER, E. J., 1943. Apparent control of the Pacific mite with xanthone. *J. econ. Ent.* **36**, 344–5

NOLTE, H. W., 1939. Über den Kot von Fichten- und Kieferninsekten. *Tharandter forstl. Jahrb.* **90**, 740–61.

ORTMAN, E. E. and PAINTER, R. H., 1960. Quantitative measurements of damage by the greenbug, *Toxoptera graminum* to four wheat varieties. *J. econ. Ent.* **53**, 798–802.

PARAMONOV, A., 1959. A possible method of estimating larval numbers in tree crowns. *Ent mon. Mag.* **95**, 82–3.

POND, D. D., 1961. Frass studies of the armyworm, *Pseudaletia unipuncta*. *Ann. ent. Soc. Amer.* **54**, 133–40.

PRASAD, S. K., 1961, (1962). Quantitative estimation of damage to cabbage by cabbage worm, *Pieris rapae* (Linn.). *Indian J. Ent.* **23**, 54–61.

RHUMBLER, L., 1929. Zur Begiftung des Kiefernspanners (*Bupalus piniarius* L.) in der Oberförsterei Hersfeld – Ost 1926. *Z. angew. Ent.* **15**, 137–58.

SEN, A. R. and CHAKRABARTY, R. P., 1964. Estimation of loss of crop from pests and diseases of tea from sample surveys. *Biometrics* **20**, 492–504.

STERN, V. M., SMITH, R. F., VAN DEN BOSCH, R. and HAGEN, K. S., 1959. The integrated control concept. *Hilgardia* **29** (2), 81–101.

STRANDINE, E. J., 1940. A quantitative study of the periodical cicada with respect to soil of three forests. *Amer. Midl. Nat.* **24**, 177–83.

STRICKLAND, A. H., 1956. Agricultural pest assessment. I – The problem. *N.A.A.S. quart. Rev.* (H.M.S.O., London) **33**, 112–18. II – A partial solution. *ibid.* **34**, 156–62.

TINBERGEN, L., 1960. The natural control of insects in pinewoods. 1. Factors influencing the intensity of predation by song birds. *Arch. Neérl. Zool.* **13**, 266–343.

TOTHILL, J. D., 1922. The natural control of the fall webworm (*Hyphentia cunea* Drury) in Canada. *Bull. Canad. Dept. Agric.* **3** (n.s) (*Ent. Bull.* **19**), 1–107.

VARLEY, G. C. and GRADWELL, G. R., 1962. The effect of partial defoliation by caterpillars on the timber production of oak trees in England. *Proc. XI int. Congr. Ent.* **2**, 211–14.

WALDBAUER, G. P., 1964. Quantitative relationships between the numbers of fecal pellets, fecal weights and the weight of food eaten by tobacco hornworms, *Protoparce sexta* (Johan.) (Lepidoptera: Sphingidae). *Ent. exp. appl.* **7**, 310–14.

WATERS, W. E., HELLER, R. C. and BEAN, J. L., 1958. Aerial appraisal of damage by the spruce budworm. *J. Forest.* **56** (4), 269–76.

WEAR, J. F., POPE, R.B. and LAUTERBACH, P. G., 1964. Estimating beetle-killed Douglas fir by photo and field plots. *J. Forest.* **62** (5), 309–15.

WEISS, H. B. and BOYD, W. M., 1950, 1952. Insect feculae I. *J. New York Ent. Soc.* **58**, 154–68. Insect feculae II. *ibid.* **60**, 25–30.

CHAPTER 9

Observational and Experimental Methods for the Estimation of Natality, Mortality and Dispersal

Values for the 'pathways' through which population size changes may also be obtained by the subtraction or integration of census figures in a budget: methods of calculation and of analysis of budgets are discussed in the next chapter, but there is no hard and fast distinction between the contents of the two chapters. As is indicated below, in the appropriate sections, *the terms 'natality' and 'dispersal' are used in their widest sense.*

NATALITY

Natality is the number of births, that is strictly speaking the number of living eggs laid; however, from the practical point of view of constructing a population budget the number of individuals entering a post-ovarian stage, i.e. larval instar, pupa or adult, can be considered as the 'natality' of that stage.

Fertility

Fertility is the number of viable eggs laid by a female and fecundity is a measure of the total egg production; the latter is often easier to measure. In those insects where all the eggs are mature on emergence the *total potential fecundity* may be *estimated by examining the ovaries* as Davidson (1956) did with sub-imagines of a mayfly, *Cloeon.* The ovaries were removed and lightly stained in methylene blue, the eggs were separated by sieving through bolting silk and then counted in a Sedwick–Rafter plankton-counting cell.

More often eggs are matured throughout much of adult life and fecundity is *measured directly by keeping females caged* under as natural conditions as possible and recording the total number of eggs laid (e.g. Huffaker & Spitzer, 1950; Spiller, 1964); if viable eggs can be distinguished from non-viable ones, usually by the onset of development, then fertility may be measured (e.g. Fewkes, 1964). In some insects egg cannibalism may interfere with the estimation of fecundity; the influence of this behaviour may be calculated from the decimation of a known number of marked eggs (Rich, 1956).

240

It has been found in a wide range of insects that the *fecundity of the female is proportional to her weight* (e.g. Prebble, 1941; Richards & Waloff, 1954; Waloff & Richards, 1958; Colless & Chellapah, 1960; Lozinsky, 1961). Female weight is directly related to size, so that measures of size such as wing-length (Gregor, 1960) or pupal length (Miller, 1957) may be substituted for weight. Once the relation between size and fecundity has been established (regression analysis is a convenient method) it may be applied to estimate the natality in field populations by measuring wild females or female pupae – the length of the empty pupal cases is a particularly suitable criterion (Miller, 1957).

Within a given population the rate of oviposition will be influenced by temperature and the extent to which the potential fecundity is realized is influenced by the longevity of the females. The influence of temperature can be studied in the laboratory and incorporated into the regression equation; the observations of Richards & Waloff (1954) show that it may be justified to apply data from the laboratory to populations in the field. Information on longevity may be obtained from wild populations by marking and recapture. An equation incorporating all these variables will be in the form (Richards & Waloff, 1954):

No. of eggs = regression coeff. × weight ± reg. coeff. × temp. + reg. coeff.
× longevity + constant

Such equations cannot, however, be applied outside the populations for which they were derived; females that have developed under other conditions, more especially of nutrition and of crowding, will have different potential fecundities (Blais, 1953; Clark, 1963); therefore in practice it is necessary to have different equations for different stages in a pest outbreak (Miller, 1957). Larval density of course affects size and longevity directly (Miller & Thomas, 1958) but the fact that new equations are necessary shows that the effects on fecundity are not just reflections of changes in these properties. Evidence is accumulating that changes may occur in the genetic constitution of fluctuating populations and the fecundity of different forms of a species may be very different (Wellington, 1964). Therefore laboratory measurements of fertility should be continually checked, for it is important in any population study to establish not only the potential fertility, but any variation in it, for this may be the essence of a population regulation mechanism (p. 298).

When large numbers of eggs are laid together in a group the weight of the individual female will fall sharply after each oviposition and slowly rise again until the next group is deposited. Where individual animals can be marked it may be possible by frequently recapturing and weighing to establish the time of oviposition of actual egg batches; Richards & Waloff (1954) were able to do this with a field population of grasshoppers. The actual number of eggs per egg mass may vary with size or age of the female (Richards & Waloff, 1954) or from generation to generation (Iwao, 1956).

Numbers entering a stage

When an animal can be trapped as it passes from one part of its habitat to another part at a specific stage of its life-history the summation of the catches provides a convenient measure of the total populations entering the next stage. Such traps are commonly referred to as *emergence traps*. The particular design will depend on the insect and its habitat; a number are described by Peterson (1934) and Nicholls (1963). Basically the traps consist of a metal or cloth box that covers a known area of soil and glass collecting vials with 'lobster-pot' type baffles are inserted in some of the corners (fig. 70). A newly

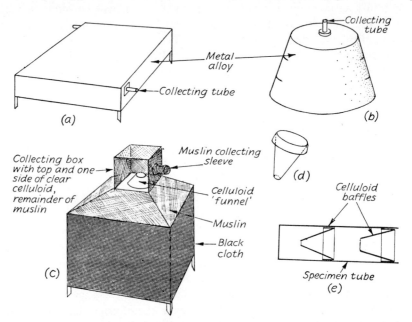

Fig. 70. Emergence traps for terrestrial habitats: *a* and *b*. metal box and tub respectively; *c*. cloth-covered, Calnaido type; *d*. celluloid baffle of collecting tube; *e*. sectional view of collecting tube with pair of baffles designed to separate, partially at least, large and small insects (*a, b* and *c* modified from Southwood & Siddorn, 1965).

emerged insect being positively phototactic will make its way into the collection vials that are emptied regularly; Turnock (1957) used an adhesive resin, 'Tanglefoot', in the collecting containers of his trap so that they could be emptied at less frequent intervals. The efficiency of a trap for a particular insect can be tested by releasing a known number of newly emerged individuals into it. The construction of the trap will influence its effect on the microclimate; all traps tend to reduce the daily temperature fluctuations (fig. 71) and the deeper they are (the greater the insulating layer of air) the smaller the fluctuations. Cloth-covered traps lose the heat less quickly than metal ones. Although

the daytime deficit may be approximately balanced by the greater warmth at
night (fig. 71), over a period of several weeks these small daily excesses or
deficits will accumulate to levels where they might influence the development
rate of pupae (Southwood & Siddorn, 1965). For this reason caution should
be exercised in using emergence trap data for phenology.

Special traps have been described by many workers, including one for fleas
(Bates, 1962) and others for ceratopogonid midges (Campbell & Pelham-
Clinton, 1960; Nielsen, 1963), for anthomyiid flies (Dinther, 1953), for
cecidomyiid midges (Speyer & Waede, 1956; Nijveldt, 1959; Guennelon &
Audemard, 1963) and beetles (Richards & Waloff, 1961).

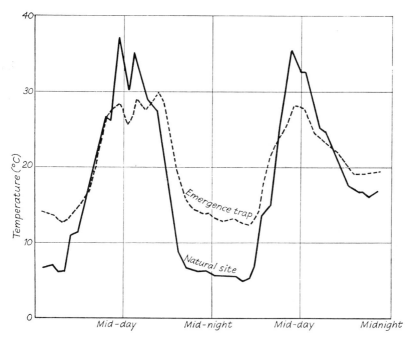

Fig. 71. The soil surface temperature over 48 hours in a Calnaido cloth-covered emergence
trap compared with that from a natural site (after Southwood & Siddorn, 1965).

Emergence traps have been used extensively in aquatic environments for
measuring the quality, quantity and biomass of insects emerging from the
habitat. In shallow water, amongst emergent vegetation and in sheltered
situations floating box traps have been utilized (Adamstone & Harkness,
1923; Macan, 1949; Vallentyne, 1952; Sommerman, Sailer & Esselbaugh,
1955; Judge, 1957; Morgan & Waddell, 1961). In exposed situations submerged funnel traps have been used as these avoid damage from wind and
rain (Grandilewskaja-Decksbach, 1935; Brundin, 1949; Jónasson, 1954;
Palmén, 1955, 1962; Mundie, 1956; Darby, 1962). A careful comparison of
these two types of trap has been made by Morgan, Waddell & Hall (1963)

from which the following conclusions may be drawn. Funnel traps are generally much less efficient than floating box traps. A number of factors probably contribute to this: one is the decomposition of the catch in the small air space of the collecting jar of the funnel trap; losses due to this cause will be proportionally greater the denser the population of emerging insects and the longer the intervals between emptying the trap, which should therefore be

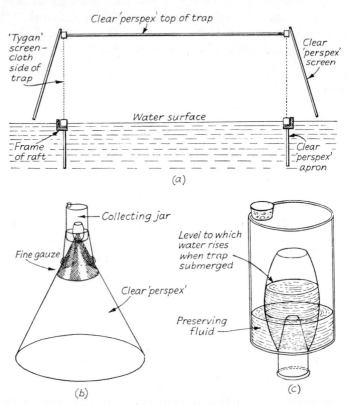

Fig. 72. Emergence traps for aquatic habitats: *a.* floating box trap for use under exposed situations; the screen may be omitted in sheltered situations (after Morgan, Waddell & Hall, 1963); *b.* submerged funnel trap; *c.* collecting jar (after Borutsky, 1955).

done daily. The ascending pupae and larvae are strongly phototactic and the slight shade produced by the gauze of the funnel trap will cause it to be avoided; furthermore some insects, e.g. Odonata, will crawl out again. It is impossible to exclude small predatory insects from the traps and they may consume much of the catch. Lastly the effective trapping area is reduced if the trap becomes tipped. However, in very exposed situations these traps must be used and Morgan *et al.* (1963) recommend a design, similar to that in fig. 72*b,* to overcome as many of these faults as possible. The collecting jar was originally devised by Borutsky (1955); it is very important that the 'Perspex' be kept clean for algal growth will soon render it opaque.

The most important causes of loss of efficiency of floating box traps are waves that will swamp the catch, and the shading effect of the trap itself on the ascending larvae and pupae. Morgan *et al.* (1963) point out that as it is probably only those animals that ascend near the edges of the trap, that can take successful avoiding reaction, the larger the area of the trap the smaller this edge-effect relative to the size of the catch. The trap designed by Morgan *et al.* (fig. 72*a*) is constructed mainly from clear 'Perspex';* the apron projecting in the water retains floating exuviae within the trap and helps to reduce wave damage; the latter function is also served by the lateral screens. The wooden frame should be as narrow as possible and painted white to minimize shadow; wire netting stretched under the frame reduces predation by fish. The trap needs to be emptied every two days and this is a difficult process: a floating tray is inserted under the trap and the whole towed to a boathouse or similar site where the unidirectional light source ensures that the edge on the darkest side may be lifted, to allow the entrance of an entomological pooter (=aspirator, Fig. 52), without any of the insects escaping. On dull days or at night, the trap may be tilted towards a paraffin lamp during emptying. In view of the time-consuming nature of this operation it would seem worthwhile to determine whether shrouding the traps for a short while in the day would drive a large proportion of the catch into a collecting tube, inserted in the roof; which is the method of collection from tents (p. 119).

In very shallow fast-running streams it may be necessary to use a tent trap of the type described by Ide (1940); basically it resembles a gauze tent that is attached to the substrate. A rather unsatisfactory feature of Ide's design is that the observer has to enter the trap to remove the insects; not only, as Ide mentions, is he exposed to noxious insects (e.g. Simuliidae), but the resultant trampling of the substrate must affect future emergences. Possibly a smaller tent should be used – one that can be emptied from the exterior.

Chironomids were sampled from very shallow rock pools by Lindeberg (1958) using a trap similar in appearance to the submerged funnel type, but the funnel was made of glass and the whole upper part of the trap was airtight so that it could be kept full of water, even though it projected well above the level of water in the pool.

The trapping in the field of beetles and other insects, emerging from tree trunks, demands a different basic technique; Reid (1963) has devised one that also allows the recording of the pattern of emergence on the trunk: the trunk is divided into small areas delimited by ropes sunk into grooves in the bark; the shallow cages so formed are completed with muslin lids.

Material containing the resting stage of the animal may be collected and exposed under field conditions or in the laboratory. Bark beetle emergence from logs may be measured under natural conditions by placing the logs in

* 'Plexiglass' is a similar material.

screened cages (McMullen & Atkins, 1959; Clark & Osgood, 1964) and emergence of flies from heads of grass and corn determined by placing these in muslin bags in the field (Southwood *et al.*, 1961). The emergence of mites from overwintered eggs on twigs or bark was measured by Morgan & Anderson (1958) by attaching the substrate to the centre of a white card and surrounding it with a circle of 'Deadline', a fruit-tree banding resin.* As the mites crawled out they were caught in the 'Deadline' and being red were easily counted.

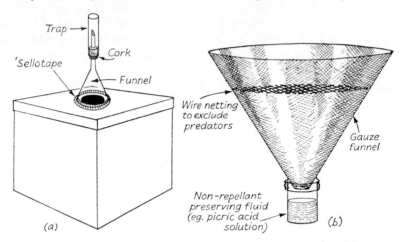

Fig. 73. *a*. Emergence tin to determine in the laboratory the emergence of insects from samples (after van Emden, 1962). *b*. Funnel trap for the collection of descending arboreal larvae.

Unseasonal emergence may be forced in the laboratory (Wilbur & Fritz, 1939; Terrell, 1959; van Emden, 1962). Commercial containers such as shoe-boxes, ice-cream cartons and biscuit tins have been found useful in such studies (fig. 73*a*).

Insects that are arboreal for part of their life may often be trapped on their upward or downward journeys. Wingless female moths and others moving up tree trunks may be trapped in sackcloth and other trap-bands (DeBach, 1949; Reiff, 1955) or in inverted funnel traps (Varley & Gradwell, 1963). Larvae descending to pupate may be caught in funnel traps (fig. 73*b*) (Ohnesorge, 1957; Pilon *et al.*, 1964).

The birth-rate from mark and recapture data

The details of marking animals and of the equations for estimating the birth-rate are given in chapter 3. This birth-rate includes immigration and it is often, more correctly, referred to as the dilution rate.

* Some brands of banding resin are listed on p. 196.

MORTALITY

Total

Measurements of total mortality are also commonly obtained by the subtraction of population estimates for successive stages (e.g. Miller, 1958; Cook & Kettlewell, 1960; see chapter 10).

i. Successive observations on the same cohort. When it is possible to make these, mortality may be measured directly. Completely natural cohorts can in general only be followed in sedentary or relatively immobile animals (e.g. the egg and pupal stages, scale insects, some aphids). Colonies present in the field in accessible positions may be repeatedly examined, each colony being identified by labelling the plant (e.g. MacLellan, 1962; van Emden, 1963); and with an animal as large as the hornworm (Sphingidae) Lawson (1959) was able to follow the larvae as well as eggs. In other situations it may be necessary to delimit the sample population or even to 'plant' it. Examples of the former are Ives & Prentice's (1959) and Turnock & Ives' (1962) studies where they placed pupal-free moss-filled trays or blocks of peat with screen bottoms and sides under the host trees of certain sawflies at pupation. Later in the season these 'natural traps' may be removed and the pupae classified. More mobile animals will need to be retained by a more extensive 'field cage' (Dobson, Stephenson & Lofty, 1958; see p. 78). It is important to remember, however, that the screens and cages are bound to alter, albeit only slightly, the situation one is trying to assess. The planting of known populations in the field and their subsequent re-examination gives a measure of the level of mortality; sometimes it is possible to recover the remains of the dead individuals in such experiments and then further information may be gained about the cause of death (Graham, 1928; Morris, 1949; Buckner, 1959; Pavlov, 1961).

When an insect leaves a mark of its presence, as many that bore into plant tissue do, a single count at, for example, the pupal stage enables the still living and the dead to be distinguished (see also p. 233). Furthermore the latter may be divided into those whose burrows have been opened by predators and those killed by parasites and disease. Such a study, which of course is in effect population estimates of two successive stages (i.e. total young larvae = total burrows, and pupae), was made by Gibb (1958) for the Eucosmid moth, *Ernarmonia conicolana*, in pine cones.

ii. The recovery of dead or unhealthy individuals. This gives another measure of mortality. Although Gary (1960) has devised a trap for collecting dead and unhealthy honey-bees, it is unusual to be able to recover the non-survivors of a mobile stage. However, unhatched eggs can often be examined to ascertain the cause of their death (e.g. Bess, 1961; Way & Banks, 1964).

The death-rate from mark and recapture data

Details of these models and the calculation of the death-rate, which includes emigration, are given in chapter 3 (see also p. 268).

Climatic factors

Apart from direct observations on a known cohort, the main method of establishing the role of climate in the total mortality has been experimental. A known number of individuals may be exposed to field conditions (e.g. Lejeune, Fell & Burbidge, 1955) or predictions may be made from laboratory experiments (MacPhee, 1961, 1964; Green, 1962; Sullivan & Green, 1964); in the latter case it is important to allow for the effect of acclimatization.

Biotic factors

As with climatic factors a knowledge of the role of various biotic ones is often obtained from successive observations on the same cohort (see above); this section is restricted to techniques for the recognition of the role of individual factors. It is important to remember that the effect of a parasite will vary with the host, as has been demonstrated by Loan & Holdaway (1961) with the braconid parasite of a weevil, which has no effect on the adult male, but causes the egg production of the female to fall off quickly. There are five approaches to the assessment of the role of biotic factors.

1. Examination of the host

Parasitic insects may often be detected in their hosts by dissection (e.g. Miller, 1955; Hafez, 1961; Evenhuis, 1962) or by breeding out the parasites from a sample of hosts (e.g. Richards, 1940). As the rate of parasitism varies throughout a generation of the host, a single assessment will not give an adequate degree of precision unless the hosts are closely synchronized. Parasites may sometimes be detected within their hosts without dissection by the use of soft X-rays (wavelength >0.25 Å) and fine-grain film (Holling, 1958). It is possible that elutriation (p. 142) could also be used to diagnose parasitism. The proportion of hosts attacked by a parasite is referred to as the '*apparent parasitism*'. The problems involved in the combination of a series of apparent mortalities and its interpretation are discussed in the next chapter.

Sometimes it is possible to find a fair proportion of the corpses of insects killed by a predator, generally when the predator collects the food together in one place, e.g. spiders' webs (Turnbull, 1960), hunting wasps' nests (Rau & Rau, 1916; Richards & Hamm, 1939; Evans & Yoshimoto, 1962), thrushes' anvils (Goodhart, 1958), shrikes' larders. A semi-natural assessment of the role of predators may be made by 'planting' a known number of prey in natural situations; Buckner (1958) describes how sawfly cocoons were exposed in this way and the type of predator determined by the markings left on the opened cocoons.

The diagnosis and determination of the extent of infection by pathogens in an insect population is a complex and specialized problem outside the scope of this book; reference should be made to works as Martignoni & Steinhaus (1961), Steinhaus (1963) and Wittig (1963). A good example of the application of such data in population ecology is Neilson's (1963) study of the incidence of disease in the spruce budworm (*Choristoneura*).

2. Examination of the predator

As the young of many birds remain in the nest it is possible to record their food. The simplest method is to observe feeding through the glass side of a nesting box (Tinbergen, 1960); however, identification and counting of the prey is often difficult and Promptow & Lukina (1938) and Betts (1954, 1958) have shown that parent birds may be induced to put the whole, or at least part, of the food for the young into an artificial gape, from which it may be removed. The young of some birds will regurgitate the food if their necks are manipulated shortly after feeding (Errington, 1932; Lack & Owen, 1955), with others a neck ring needs to be used to prevent swallowing. The remains of insects and other prey in the pellets of owls provides a further source of evidence of the role of these predators (Hartley, 1948; Miles, 1952; Southern, 1954); although it is possible that if the prey were marked in some way this might be made quantitative. Apparently the relationship between the analysis of pellets and the actual food is not reliable in herons and possibly other birds (Hartley, 1948).

Other methods involve the slaughter of the predator, and although the removal of a small number of invertebrate predators may not have a significant effect on the population being studied, it is clearly undesirable (quite apart from conservational and legal considerations) to kill large numbers of birds. When practical, therefore, the role of adult birds is best determined by exclusion techniques (see below), with only qualitative confirmation from gizzard analyses. Much information on the possible role of vertebrates as insect predators has been obtained by the examination of the gizzard and stomach contents (Hartley, 1948; Kennedy, 1950; Betts, 1955; Mook, 1963) and the excreta of mammals (Chapman, Romer & Stark, 1955).

Occasionally prey remains can be detected and identified from the guts of large predatory insects (James, 1961), but in general more refined methods of detection are needed; these are:

a. the precipitin test in which the specific proteins of the prey are identified by their reaction with the serum of a sensitized mammal (usually a rabbit);

b. the use of radioactive isotope labelled prey which if eaten will impart their radioactivity to the predator.

a. The precipitin test

Serological techniques, originally developed by vertebrate zoologists, have been used in entomology for the investigation of systematic relationships and metamorphosis, the identification of blood meals of biting flies and predator/ prey relations: here we are only concerned with the last named aspect, relevant studies having been made by Brooke & Proske (1946), West (1950), Hall, Downe, MacLellan & West (1953), Downe & West (1954), Fox & MacLellan (1956), Dempster, Richards & Waloff (1959), Dempster (1964) and Loughton, Derry & West (1963). For the population ecologist the method may be limited by (1) the specificity of the antiserum, (2) the rate of digestion, (3) the confusion of multiple with single meals. Antisera, as most easily produced from a single rabbit, will be found to be sensitive to other related insects; e.g. that used by Loughton & West (1962) for the spruce budworm(*Choristoneura*) was sensitive to other tortricids. This sensitivity to 'false positives' can be eliminated, at least to a large extent, by absorption of the appropriate antigens, but the resulting serum is much weaker so that it may give a 'false negative' if the prey proteins are dilute; furthermore a very sensitive serum might react for only a particular instar of the appropriate species (Telfer & Williams, 1953). Therefore it may be concluded that at present it is not practical to use this technique to distinguish fairly closely allied species of prey and that the antisera used will be relatively powerful, but with a wide spectrum, so that one must be able to neglect the rare cross-reaction with another species (Loughton & West, 1962).

The rate of digestion will determine, for a given antisera, the length of time a meal can be detected. This is partly a matter of the relative size of the predator and the meal, but the data of Hall *et al.* (1953), Dempster (1960) and Loughton *et al.* (1963), for a number of predators (ranging in size from mites and mirids to earwigs and reduviid bugs) with lepidopterous and coleopterous prey, are in remarkable agreement: eggs were detectable for 18–48 hours after feeding and large larvae for about 5 days. Feeding trials (see below) may be used to determine the size of prey normally eaten and hence the detectable time of a meal. For precise population studies it is desirable to know not only that a given predator has eaten the prey during the last x hours, but also whether it has eaten one or many individuals. By studying the dispersion of the prey in the field and the rate of movement of the predator, Dempster (1960) was able to argue, supported by laboratory feeding trials, that the chance of a positive representing more than one feed was very small. Therefore it was possible to estimate the number of prey consumed by the predator in the total population during the digestion period; e.g. if in a sample of 200 predators, 6 were shown to contain meals of the prey, which remain detectable for 1 day, we may say that the total number of prey destroyed by that predator during the previous 24 hours is $= 6 \times$ total pop. of predator $\div 200$ (Dempster, 1960).

If one is concerned merely with determining which of a range of predators is preying on the particular species, as were Loughton *et al.* (1963), then it is possible to claim (as they did) that when the period of detection is longer than the feeding interval the precipitin test is adequate. Normally, however, as shown above, the reverse is true and thus the test is least useful with a voracious predator.

The technique of the precipitin test is as follows (Leone, 1947; Dempster, 1960; Loughton *et al.*, 1963):

i. Preparation of antigen. Numbers of the prey are starved to empty the gut, killed with cyanide and, with large insects, the legs and wings removed; they are then crushed in a pestle and mortar with normal buffered saline solution (0·9% NaCl, pH 7·0) and kept at about 4°C for one or two days; if necessary, they are subsequently pressed through bolting silk to remove the sclerotized particles and then centrifuged for about 15 minutes at 6000 r/m (longer at a slower speed). The supernatant liquid is decanted, sterilized by passing through a Seitz EK sterilizing filter pad. Working with the beetle *Phytodecta* Dempster (1960) found it necessary to add M/1000 crushed potassium cyanide to prevent the deposition of melanin at this stage. After filtering, the clear sterile antigen is conveniently freeze-dried and stored in serum vials.

ii. Production of antiserum. The antigen is reconstituted with distilled water, the soluble proteins precipated with 0·4% potassium alum, the pH adjusted to 6·8 and the resulting suspension injected into a rabbit. One large (2·5 ml) intramuscular injection may be given, but there are probably advantages in using three smaller (1 ml) subcutaneous injections over 6 days. About 10 days to 2 weeks after inoculation a blood sample can be taken from the rabbit and tested against an extract of the insect; injections are continued until a sufficiently high level of sensitivity is built up. (The sensitivity reaches a peak and then falls off.) 50 ml of blood can then be taken from the rabbit and the serum separated, the lipoids removed from it by extracting with ether at a temperature below $-25°C$ and then it is freeze-dried and stored in a deep freeze.

iii. Collection of predator meals. The predators are killed with cyanide and either the whole animal (small species) or the gut (larger ones) smeared on to filter paper strips that are labelled and rapidly dried over phosphorus pentoxide, and such smears may usually be stored for 2 years or more (but see Loughton *et al.*, 1963).

iv. The conduct of the test. The smear of a predator is allowed to soak for a day in a small quantity (e.g. 0·2 ml) of normal saline and then is centrifuged. About 0·02 ml of this is then underlayed in a serological test tube with an equivalent volume of antiserum and a positive result is given by the formation of a visible ring of precipitate at the interface of the liquids. It may be necessary to leave the tube to stand for 2 hours at room temperature, to allow the ring to form, and to view it against a black background. It is essential that both liquids be completely clear.

b. Radio-isotope labelled prey

If the prey are marked with a radio-isotope the development of radioactivity by the predator will be a clear indication of feeding; furthermore if each of the prey could be made to carry a similar burden of radionuclide the level of radioactivity in the predator would be a measure of the number of prey consumed. Theoretically, therefore, this method could be of value with voracious predators that consume prey at frequent intervals, a situation in which the precipitin test is unsuitable for quantitative studies. However, in practice it is difficult to arrange for all the prey to carry an equal burden of radionuclide. Most studies using this technique have involved prey tagged with phosphorus-32 (see chapter 3 for marking methods) and have had as their objective the identification of the predators (Jenkins & Hassett, 1950; Fredeen *et al.*, 1953; Pendleton & Grundmann, 1954; Baldwin, James & Welch, 1955; James, 1961; Jenkins, 1963). An approximate measure of the number of prey taken may be obtained from the level of activity in the predator. However, Baldwin *et al.* (1955) showed, in laboratory tests, that the same level of radioactivity (in counts per minute) could result from the consumption of different numbers of prey; this may be due to the variable radionuclide burdens of the prey, but could arise from different assimilation rates on the part of the predator (p. 362). If a large number of results were obtained and the radioactivity of the prey were normally distributed, it would be justifiable to calculate the number of prey eaten from the mean counts for 1, 2, . . . *x* prey. In essence this was the approach of Pendleton & Grundmann (1954), who made a thistle plant radioactive by placing 1 μc P^{32} in 3 c.c. of water in a hollow in the pith; the aphids feeding on the plant gave an average of 250 c.p.m. and the predators that eat *whole* aphids gave counts roughly in multiples of 250 c.p.m.; those such as spiders that consume only part of the aphid gave lower counts and so the lowest group of counts (120–180) was taken to represent the killing of a single aphid and approximate multiples of this, the killing of two or more.

Greater precision for more continuous studies might be introduced by using a modification of the approach of Crossley (1963) which was developed for measuring the consumption of vegetation by insects. He points out that if the biological half-life of the nuclide is long relative to the life-span of the insect, the amount in the insect (Q_t) may be given by:

$$Q_t = \frac{ra}{K}(1 - e^{-Kt})$$

where r=rate of ingestion, a=proportion of ingested nuclide assimilated, K=average elimination constant and t=time. (This approach could not be used in a situation when the radionuclide in the predator reaches equilibrium with that of its food, when the relationship $Q_e = ra/K$ holds; this is discussed on p. 361). Now if the isotope used had a long biological half-life (e.g. Ca^{45}, Zn^{65}) for any predator Q_t could be measured, and if a and K were known from laboratory studies, it should be possible to calculate r which would give a measure of the total number of isotope marked prey eaten. If the proportion of these in the total population was known (it would probably have to be fairly high), it could be assumed that the marked and unmarked prey were taken equally and the total prey consumption easily estimated. Gamma emitters and the use of a scintillation counter would be particularly suitable for measuring radioactivity in these studies, since it would eliminate problems of counting geometry associated with whole body counts.

Extreme caution should be exercised in all work of this type to ensure that the predator's intake of radionuclide came only from the prey. Baldwin *et al.* (1955) point out that if mosquito larvae are returned to a pond directly after marking by immersion in a solution of P^{32}, their radioactive excreta contaminates the whole pond. They overcome this by washing the larvae twice and keeping them for two days in freshwater before release. If the prey are marked through the host plant it must be remembered that some predators also feed, to a greater or lesser extent, on the plant.

Theoretically there is no reason why predator/prey relations should not be studied by tagging the prey with a known quantity of dye (e.g. rhodamine B) or other marker if this could be easily assayed in the predator's gut or excreta and if it was unaffected by the digestion processes.

3. Predator or parasite exclusion techniques

These methods demonstrate the effects of predators or parasites by artificially excluding them and measuring the increase in the prey's population under the new conditions; this increase represents the action of the predator (or parasite) in the exposed situation. Conceptually the method is very attractive but its weakness is that the techniques of excluding the predators often affect the microclimate and other aspects of the habitat, so that it is difficult to be certain that the observed effects are entirely due to the predator (Fleschner, 1958).

a. Mechanical or other barriers

Mammals and birds are relatively easily excluded by wire netting or nets, and it is unlikely that such methods have marked side-effects on the prey species, unless of course they also exclude herbivorous mammals whose activities have an important role on the vegetation. Buckner (1959) used mammal exclusion

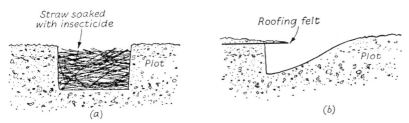

Fig. 74. Barriers to carabid beetles: *a.* exclusion barrier of straw soaked with insecticide; *b.* emigration barrier that allows beetles to enter plot but not to leave (based on Wright, Hughes & Worrall, 1960).

cages in his study of the predation of larch sawfly, *Pristiphora*, cocoons; in this case both the protected and exposed cocoons were 'planted' and therefore there was the risk that the resulting artificially high density might have acted as a bait to the mammals.

Predatory insects need to be excluded by smaller muslin cages of the sleeve-cage type (Smith & DeBach, 1942), but as Fleschner (1958) has shown such cages may affect the population directly and therefore, even if some cages are left open for predator access, as the cages are affecting the rate of increase the natural situation cannot be measured.

Non-flying insects can be more easily excluded by mechanical or insecticidal barriers. Wright, Hughes & Worrall (1960) and Coaker (1965) demonstrated the effects of carabid beetles on populations of the cabbage root fly (*Erioischia brassicae*) by means of trenches round the plots, filled with straw soaked with an insecticide (fig. 74). Ants can often be eliminated by similar barriers or bands on trees (p. 246).

b. Elimination of predator or parasite

Vertebrates may be shot (Dowden, Jaynes & Carolin, 1953), or trapped (Buckner, 1959), until their numbers are extremely low; as this must be done over a fairly large area to be effective it will lead to major disturbance in the habitat; this is undesirable in ecological studies. Fleschner (1958) found hand-picking of invertebrate predators from a part of the tree was both a feasible and reliable method.

As some predators are very susceptible to certain insecticides to which the prey are resistant, it is possible to assess their effects by an *insecticidal check method* (DeBach, 1946, 1955). It is very important to ensure that the pesticide has no side-effects on the prey species. Although this method was found reliable for studies on predators of *Aonidiella* scale insects (DeBach, 1955), it was not satisfactory for various plant-feeding tetranycid mites (Fleschner, 1958).

A *biological check method* has also been described in which large populations of ants are built up; these attack and often prevent predator and parasite action (Fleschner, 1958). Although such observations do give a measure of predator importance, there are so many other factors involved that they cannot be considered as equivalent to the quantitative estimation of predation.

4. Direct counts of parasites

When a single parasite larva emerges from each individual of an arboreal host and drops to the ground to pupate, these may be collected in trays or cone traps (see p. 246) to give an absolute measure of their own population, which is equivalent to the number of hosts they have killed. Such conditions are fulfilled, for example, in many tachinid parasites of Lepidoptera. When the percentage parasitism of the host is known *accurately* such figures may also be used to calculate the actual host population (Dowden, Jaynes & Carolin, 1953; Bean, 1958):

$$\text{Total host population} = \frac{\text{Total parasites} \times 100}{\% \text{ parasitism}}$$

5. Experimental assessment of performance

a. Feeding and searching capacity of predator

Measurement of the potential influence of a predator may be made under experimental conditions. There have been many such studies on feeding (e.g. Fewkes, 1960; Hukusima, 1961; Hukusima & Kondô, 1962; Turnbull, 1962), but they are difficult to apply in the field, except as a measure of potentiality, unless the predator is virtually monophagous (Evans, 1962). In the case of general predators differences in the acceptability of various prey, long recognized for vertebrates (e.g. Lane, 1957), are now being demonstrated in invertebrates (e.g. Coccinellidae; Hodek, 1962). The influence of a predator is, however, due not only to its feeding capacity, but also to its searching ability (Fleschner, 1950) and, depending on the time scale being considered, its rate of reproduction. MacLellan (1962) made semi-natural trials of the two former attributes by confining predators with known numbers of codling moth eggs on twigs in the field. The net result of all three properties may be studied by the introduction of a known number of predators and a known number of prey into a restricted environment and making assessments over several generations (e.g. Collyer, 1958).

b. The searching and reproductive capacity of a parasite

The roles of these two properties of the parasite in relation to changes in host and parasite density is a controversial subject of great theoretical importance. Laboratory studies on their interactions have been made by DeBach & Smith (1941), Burnett (1959, 1960), Varley & Edwards (1957), Edwards (1961) and others. These measurements are also important in the analysis of parasite/ prey interactions by computers. Nicholson & Bailey (1935) showed that a measure of the efficiency of search of a parasite, that they called the *area of discovery* (a), could be calculated:

$$a = \frac{1}{P_n}\left(\log_e \frac{u}{u_1}\right)$$

where P_n = the density of the parasite, u = the initial density of hosts and u_1 = the density of hosts still unparasitized after the search by the parasite. If pre- and post-parasitism estimates of the host are not available, but the fecundity of the host, together with earlier mortality factors, are known (these two being expressed as the coefficient of increase, f), then a may be calculated from the estimates of unparasitized individuals in successive populations (Varley & Edwards, 1957; Edwards, 1961):

$$a = \frac{1}{P_n}\left(\log_e \frac{fH_n}{H_{n+1}}\right)$$

where f = coefficient of increase, H_n = density of unparasitized hosts in generation n and H_{n+1} = density of unparasitized hosts in generation $n+1$, the generation for which the area of discovery is calculated in the same units as the parasite and host densities are expressed.

The reproductive capacity of a parasite may be estimated by laboratory studies or from field data (e.g. Varley, 1947).

DISPERSAL

The term dispersal covers any movement away from an aggregation or a population and may refer to the movement of newly hatched larvae away from their egg mass, a secondary dispersive process (Henson, 1959) (=interspersal of MacLeod & Donnelly, 1963) or the migration of adults away from their population territory (Southwood, 1962). Methods of estimating dispersal from life-table data are discussed in the next chapter.

The use of marked animals

1. The measurement and description of dispersal

a. The demonstration of the dispersive potential
Numerous studies have been made with marked animals released at a point and subsequently recaptured some distance away. Laboratory-bred material has sometimes been used and although this is best avoided when possible, MacLeod & Donnelly (1956) present evidence that under some circumstances the differences in behaviour between laboratory-reared and wild flies may not be great. Many workers (e.g. Quarterman, Mathis & Kilpatrick, 1954) have trapped wild insects, marked and released them, but this disturbance may lead to exceptional dispersal during the first few days after release (Clark, 1962; Greenslade, 1964). In dispersal studies the ideal method is to mark the insects in the field; this may be done by spraying with a dye (e.g. Greenberg & Bornstein, 1964) or by placing baits incorporating a radio-isotope at a fixed point in the field. Details of marking and release techniques are given in chapter 3. The marked animals may be trapped at selected sites or the traps may be arranged in a geometric pattern around the release site (e.g. Doane, 1963). The recovery of these marked individuals gives a measure of the actual movement of the individual and hence the potentiality for dispersal in the population. For some purposes this may be sufficient or the data may be analysed further, as outlined below. In analyses of the spread of marked animals where these are being estimated by a trapping technique, the influence of the dispersion pattern may be reduced by using the ratio of unmarked to marked animals in the traps rather than actual numbers (Gilmour, Waterhouse & McIntyre, 1946; MacLeod & Donnelly, 1963).

b. The detection of heterogeneity, with respect to the rate of dispersal, in the individuals of the population

In an experiment on the dispersal of marked *Drosophila* from a central point of a cross of traps, Dobzhansky & Wright (1943) demonstrated that the flies were heterogeneous with respect to the distance they travelled. This was detected by determining the departure from the normal curve of the frequency curve of numbers with distance from the point of release on a given day. The departure or kurtosis is given by the formula:

$$Ku = \frac{N \sum\limits_{p=0 \to l} d_p^4 n_p}{\left(\sum\limits_{p=0 \to l} d_p^{\cdot 2} n_p \right)^2}$$

where N=total animals caught in all traps, d_p=distance of the recapture point (p) from the point of release and n_p=total number caught in traps at recapture points the same distance from the point of release.

A normal curve has a $Ku=3$, a flat curve $Ku>3$ and a steep curve $Ku<3$. Values of Ku significantly greater or smaller than 3 therefore indicate some heterogeneity with respect to dispersal.

c. The rate of dispersal in terms of distance

In the experiment with *Drosophila* referred to above Dobzhansky & Wright (1943, 1947) determined the speed of dispersal by comparing the change in variance on successive days. If the speed of dispersal is constant the variance should change by a constant amount from day to day. They suggested that as the curve of numbers on distance was not normal variance should be estimated:

$$s^2 = \frac{\pi \sum\limits_{p=1 \to l} d_p^3 \bar{n}_p}{\sum\limits_{p=1 \to l} d_p \bar{n}_p + c}$$

where the symbols are as above, $\bar{n}_p$=the mean number of animals found in traps p at a given distance from the release point, c=the number of flies found in the central trap and $\pi=3 \cdot 14$.

In an interesting study on grasshoppers Clark (1962) demonstrated, by slightly different approach, that the rate of dispersal (or spread) varied with time after release. For each day after release the root mean square of the distances travelled (D) was calculated:

$$D = \sqrt{\frac{\Sigma (d^2)}{N}}$$

where d=distance of recapture point of an individual from the release point and N=total number of animals recaptured. If D is plotted against time and it rises steeply at first and then falls off, as it did in Clark's experiment, then the rate of dispersal falls with time. Indeed once the value of D has ceased to increase, then migration has ceased and movement is entirely trivial.

d. The fall-off of density with distance

Following the comprehensive review of Wolfenbarger (1946), a number of workers have attempted to find the most suitable regression equation to describe the fall-off of density with distance from the point of release (natural or artificial) of a number of animals. Some of the equations have a theoretical base, most are purely empirical. Where Y=the density of the population at x distance from the point of release and a, b and c are constants the equations are:

$$Y = a + b \log x \qquad (1) \text{ (Wolfenbarger, 1946)}$$

$$Y = a + b \log x + \frac{c}{x} \qquad (2) \text{ (Wolfenbarger, 1946)}$$

$$\log Y = \log a' + bx \qquad (3) \text{ (Kettle, 1951)}$$

$$\log Y = \log a + b \log x \qquad (4) \text{ (MacLeod \& Donnelly, 1963)}$$

$$Y = a + \frac{c}{x} \qquad (5) \text{ (Paris, 1965)}$$

Assuming the dispersal rate is constant and the population is homogeneous with respect to dispersal, then the fall-off of numbers with distance will be compounded of a 'dilution factor' due to the increasing area occupied as the circle of colonized habitat expands, and a 'loss factor' due to mortality or disappearance (e.g. entry into the soil). Wolfenbarger (1946) fitted equations 1 or 2 to a wide range of organisms with varying closeness of fit. Working with blowflies MacLeod and Donnelly (1963) found that equation 1 applied over the first half-mile of a two-mile dispersal radius, whereas equation 4 held for the first mile. Both these equations relate the fall-off of numbers (provided b is negative) to a power of the distance. Wadley (1957) has suggested that this factor may correspond to the 'loss factor'. Now if D does in fact correspond with a loss factor then the only explanation of it becoming less severe with distance, that I can envisage, is that the population is not homogeneous: those that have moved furthest are less liable to dropping out (mortality or failure to trap) than those that have remained closer to the release point. I would therefore suggest that, as migration is generally a feature of young animals (Johnson, 1960), this type of change in survival rate with distance, could well occur when a population of mixed ages was released, as in MacLeod and Donnelly's experiments. It could also be associated with the greater liability to trapping of those animals that have moved furthest or to a population being heterogeneous for movement and survival, the more active members having the greatest chance of survival. Therefore, perhaps equations 1 and

4 may be expected to apply to comparatively short-lived and heterogeneous populations, showing variation in vulnerability to trapping or mortality.

Equation 3 implies that density decreases at a constant rate per unit increase of distance, and was found by Kettle (1951) to describe the dispersal of *Culicoides* midges from their breeding ground; a similar equation has also been used to describe the spread of an aphid-transmitted virus in a field (Gregory & Read, 1949). In Kettle's equation a' = the density of midges at the breeding ground. It would seem that this equation approximates towards a description of the dispersal of animals, from a source, fanning out in one direction: thus it particularly applies to small insects carried by the wind, such as aphids and midges, the constant rate resulting from the dilution due to spread in a segment of a circle and to loss.

Equations 2 and 5 emphasize the dilution of density linearly as the reciprocal of distance; both were found by Paris (1965) to describe the dispersal of woodlice from a release point and the simpler formula that he developed has a precise geometrical analogue that considers the number of animals at the circumference of a circle. These equations seem to describe the dispersal of animals that spread out in most directions from the point of release (Paris found in six out of eight radii the rate of spread was similar), and whose dispersive ability, survival rate and vulnerability to trapping do not change significantly during the period of observation.

e. The demonstration of drift and non-randomness in direction of dispersal
One approach to this is to superimpose upon the map of the release and recapture sites a horizontal and vertical grid, and the mean and the variance are calculated for each day in terms of these grids (Clark, 1962). If the means differ significantly, then there was markedly more dispersal in one direction than another – drift. If the means are similar, but the variances differ, then movement was non-random. Clark (1962) describes a method for testing whether the resulting spatial distribution is circular or elliptical.

Another approach is that of Paris (1965), who, in a series of experiments, determined the number of woodlice in different radii and compared the results for eight radii using Friedman's (1940) analysis of variance by ranks test, which is non-parametric.

Both the above methods are limited to situations when a group of marked animals are released from a central point. When the members of a natural population have been marked individually it may be possible to use the approach of Frank (1964), who demonstrated that individual limpets (*Acmaea digitalis*) were not moving randomly and hence concluded that they had home ranges. The hatitat is regarded as a grid of identical squares; if the probability of movement from one square to the next remains constant, then, knowing the movement in one time period, it is possible to calculate, by applying a Markov process, the transition matrix at the end of a given number of time periods for the probabilities of movement from one square to another. The actual movements may then be compared with the expected using the χ^2 test.

f. The number of marked individuals that have left an area
If animals are released at a central point it is possible, making the assumptions of random flight movements and constant speed, to calculate theoretical curve for the fall-off in numbers of marked individuals with distance. By relating this curve to actual data of the ratio of marked to unmarked flies Gilmour, Waterhouse & McIntyre (1946) were able to calculate the number of marked blowflies beyond the last ring of traps.

The actual number of animals migrating into or out of a population may also be determined from mark and recapture analysis (see chapter 3). If there are no births or deaths, then the loss and dilution rates may be taken as equivalent to migration rates; alternatively the two components may be separated by measuring natality and mortality separately (see pp. 240–56).

The simple Lincoln Index may be used to calculate the proportion of a population that has migrated if the total population is known from some other method and there are no births or deaths. A number of marked individuals are released; knowing this number, the total population and the size of subsequent samples, expected recapture values may be calculated. The proportion of the marked insects that have migrated is given by the ratio of actual to expected recaptures. Such an approach is of particular value with a highly mobile insect.

g. The rate of population interchange between two areas
Richards & Waloff (1954) described a method for studying the movement between two grasshopper colonies; their basic assumption was that the survival rates in the two colonies were similar. Their method has been further developed by Iwao (1963), who has derived equations that are applicable to populations where both the survival rates and sampling ratios differ. A series of three sets of observations on days 1 (t_1), 2 (t_2) and 3 (t_3) are necessary as with Bailey's triple catch (p. 82). A number (a_1) of animals are marked and released in both areas on day 1; on day 2 a sample (n_2) is taken and the number of already marked individuals recorded, all the individuals (a_2) are then given a distinctive mark and released. On the third day samples are again taken in both areas and the number of already marked individuals recorded together with the details of their marks.

Thus the estimate of the emigration rate from area x to area y during the time interval from day 1 to day 2 is given by:

$$_{xy}\hat{e}_1 = \frac{\left(\dfrac{_{yy}r_{31}\ _{y}a_2 + _{yy}r_{21}\ _{yy}r_{32}}{_{yy}r_{32}\ _{y}a_1}\right)_{y}a_1\ _{xy}r_{21}}{_{x}a_1\ _{yy}r_{21}} \tag{1}$$

where the notation has been adapted to conform with that in chapter 3, the anterior subscripts being added to denote the areas; with both the anterior and posterior subscripts the symbol nearest the character represents the actual condition and that furthest away its previous history, thus $_{xy}r_{21}$ represents the recaptures in area y on day 2 that were marked in area x on day 1. To recapitulate the notation for the above equation:

$_{x}a_1 =$ no. of marked individuals released in area x on day 1

$_{y}a_1 =$,,   ,,   ,,   ,,   ,, y ,, 1

$_{y}a_2 =$,,   ,,   ,,   ,,   ,, y ,, 2

$_{yy}r_{21} =$ recaptures in area y on day 2 marked in area y on day 1

$_{yy}r_{31} =$,,   ,, y ,, 3 ,, y ,, 1

$_{yy}r_{32} =$,,   ,, y ,, 3 ,, y ,, 2

The equivalent equation for the estimation of the emigration rate from y to x is:

$$_{yx}\hat{e}_1 = \frac{\left(\dfrac{_{xx}r_{31}\,_{x}a_2 + _{xx}r_{21}\,_{xx}r_{32}}{_{xx}r_{32}\,_{x}a_1}\right)_{x}a_1\,_{yx}r_{21}}{_{y}a_1\,_{xx}r_{21}} \tag{2}$$

If the total populations (P) have been estimated by capture–recapture or some other way, then the actual numbers that have emigrated $\hat{E}$ are:

$$_{xy}\hat{E} = _{x}P_1 \times _{xy}\hat{e}_1$$

and

$$_{yx}\hat{E} = _{y}P_1 \times _{yx}\hat{e}_1$$

Survival rates (K) may also be calculated:

$$_{x}K_1 = _{xx}\mu_1 + _{xy}\hat{e}_1$$

where

$$_{xx}\mu_1 = \frac{_{yy}r_{31}\,_{y}a_2 + _{yy}r_{21}\,_{yy}r_{32}}{_{yy}r_{32}\,_{y}a_1}$$

i.e. the bracket term in equation 1 above, and

$$_{y}K_1 = _{yy}\mu_1 + _{yx}\hat{e}_1$$

where $_{yy}\mu_1 =$ the bracket term in equation 2 above

2. The measurement and description of home range and territory

The determination of the home range or territory of an individual or, for social animals, of a colony, is of value in the analysis of competition and density effects, the assessment of resources and similar problems. Although many studies have been made on the territories of vertebrates, little work has been done with insects except for crickets (Alexander, 1961), dragonflies (Borror, 1934; Moore, 1952, 1957), and ants (Elton, 1932). Some insects may be marked and recaptured on a number of occasions (e.g. Borror, 1934; Green & Pointing, 1962; Greenslade, 1964); this type of experiment gives data that would be suitable for the computation of the home range, using the methods of vertebrate ecologists. Ten recaptures are usually taken as sufficient to calculate the home range, but considerably more data would be required to use the method of Frank (1964) (p. 259) and ensure that one was not measuring an artifact.

The term territory implies the exclusion of at least certain other individuals, as occurs in crickets and dragonflies (Alexander, 1961; Moore, 1952, 1957); it is probable that this is the exception rather than the rule in insects; nevertheless most insects will have a home range, over which they forage and search for mates and where they rest; that is the area over which they engage in trivial movement (*sensu* Southwood, 1962). As Moore (1957) points out, the home range, especially for insects, should not be regarded as a hard and fast geographical area, but provided it is measured in a strictly comparative way it should be possible to detect changes due to inter- or intra-specific competition, to variation in the available resources or to changes in the behaviour of the animals themselves (e.g. Wellington, 1964). The calculation of the home range of vertebrates is important to the student of arthropod ectoparasites (e.g. Mohr & Stumpf, 1964a and b). There are a number of methods of calculating home range of vertebrates; these have been reviewed for mammals by Brown (1962).

a. Minimum area method

The points of recapture are mapped and the outermost points joined up to enclose the area, which may be measured (Mohr, 1947; Odum & Kuenzler, 1955). This method has the advantage that no assumption is made about the shape of the range and it has been shown that in some animals, at least, they may be linear (Stumpf & Mohr, 1962). However, with such a method the worker may feel it necessary to exclude 'incidental forays outside the area' (Jorgensen & Tanner, 1963). Furthermore, unless all re-entrant angles are avoided (as in fig. 75a), the depth to which they are drawn will depend on individual judgement and thus different results may be obtained from the same set of data.

b. Boundary strip methods

These are basically similar to the minimum area method, but an additional strip, arbitrarily extending the range halfway to the next trap, is added on (fig. 75b). There are two variants of this approach: the inclusive boundary strip in which the outer corners of the squares round each of the outer traps are joined, and the exclusive method in which the nearest corners of adjacent squares are joined – this encloses less area. Stickel (1954) considered that the exclusive boundary strip method gave truer results than the inclusive or minimum area methods.

c. Range length

This is the distance between the most widely separated captures (fig. 75a) and has been used by Linsdale (1946) and others; when there is little vagrancy this

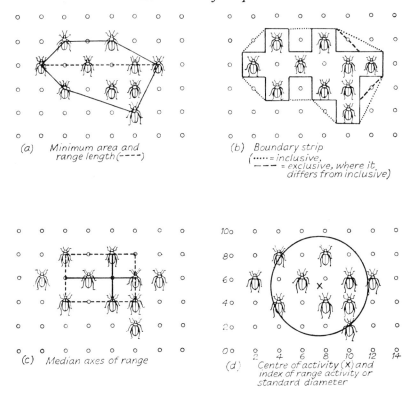

Fig. 75. Various methods of calculating home range from the recaptures of an individual animal in a grid of traps:

is a useful relative measure and has the advantage that no assumptions are made. To calculate the *adjusted range length*, half the distance to the next trap is added on, a process analagous to the boundary strip area.

d. Centre of activity

This concept was devised by Hayne (1949) as a method of overcoming the difficulties of fixing the boundaries of the home range, of determining the influence of the traps themselves on movement and of the relation of the trap catches to actual movement (see also Linsdale, 1946). It should be noted here that some of these problems do not arise if our information is based on following an individual, tagged with radio-isotope or in some other way (see pp. 57–73), so that it can be identified without recapture. The centre of activity is the geometric centre of all points of capture or observation (fig. 75d). It is calculated as follows: a grid system is applied to the map of capture points and each point will have two values – one on the vertical grid and one on the horizontal grid. All the values on the vertical grid are summed and divided by the number of observations to give a mean; likewise with those on the horizontal grid. These two means fix a point – the centre of activity. It should perhaps be mentioned that a series of centres of activity might be analysed with nearest neighbour type techniques (see p. 39).

e. Index of range activity

This is the simplified culmination of a series of concepts developed from the centre of activity (White, 1964). Dice & Clark (1953) and Harrison (1958) both considered that although the centre of activity might be a useful concept and that ranges probably have no fixed boundaries, what was required was the probability of the animal being taken at various distances away from this centre. For this purpose the range is assumed to be circular and the distances of the difference recapture points away from the centre of activity to represent the radii of these circles of probability of capture. Dice & Clark (1953) termed the distance between the centre and the recapture point or locus, the *recapture radius*. It was found for the deer mouse (*Peromyscus*) that a square-root transformation would normalize the distribution of these recapture radii around the recapture centre and then the differences in mean recapture radii of different sexes and ages and in different years could be tested by normal statistical means. Harrison's (1958) approach was basically similar and he expressed home range as the *standard diameter*, which was the diameter of the circle whose radius is equal to a single standard deviation of the values of the recapture radii (fig. 75*d*). That is, the animal would be expected to spend 68% of its time within this circle. The probability of capture within a given distance of the centre of activity (the density function) in relation to the time spent in this area has been further considered by Calhoun & Casby (1958), who introduced the concept that the animal will spend more time, area for area, closer to the centre, its home. It is doubtful, however, whether this refinement is justified, or even true for insects, and the most convenient measure of the entomologist is either the recapture radii of Dice & Clark (1953) or Harrison's method, termed an Index of Range Activity by White (1964). To find this index the geometric centre of activity is calculated as described by Hayne (1949) (see above), the distance of each recapture or observation point from this centre measured and doubled and these recapture diameters (D) used to calculate their standard deviation – the index, i.e. the standard diameter of Harrison:

$$\text{Index} = \sqrt{\left(\frac{\Sigma\, D^2}{N-1}\right)}$$

where N = the number of observations.

f. Median axes of range and composite ranges

Stumpf & Mohr (1962) have demonstrated that ranges may be linear and have proposed (Mohr & Stumpf, 1964*a* and *b*) that as recapture points and sighting are not necessarily normally distributed they be analysed by the use of the median point and axes. When the median axes have been calculated the range may be indicated by the construction of a parallelogram or convex polygon round them, so as to exclude a third of the recaptures. A composite range for a species in a habitat may be obtained by superimposing the axes of several individual ranges one above another. Mohr & Stumpf found that ranges often tend to be mirror images of each other and therefore it may be necessary to reverse some patterns when constructing the composite range, so that the longest arm of each axis is directly superimposed. The length of the arms is

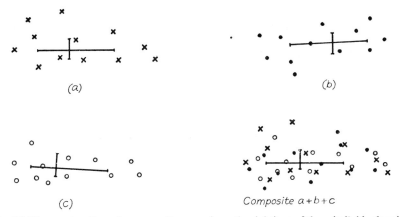

Fig. 76. The construction of a composite range from the sightings of three individuals using the method of Mohr & Stumpf (1964a & b).

taken so that it extends to the median of the sighting points in that direction, i.e. the sub-median (fig. 76). This method is particularly suitable for the analysis of sightings.

Apart from difficulties of observation and repeated capture, one of the main objections to the use of this concept in entomological work is that only a few insects such as pond skaters (Gerridae) and various mud or bare soil surface dwellers really move in only two dimensions; however, in a larger number, such as some grasshoppers, carabid beetles and ant colonies, the vertical component of the range may perhaps be neglected. A further difficulty is that the tendency of range to change with time – a variable that has to be eliminated in vertebrate studies – is likely to be well marked in many insects.

The elimination of emigration

With a very few insects, such as apterous ground beetles, it may be possible to allow immigration, but prevent emigration by a barrier of some type (e.g. fig. 74b).

The use of quadrat counts of unmarked individuals

Where the habitat is uniform and it is possible to assume random diffusion, movement may be separated from mortality by using the method of Dempster (1957), which is based on random diffusion theory. The changes in the numbers of insects (f) with time will be represented (Skellam, 1951) by:

$$\frac{df}{dt} = \alpha\left(\frac{d^2f}{dx^2} + \frac{d^2f}{dy^2}\right) - \mu f \tag{1}$$

where α = the mobility of the insects; $d^2f/dx^2 + d^2f/dy^2$ = a measure of the density gradient along the two axes of the quadrat in which the insects occur and μ = mortality rate.

Dempster shows that a representation of density gradient expression is given:

$$\frac{d^2f}{dx^2} + \frac{d^2f}{dy^2} = \frac{1}{3}(3 \ \Sigma \ x^2 f'_{(x,y)} + 3 \ \Sigma \ y^2 f'_{(x,y)} - 4 \ \Sigma \ f'_{(x,y)}) \tag{2}$$

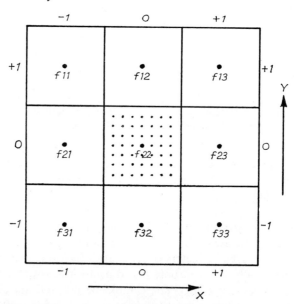

Fig. 77. The populations ($f_{11}, f_{12} \ldots$) along the two axes (x and y) across a central quadrat surrounded by quadrats of equal area (from Dempster, 1957).

Now if we consider a block of 9 quadrats (fig. 77) and take quadrat f_{11}, its numerical value in this expression would be

$$3 \times (-1)^2 + 3 \times (1)^2 - 4 = 2$$

Similarly for all the other squares in turn, so that:

$$\frac{d^2f}{dx^2} + \frac{d^2f}{dy^2} = \tfrac{1}{3}(2f_{11} - 1f_{12} + 2f_{13} - 1f_{21} - 4f_{22} - 1f_{23} + 2f_{31} - f_{32} + 2f_{33}) \tag{3}$$

Thus for a central quadrat surrounded by 8 other quadrats the best estimator for $d^2f/dx^2 + d^2f/dy^2$ is given by equation 3 and this value may be substituted in equation 1, the only unknowns then are α and μ. A series of simultaneous equations can therefore be developed for a number of central squares; as these must be more than the number of unknowns (2 in this case), the absolute minimum number of equal sized quadrats would be 15 arranged in a block of 3×5. A larger number would be preferable and Dempster used 18. Equations for the four middle squares can be calculated. The df/dt value being the changes in numbers normally decrease, from one instar to the next (or whatever the period of time). For the values of the estimator of $d^2f/dx^2 + d^2f/dy^2$, equation 3, the estimates of the populations in the quadrats used are those for the commencement of the period in question. The equations are then solved by normal mathematical procedures. The value for μ will be fractional and that for α should be positive; when mobility is extremely small negative values of α may occur by chance.

EXAMPLE (from Dempster, 1957): Consider square B_2 in fig. 78. The number of insects in this square has changed from 50,500 to 26,475.

$$\therefore \frac{df}{dt} = -24,025$$

and
$$\left(\frac{d^2f}{dx^2} + \frac{d^2f}{dy^2}\right) = \frac{1}{3}\begin{pmatrix} 2 \times 44,230 - 45,650 + 2 \times 6478 - \\ 47,370 - 4 \times 50,500 - 16,650 + 2 \times \\ 50,720 - 103,900 + 2 \times 89,160 \end{pmatrix} = -11,465$$

Substituting in the equation
$$\frac{df}{dt} = \alpha\left(\frac{d^2f}{dx^2} + \frac{d^2f}{dy^2}\right) - \mu f$$

we get
$$\underset{A}{-24,025} = \underset{B}{-11,465\alpha \times} \underset{C}{-50,500\mu}$$

	A	B	C
1	44,230 / 14,600	45,650 / 16,145	6,478 / 5,840
2	47,370 / 22,580	50,500 / 26,475	16,650 / 6,623
3	50,720 / 30,015	103,900 / 52,680	89,160 / 57,860

Fig. 78. The estimated number of locusts entering the first (upper figure) and second instar (lower figure) in a number of quadrats (from Dempster, 1957).

At least 3, preferably more, similar equations are obtained. Then the normal equation for μ is found by multiplying each equation by the coefficient of μ in it and adding all equations. The normal equation for a is found in the same way. These two equations are then solved.

The rate of colonization of a new habitat

This property, which is related to migration, may be measured by planting virgin artificial habitats (e.g. new plants in a field or stones in a stream) and determining the rate of colonization (Breymeyer & Pieczynski, 1963) (see also pp. 163 and 208).

The direction of migration

There are a number of traps (pp. 191–9) that enable one to determine the direction an animal was flying at the time of capture. It is possible that the proportionality values obtained from a series of such traps round a habitat might be used in conjunction with measures of either the net change in population or a measurement of migration to determine values for immigration and emigration. Furthermore it has been pointed out how the dilution and 'loss' rates obtained from multiple capture–recapture analysis are compounded of birth and immigration and death and emigration respectively. Sometimes it is possible to separate the two components of the dilution rate from a knowledge of natality or the numbers entering the stage, When 'births' are known, the proportion of emigration to immigration determined from a 'directional trap', might be used to give an indication of the amount of immigration and hence allow the partitioning of the death-rate into mortality and immigration. Caution would need to be used in such an approach, particularly to ensure an adequate distribution of traps around the habitat and difficulty would be experienced in determining the numbers of animals leaving and arriving in vertical air currents, i.e. only crossing the habitat boundaries at a considerable height.

A measure of drift in a dispersing population may also be obtained from the analysis of data from marked individuals (see p. 259).

REFERENCES

ADAMSTONE, F. B. and HARKNESS, W. J. K., 1923. The bottom organisms of Lake Nipigon. *Univ. Toronto Stud. Biol.* **22,** 121–70.

ALEXANDER, R. D., 1961. Aggressiveness, territoriality and sexual behaviour in field crickets (Orthoptera: Gryllidae). *Behaviour* **17,** 130–223.

BALDWIN, W. F., JAMES, H. G. and WELCH, H. E., 1955. A study of predators of mosquito larvae and pupae with a radio-active tracer. *Canad. Ent.* **87,** 350–6.

BATES, J. K., 1962. Field studies on the behaviour of bird fleas. 1. Behaviour of the adults of three species of bird flea in the field. *Parasitology* **52,** 113–32.

BEAN, J. L., 1958. The use of larvaevorid maggot drop in measuring trends in spruce budworm populations. *Ann. ent. Soc. Amer.* **51**, 400–3.

BESS, H. A., 1961. Population ecology of the gipsy moth, *Porthetria dispar* L. (Lepidoptera: Lymantridae). *Bull. Conn. agric. Exp. Sta.* **646**, 43 pp.

BETTS, M. M., 1954. Experiments with an artificial nestling. *Brit. Birds* **47**, 229–31.

BETTS, M. M., 1955. The food of titmice in oak woodlands. *J. anim. Ecol.* **24**, 282–323.

BETTS, M. M., 1958. Further experiments with an artificial nestling gape. *Brit. Birds* **49**, 213–5.

BLAIS, J. R., 1953. The effects of the destruction of the current year's foliage of balsam fir on the fecundity and habits of flight of the spruce budworm. *Canad. Ent.* **85**, 446–8.

BORROR, D. J., 1934. Ecological studies of *Agria moesta* Hogen (Odonata: Coenagrionidae) by means of marking. *Ohio J. Sci.* **34**, 97–108.

BORUTSKY, E. V., 1955. [A new trap for the quantitative estimation of emerging chironomids.] [In Russian.] *Trudy̆ vses. gidrobiol. Obshch.* **6**, 223–6.

BREYMEYER, A. and PIECZYNSKI, E., 1963. Review of methods used in the Institute of Ecology, Polish Academy of Sciences, for investigating migration. [In Polish.] *Ekol. Polska B* **9**, 129–44.

BROOKE, M. M. and PROSKE, H. O., 1946. Precipitin test for determining natural insect predators of immature mosquitoes. *J. Nat. Malaria Soc.* **5**, 45–56.

BROWN, L. E., 1962. Home range in small mammal communities. *In* Glass, B. (ed.), *Survey of biological progress* **4**, 131–79.

BRUNDIN, L., 1949. Chironomiden und andere Bodentiere der Südschwedischen Urgebirgsseen. *Rep. Inst. Freshw. Res. Drottringholm* **20**, 915 pp.

BUCKNER, C. H., 1958. Mammalian predators of the larch sawfly in eastern Manitoba. *Proc. X int. Congr. Ent.* **4**, 353–61.

BUCKNER, C. H., 1959. The assessment of larch sawfly cocoon predation by small mammals. *Canad. Ent.* **91**, 275–82.

BURNETT, T., 1959. Experimental host–parasite populations. *A. Rev. Ent.* **4**, 235–50.

BURNETT, T., 1960. An insect host–parasite population. *Canad. J. Zool.* **38**, 57–75.

CALHOUN, J. B. and CASBY, J. U., 1958. Calculation of home range and density of small mammals. *U.S. Pub. Hlth Monog.* **55**, 1–24.

CAMPBELL, J. A. and PELHAM-CLINTON, E. C., 1960. A taxonomic review of the British species of 'Culicoides' Latreille (Diptera, Ceratopogonidae). *Proc. R. Soc. Edin. B* **67** (3), 181–302.

CHAPMAN, J. A., ROMER, J. I. and STARK, J., 1955. Ladybird beetles and army cut-worm adults as food for grizzly bears in Montana. *Ecology* **36**, 156–8.

CLARK, D. P., 1962. An analysis of dispersal and movement in *Phaulacridium vittatum* (Sjöst.) (Acrididae). *Aust. J. Zool.* **10**, 382–99.

CLARK, E. W. and OSGOOD, E. A., 1964. An emergence container for recovering southern pine beetles from infested bolts. *J. econ. Ent.* **57**, 783–4.

CLARK, L. P., 1963. The influence of population density on the number of eggs laid by females of *Cardiaspina albitextura* (Psyllidae). *Aust. J. Zool.* **11**, 190–201.

COAKER, T. H., 1965. Further experiments on the effect of beetle predators on the numbers of the cabbage root fly, *Erioischia brassicae* (Bouché), attacking brassica crops. *Ann. appl. Biol.* **56**, 7–20.

COLLESS, D. H. and CHELLAPAH, W. T., 1960. Effects of body weight and size of blood-meal upon egg production in *Aëdes aegypti* (Linnaeus) (Diptera, Culicidae). *Ann. trop. Med. Parasit.* **54**, 475–82.

COLLYER, E., 1958. Some insectary experiments with predacious mites to determine their effects on the development of *Metatetranychus ulmi* (Koch) populations. *Ent. exp. appl.* **1**, 138–46.

COOK, L. M. and KETTLEWELL, H. B. D., 1960. Radioactive labelling of lepidopterous larvae: a method of estimating late larval and pupal mortality in the wild. *Nature, Lond.* **187,** 301–2.

CROSSLEY, D. A., 1963. Consumption of vegetation by insects. *In* Schultz, V. & Klement, A. W. (eds.), *Radioecology,* 431–40.

DARBY, R. E., 1962. Midges associated with California rice fields, with special reference to their ecology (Diptera: Chironomidae). *Hilgardia* **32,** 1–206.

DAVIDSON, A., 1956. A method of counting Ephemeropteran eggs. *Ent. mon. Mag.* **92,** 109.

DEBACH, P., 1946. An insecticidal check method for measuring the efficacy of entomophagous parasites. *J. econ. Ent.* **39,** 695–7.

DEBACH, P., 1949. Population studies of the long-tailed mealy bug and its natural enemies on citrus trees in Southern California, 1946. *Ecology* **30,** 14–25.

DEBACH, P., 1955. Validity of the insecticidal check method as a measure of the effectiveness of natural enemies of Diaspine scale insects. *J. econ. Ent.* **48,** 584–8.

DEBACH, P. and SMITH, H. S., 1941. The effect of host density on the rate of reproduction of entomophagous parasites. *J. econ. Ent.* **34,** 741–5.

DEMPSTER, J. P., 1957. The population dynamics of the Moroccan locust (*Dociostaurus maroccanus* Thunberg) in Cyprus. *Anti-Locust Bull.* **27,** 1–60.

DEMPSTER, J. P., 1960. A quantitative study of the predators on the eggs and larvae of the broom beetle, *Phytodecta olivacea* Forster, using the precipitin test. *J. anim. Ecol.* **29,** 149–67.

DEMPSTER, J. P., 1964. The feeding habits of the Miridae (Heteroptera) living on broom (*Sarothamnus scoparius* (L.) Wimm.). *Ent. exp. appl.* **7,** 149–54.

DEMPSTER, J. P., RICHARDS, O. W. and WALOFF, N., 1959. Carabidae as predators on the pupal stage of the Chrysomelid beetle, *Phytodecta olivacea* (Forster). *Oikos* **10,** 65–70.

DICE, L. R. and CLARK, P. J., 1953. The statistical concept of home range as applied to the recapture radius of the deermouse (*Peromyscus*). *Contrib. Lab. Vert. Biol.* **62,** 1–15.

DINTHER, J. B. M. VAN, 1953. Details about some flytraps and their application to biological research. *Ent. Ber.* **14,** 201–4.

DOANE, J. F., 1963. Dispersion on the soil surface of marked adult *Ctenicera destructor* and *Hypolithus bicolor* (Coleoptera: Elateridae), with notes on flight. *Ann. ent. Soc. Amer.* **56,** 340–5.

DOBSON, R. M., STEPHENSON, J. W. and LOFTY, J. R., 1958. A quantitative study of a population of wheat bulb fly, *Leptohylemyia coarctata* (Fall.), in the field. *Bull. ent. Res.* **49,** 95–111.

DOBZHANSKY, T. and WRIGHT, S., 1943. Genetics of natural populations: X. Dispersion rates in *Drosophila pseudoobscura*. *Genetics* **28,** 304–40.

DOBZHANSKY, T. and WRIGHT, S., 1947. Genetics of natural populations. XV. Rate of diffusion of a mutant gene through a population of *Drosophila pseudoobscura*. *Genetics* **32,** 303–24.

DOWDEN, d. B., JAYNES, H. A. and CAROLIN, V. M. 1953. The role of birds in a spruce budworm outbreak in Maine. *J. econ. Ent.* **46,** 307–12.

DOWNE, A. E. R. and WEST, A. S., 1954. Progress in the use of the precipitin test in entomological studies. *Canad. Ent.* **86,** 181–4.

EDWARDS, R. L., 1961. The area of discovery of two insect parasites, *Nasonia vitripennis* (Walker) and *Trichogramma evanescens* Westwood, in an artificial environment. *Canad. Ent.* **93,** 475–81.

ELTON, C., 1932. Territory among wood ants (*Formica rufa* L.) at Picket Hill. *J. anim. Ecol.* **1,** 69–76.

EMDEN, H. F. VAN, 1962. A preliminary study of insect numbers in field and hedgerow. *Ent. mon. Mag.* **98,** 255–9.

EMDEN, H. F. VAN, 1963. A field technique for comparing the intensity of mortality factors acting on the cabbage aphid, *Brevicoryne brassicae* (L.) (Hem., Aphididae) in different areas of a crop. *Ent. exp. appl.* **6,** 53–62.

ERRINGTON, P., 1932. Technique of raptor food habits study. *Condor* **34**, 75–86.

EVANS, D. E., 1962. The food requirements of *Phonoctonus nigrofasciatus* Stål (Hemiptera, Reduviidae). *Ent. exp. appl.* **5**, 33–9.

EVANS, H. E. and YOSHIMOTO, C. M., 1962. The ecology and nesting behaviour of the Pompilidae (Hymenoptera) of the Northeastern United States. *Misc. Pub. ent. Soc. Amer.* **3** (3), 65–119.

EVENHUIS, H. H., 1962. Methods to investigate the population dynamics of aphids and aphid parasites in orchards. *Entomophaga* **7**, 213–20.

FEWKES, D. W., 1960. The food requirements by weight of some British Nabidae (Heteroptera). *Ent. exp. appl.* **3**, 231–7.

FEWKES, D. W., 1964. The fecundity and fertility of the Trinidad sugar-cane froghopper, *Aeneolamia varia saccharina* (Homoptera, Cercopidae). *Trop. Agriculture, Trin.* **41**, 165–8.

FLESCHNER, C. A., 1950. Studies on searching capacity of the larvae of three predators of the citrus red mite. *Hilgardia* **20** (13), 233–65.

FLESCHNER, C. A., 1958. Field approach to population studies of Tetranychid mites on citrus and Avocado in California. *Proc. X int. Congr. Ent.* **2**, 669–76.

FOX, C. J. S. and MACLELLAN, C. R., 1956. Some Carabidae and Staphylinidae shown to feed on a wireworm, *Agnotes sputator* (L.) by the precipitin test. *Canad. Ent.* **88**, 228–31.

FRANK, P. W., 1964. On home range of limpets. *Amer. Nat.* **98**, 99–104.

FREDEEN, F. J. H., SPINKS, J. W. T., ANDERSON, J. R., ARNASON, A. P. and REMPEL, J. G., 1953. Mass tagging of blackflies (Diptera: Simuliidae) with radio-phosphorus. *Canad. J. Zool.* **31**, 1–15.

FRIEDMAN, M., 1940. A comparison of alternative tests of significance for the problem of *m* rankings. *Ann. math. Stat.* **11**, 86–92.

GARY, N. E., 1960. A trap to quantitatively recover dead and abnormal honey bees from the hive. *J. econ. Ent.* **53**, 782–5.

GIBB, J. A., 1958. Predation by tits and squirrels on the Eucosmid *Ernarmonia conicolana* (Heyl.). *J. anim. Ecol.* **27**, 375–96.

GILMOUR, D., WATERHOUSE, D. F. and MCINTYRE, G. A., 1946. An account of experiments undertaken to determine the natural population density of the sheep blowfly, *Lucilia cuprina* Wied. *Bull. Coun. sci. indust. Res. Aust.* **195**, 1–39.

GOODHART, C. B., 1958. Thrush predation on the snail *Cepaea hortensis. J. anim. Ecol.* **27**, 47–57.

GRAHAM, S. A., 1928. The influence of small mammals and other factors upon larch sawfly survival. *J. econ. Ent.* **21**, 301–10.

GRANDILEWSKAJA-DECKSBACH, M. L., 1935. Materialien zur Chironomidenbiologie verschiedener Becken. Zur Frage über die Schwankungen der Anzahl und der Biomasse der Chironomidenlarven. *Trudy limnol. Sta. Kosine* **19**, 145–82.

GREEN, G. W., 1962. Low winter temperatures and the European pine shoot moth, *Rhyacionia buoliana* (Schiff.) in Ontario. *Canad. Ent.* **94**, 314–36.

GREEN, G. W. and POINTING, P. J., 1962. Flight and dispersal of the european pine shoot moth, *Rhyacionia buoliana* (Schiff.). II. Natural dispersal of egg-laden females. *Canad. Ent.* **94**, 299–314.

GREENBERG, B. and BORNSTEIN, A. A., 1964. Fly dispersion from a rural mexican slaughterhouse. *Amer. J. trop. Med. Hyg.* **13** (6), 881–6.

GREENSLADE, P. J. M., 1964. The distribution, dispersal and size of a population of *Nebria brevicollis* (F.) with comparative studies on three other carabidae. *J. anim. Ecol.* **33**, 311–33.

GREGOR, F., 1960. Zur Eiproduktion des Eichenwicklers (*Tortrix viridana* L.). *Zool. Listy.* **9**, 11–18.

GREGORY, P. H. and READ, D. R., 1949. The spatial distribution of insect-borne plant-virus diseases. *Ann. appl. Biol.* **36**, 475–82.

GUENNELON, G. and AUDEMARD, M. H., 1963. Enseignements écologiques donnés par la méthode de captures par cuisses-éclosion de la cécidomyie des lavandes (*Thomasiniana lavandulae* Barnes). Critique de la méthode. Conclusions pratiques. *Ann. Épiphyt. C* **14**, 35–48.

HAFEZ, M., 1961. Seasonal fluctuations of population density of the cabbage aphid, *Brevicoryne brassicae* (L.) in the Netherlands, and the role of its parasite, *Aphidius* (*Diaeretiella*) *rapae* (Curtis). *Tijdschr. PlZiekt.* **67**, 445–548.

HALL, R. R., DOWNE, A. E. R., MACLELLAN, C. R. and WEST, A.S., 1953. Evaluation of insect predator–prey relationships by precipitin test studies. *Mosq. News* **13**, 199–204.

HARRISON, J. L., 1958. Range of movement of some malayan rats. *J. Mammal.* **39**, 190–206.

HARTLEY, P. H. T., 1948. The assessment of the food of birds. *Ibis* **90**, 361–81.

HAYNE, D. W., 1949. Calculation of size of home range. *J. Mammal.* **30**, 1–18.

HENSON, W. R., 1959. Some effects of secondary dispersive processes on distribution. *Amer. Nat.* **93**, 315–20.

HODEK, I., 1962. Essential and alternative food in insects. *Proc. XI int. Congr. Ent.* **2**, 698–9.

HOLLING, C. S., 1958. A radiographic technique to identify healthy, parasitised and diseased sawfly prepupae within cocoons. *Canad. Ent.* **90**, 59–61.

HUFFAKER, C. B. and SPITZER, C. H., 1950. Some factors affecting red mite populations on pears in California. *J. econ. Ent.* **43**, 819–31.

HUKUSIMA, S., 1961. Feeding capacity of seven predators of aphids and mites, and toxicity of several pesticides to beneficial arthropods. *Res. Bull. Fac. Agric. Gifu-ken prefect Univ.* **14**, 55–67.

HUKUSIMA, S. and KONDÔ, K., 1962. Further evaluation in the feeding potential of the predacious insects and spiders in association with aphids harmful to apple and pear growing and the effect of pesticides on predators. (Studies on the insect association in crop field 27.) *Jap. J. appl. Ent. Zool.* **6** (4), 274–80.

IDE, F. P., 1940. Quantitative determination of the insect fauna of rapid water. *Univ. Toronto Stud. Biol. Ser.* **47** (*Publ. Ontario Fish. Res. Lab.* **59**), 20 pp.

IVES, W. G. H. and PRENTICE, R. M., 1959. Estimation of parasitism of larch sawfly cocoons by *Bessa harveyi* Tnsd. in survey collections. *Canad. Ent.* **91**, 496–500.

IWAO, S., 1956. On the number of eggs per egg-mass of the paddy rice borer, *Schoenobuis incertellus* Walker and the percentage of their parasitization. [In Japanese.] *Gensei* (Kochi Konchu Dokokai) **5**, 45–9.

IWAO, S., 1963. On a method for estimating the rate of population interchange between two areas. *Res. Popul. Ecol.* **5**, 44–50.

JAMES, H. G., 1961. Some predators of *Aedes stimulans* (Walk) and *Aedes trichurus* (Dyar) (Diptera: Culicidae) in woodland pools. *Canad. J. Zool.* **39**, 533–40.

JENKINS, D. W., 1963. Use of radionuclides in ecological studies of insects. *In* Schultz, V. and Klement, A. W. (eds.), *Radioecology* 431–40.

JENKINS, D. W. and HASSETT, C.C., 1950. Radioisotopes in entomology. *Nucleonics* **6** (3), 5–14.

JOHNSON, C. G., 1960. A basis for a general system of insect migration and dispersal by flight. *Nature, Lond.* **186**, 348–50.

JÓNASSON, P. M., 1954. An improved funnel trap for capturing emerging aquatic insects, with some preliminary results. *Oikos* **5**, 179–88.

JORGENSEN, C. D. and TANNER, W. W., 1963. The application of the density probability function to determine the home ranges of *Uta stansburiana stansburiana* and *Cnemidophorus tigris tigris*. *Herpetologica* **19**, 105–15.

JUDGE, W. W., 1957. A study of the population of emerging and littoral insects trapped as adults from tributary waters of the Thames River at London, Ontario. *Amer. midl. Nat.* **58**, 394–412.

KENNEDY, C. H., 1950. The relation of American dragonfly-eating birds to their prey. *Ecol. Monogr.* **20**, 103–42.

KETTLE, D. S., 1951. The spatial distribution of *Culicoides impunctatus* Goet under woodland and moorland conditions and its flight range through woodland. *Bull. ent. Res.* **42**, 239–91.

LACK, D. and OWEN, D. F., 1955. The food of the swift. *J. anim. Ecol.* **24**, 120–36.

LANE, C., 1957. Preliminary note on insects eaten and rejected by a tame Shama (*Kittacincta malabarica* G. M.) with the suggestion that in certain species of butterflies and moths, females are less palatable than males. *Ent. mon. Mag.* **93**, 172–9.

LAWSON, F. R., 1959. The natural enemies of the hornworms on tobacco (Lepidoptera: Sphingidae). *Ann. ent. Soc. Amer.* **52**, 741–55.

LEJEUNE, R. R., FELL, W. H. and BURBIDGE, D. P., 1955. The effect of flooding on development and survival of the larch sawfly *Pristiphora erichsonii* (Tenthredinidae). *Ecology* **36**, 63–70.

LEONE, C. A., 1947. A serological study of some Orthoptera. *Ann. ent. Soc. Amer.* **40**, 417–33.

LINDEBERG, B., 1958. A new trap for collecting emerging insects from small rockpools, with some examples of the results obtained. *Suom. hyönt. Aikak.* (*Ann. ent. fenn.*) **24** 186–91.

LINSDALE, J. M., 1946. *The Californian ground squirrel.* Berkeley, California, 475 pp.

LOAN, C. and HOLDAWAY, F. G., 1961. *Microctonus aethiops* (Nees) auctt. and *Perilitus rutilus* (Nees) (Hymenoptera: Braconidae). European parasites of *Sitona* weevils (Coleoptera: Curculionidae). *Canad. Ent.* **93**, 1057–78.

LOUGHTON, B. G., DERRY, C. and WEST, A. S. 1963. Spiders and the spruce budworm. *Mem. ent. Soc. Canad.* **31**, 249–68.

LOUGHTON, B. G. and WEST, A. S., 1962. Serological assessment of spider predation on the spruce budworm, *Choristoneura fumiferana* (Clem.) (Lepidoptera: Tortricidae). *Proc. ent. Soc. Ontario* (1961) **92**, 176–80.

LOZINSKY, V. A., 1961. On the correlation existing between the weight of pupae and the number and weight of eggs of *Lymantria dispar* L. [In Russian.] *Zool. Zh.* **40**, 1571–3.

MACAN, T. T., 1949. Survey of a moorland fishpond. *J. anim. Ecol.* **18**, 160–86.

MACLELLAN, C. R., 1962. Mortality of codling moth eggs and young larvae in an integrated control orchard. *Canad. Ent.* **94**, 655–66.

MACLEOD, J. and DONNELLY, J., 1956. Methods for the study of blowfly populations. II. The use of laboratory-bred material. *Ann. appl. Biol.* **44**, 643–8.

MACLEOD, J. and DONNELLY, J., 1963. Dispersal and interspersal of blowfly populations. *J. anim. Ecol.* **32**, 1–32.

MACPHEE, A. W., 1961. Mortality of winter eggs of the european red mite *Panonychus ulmi* (Koch), at low temperatures, and its ecological significance. *Canad. J. Zool.* **39**, 229–43.

MACPHEE, A. W., 1964. Cold-hardiness, habitat and winter survival of some orchard Arthropods in Nova Scotia. *Canad. Ent.* **96**, 617–36.

MARTIGNONI, M. E. and STEINHAUS, E. A., 1961. *Laboratory exercises in insect microbiology and insect pathology.* Burgess, Minneapolis, 75 pp.

MᶜMULLEN, L. H. and ATKINS, M. D., 1959. A portable tent-cage for entomological field studies. *Proc. ent. Soc. B.C.* **56**, 67–8.

MILES, P. M., 1952. Entomology of Bird Pellets. *Amat. Ent. Soc. Leaflet* **24**, 8 pp.

MILLER, C. A., 1955. A technique for assessing larval mortality caused by parasites. *Canad. J. Zool.* **33**, 5–17.

MILLER, C. A., 1957. A technique for estimating the fecundity of natural populations of the spruce budworm. *Canad. J. Zool.* **35**, 1–13.

MILLER, C. A., 1958. The measurement of spruce budworm populations and mortality during the first and second larval instars. *Canad. J. Zool.* **36**, 409–22.

MILLER, R. S. and THOMAS, J. L., 1958. The effects of larval crowding and body size on the longevity of adult *Drosophila melanogaster*. *Ecology* **39**, 118–25.

MOHR, C. O., 1947. Table of equivalent populations of North American small mammals. *Amer. midl. Nat.* **37**, 223–49.

MOHR, C. O. and STUMPF, W. A., 1964a. Relation of tick and chigger infestations to home areas of California meadow mice. *J. Med. Ent.* **1** (1), 73–7.

MOHR, C. O. and STUMPF, W. A., 1964b. Louse and chigger infestations as related to host size and home ranges of small mammals. *Trans. 29th N. Amer. Wildl. nat. Res. Confr.* 181–95.

MOOK, L. J., 1963. Birds and the spruce budworm. *Mem. ent. Soc. Canad.* **31**, 268–71.

MOORE, N. W., 1952. On the so-called 'territories' of dragonflies (Odonata – Anisoptera). *Behaviour* **4**, 85–100.

MOORE, N. W., 1957. Territory in dragonflies and birds. *Bird study* **4**, 125–30.

MORGAN, C. V. G. and ANDERSON, N. H., 1958. Techniques for biological studies of Tetranychid mites, especially *Bryobia arborea* M. and A. and *B. praetiosa* Koch (Acarina: Tetranychidae). *Canad. Ent.* **90**, 212–15.

MORGAN, N. C. and WADDELL, A. B., 1961. Insect emergence from a small trout loch, and its bearing on the food supply of fish. *Sci. Invest. Freshw. Fish. Scot.* **25**, 1–39.

MORGAN, N. C., WADDELL, A. B. and HALL, W. B., 1963. A comparison of the catches of emerging aquatic insects in floating box and submerged funnel traps. *J. anim. Ecol.* **32**, 203–19.

MORRIS, R. F., 1949. Differentiation by small mammals between sound and empty cocoons of the European spruce sawfly. *Canad. Ent.* **81**, 114–20.

MUNDIE, J. H., 1956. Emergence traps for aquatic insects. *Mitt. int. Verein. theor. angew. Limnol.* **7**, 1–13.

NEILSON, M. M., 1963. Disease and the spruce budworm. *Mem. ent. Soc. Canad.* **31**, 272–88.

NICHOLLS, C. F., 1963. Some entomological equipment. *Res. Inst. Can. Dept. Agric. Belleville, Inf. Bull.* **2**, 85 pp.

NICHOLSON, A. J. and BAILEY, V. A., 1935. The balance of animal populations. Part I. *Proc. zool. Soc. Lond.* **1935**, 551–98.

NIELSEN, B. OVERGAARD, 1963. The biting midges of Lyngby Aamose (Culicoides: Ceratopogonidae). *Natura jutl.* **10**, 46 pp.

NIJVELDT, W., 1959. Overhet gebruik van vangekegels bij het galmugonderzoek. *Tijdschr. PlZiekt.* **65**, 56–59.

ODUM, E. P. and KUENZLER, E. J., 1955. Measurement of territory and home range size in birds. *Auk.* **72**, 128–37.

OHNESORGE, B., 1957. Untersuchungen über die Populationsdynamik der kleinen Fichten-blattwespe, *Pristiphora abietina* (Christ) (Hym. Tenthr.). I. Teil. Fertilität und Mortalität. *Z. angew. Ent.* **40**, 443–93.

PALMÉN, E., 1955. Diel periodicity of pupal emergence in natural populations of some chironomids (Diptera). *Ann. zool. Soc. Vanamo* **17** (3), 1–30.

PALMÉN, E., 1962. Studies on the ecology and phenology of the Chironomids (Dipt.) of the Northern Baltic. *Ann. ent. fenn.* **28** (4), 137–68.

PARIS, O. H., 1965. The vagility of P^{32}-labelled Isopods in grassland. *Ecology* **46**, 635–48.

PAVLOV, I. F., 1961. Ecology of the stem moth *Ochsenheimeria vaculella* F.-R. (Lepidoptera Tineoidea). [In Russian.] *Ent. Obozr.* **40**, 818–27 (transl. *Ent. Rev.* **40**, 461–6).

PENDLETON, R. C. and GRUNDMANN, A. W., 1954. Use of P^{32} in tracing some insect–plant relationships of the thistle, *Cirsium undulatum. Ecology* **35**, 187–91.

PETERSON, A., 1934. *A manual of entomological equipment and methods.* Pt 1. Ann Arbor.

PILON, J. G., TRIPP, H. A., McLEOD, J. M. and ILNITZKY, S. L., 1964. Influence of temperature on prespinning eonymphs of the Swaine jack-pine sawfly, *Neodiprion swainei* Midd. (Hymenoptera: Diprionidae). *Canad. Ent.* **96**, 1450–7.

PREBBLE, M. L., 1941. The diapause and related phenomena in *Gilpinia polytoma* (Hartig). IV. Influence of food and diapause on reproductive capacity. *Canad. J. Res. D* **19**, 417–36.

PROMPTOW, A. N. and LUKINA, E. W., 1938. Die Experimente beim biologischen Studium und die Ernährung der Kohlmeise (*Parus major* L.) in der Brutperiode. [In Polish.] *Zool. Zh.* **17**, 777–82.

QUARTERMAN, K. D., MATHIS, W. and KILPATRICK, J. W., 1954. Urban fly dispersal in the area of Savannah, Georgia. *J. econ. Ent.* **47**, 405–12.

RAU, P. and RAU, N., 1916. The biology of the mud-daubing wasps as revealed by the contents of their nests. *J. anim. Behavior* **6**, 27–63.

REID, R. W., 1963. Biology of the mountain pine beetle, *Dendroctonus monticolae* Hopkins, in the East Kootenay Region of British Columbia. III. Interaction between the beetle and its host, with emphasis on brood mortality and survival. *Canad. Ent.* **95**, 225–38.

REIFF, M., 1955. Untersuchungen zum Lebenszyklus der Frostspanner *Cheimatobia* (*Operophthera*) *brumata* L. und *Hibernia defoliaria* Ch. *Mitt. schweiz. ent. Ges.* **26**, 129–44.

RICH, E. R., 1956. Egg cannibalism and fecundity in Tribolium. *Ecology* **37**, 109–20.

RICHARDS, O. W., 1940. The biology of the small white butterfly (*Pieris rapae*), with special reference to the factors controlling its abundance. *J. anim. Ecol.* **9**, 243–88.

RICHARDS, O. W. and HAMM, A. H., 1939. The biology of the British Pompilidae (Hymenoptera). *Trans. Soc. Brit. Ent.* **6**, 51–114.

RICHARDS, O. W. and WALOFF, N., 1954. Studies on the biology and population dynamics of British grasshoppers. *Anti-Locust Bull.* **17**, 184 pp.

RICHARDS, O. W. and WALOFF, N., 1961. A study of a natural population of *Phytodecta olivacea* (Forster) (Coleoptera: Chrysomelidae). *Phil. Trans. B* **244**, 205–57.

SKELLAM, J. G., 1951. Random dispersal in theoretical populations. *Biometrika* **38**, 196–218.

SMITH, H. S. and DEBACH, P. 1942. The measurement of the effect of entomophagous insects on population densities of the host. *J. econ. Ent.* **35**, 845–9.

SOMMERMAN, K. M., SAILER, R. I. and ESSELBAUGH, C. O., 1955. Biology of Alaskan black flies (Simuliidae, Diptera). *Ecol. Monogr.* **25**, 345–85.

SOUTHERN, H. N., 1954. Tawny owls and their prey. *Ibis* **96**, 384–410.

SOUTHWOOD, T. R. E., 1962. Migration of terrestrial arthropods in relation to habitat. *Biol. Rev.* **37**, 171–214.

SOUTHWOOD, T. R. E., JEPSON, W. F. and EMDEN, H. F. VAN, 1961. Studies on the behaviour of *Oscinella frit* L. (Diptera) adults of the panicle generation. *Ent. exp. appl.* **4**, 196–210.

SOUTHWOOD, T. R. E. and SIDDORN, J. W., 1965. The temperature beneath insect emergence traps of various types. *J. anim. Ecol.* **34**, 581–5.

SPEYER, W. and WAEDE, M., 1956. Eine Methode zur Vorhersage des Weizengallmückenfluges. *Nachr.Bl. dtsch. PflSchDienst. Stuttg.* **8**, 113–21.

SPILLER, D., 1964. Numbers of eggs laid by *Anobium punctatum* (Degeer). *Bull. ent. Res.* **55**, 305–11.

STEINHAUS, E. A., 1963. Background for the diagnoiss of insect diseases. In Steinhaus, E. A. (ed.), *Insect pathology, an advanced treatise* **2**, 549–89.

STICKEL, L. F., 1954. A comparison of certain methods of measuring ranges of small mammals. *J. Mammal.* **35**, 1–15.

STUMPF, W. A. and MOHR, C. O., 1962. Linearity of home ranges of California mice and other animals. *J. Wildl. Mgmt.* **26**, 149–54.

SULLIVAN, C. R. and GREEN, G. W., 1964. Freezing point determination in immature stages of insects. *Canad. Ent.* **96**, 158.

TELFER, W. H. and WILLIAMS, C. M., 1953. Immunological studies of insect metamorphosis. I. Qualitative and quantitative description of the blood antigens of the *Cecropia* silkworm. *J. Gen. Physiol.* **36,** 389–413.

TERRELL, T. T., 1959. Sampling populations of overwintering spruce budworm in'the Northern Rocky Mountain region. *Res. note Intermountain Forest Range Exp. Sta., Ogden, Utah* **61,** 8 pp.

TINBERGEN, L., 1960. The natural control of insects in pinewoods. 1. Factors influencing the intensity of predation by songbirds. *Arch. Néerland. Zool.* **13,** 266–343.

TURNBULL, A. L., 1960. The prey of the spider *Linyphia triangularis* (Clerck) (Araneae: Linyphiidae). *Canad. J. Zool.* **38,** 859–73.

TURNBULL, A. L., 1962. Quantitative studies of the food of *Linyphia triangularis* Clerck (Araneae: Linyphiidae). *Canad. Ent.* **94,** 1233–49.

TURNOCK, W. J., 1957. A trap for insects emerging from the soil. *Canad. Ent.* **89,** 455–6.

TURNOCK, W. J. and IVES, W. G. H., 1962. Evaluation of mortality during cocoon stage of the larch sawfly, *Pristiphora erichsonii* (Htg.). *Canad. Ent.* **94,** 897–902.

VALLENTYNE, J. R., 1952. Insect removal of nitrogen and phosphorus compounds from lakes. *Ecology* **33,** 573–7.

VARLEY, G. C., 1947. The natural control of population balance in the knapweed gall-fly (*Urophora jaceana*). *J. anim. Ecol.* **16,** 139–87.

VARLEY, G. C. and EDWARDS, R. L., 1957. The bearing of parasite behaviour on the dynamics of insect host and parasite populations. *J. anim. Ecol.* **26,** 471–7.

VARLEY, G. C. and GRADWELL, G. R., 1963. The interpretation of insect population change. *Proc. Ceylon Assn Adv. Sci.* (*D*) (**1962**), **18,** 142–56.

WADLEY, F. M., 1957. Some mathematical aspects of insect dispersion. *Ann. ent. Soc. Amer.* **50,** 230–1.

WALOFF, N. and RICHARDS, O. W., 1958. The biology of the Chrysomelid beetle, *Phytodecta olivacea* (Forster) (Coleoptera: Chrysomelidae). *Trans. R. ent. Soc. Lond.* **110,** 99–116.

WAY, M. J. and BANKS, C. J., 1964. Natural mortality of eggs of the black bean aphid, *Aphis fabae* (Scop.), on the spindle tree, *Euonymus europaeus*. *Ann. appl. Biol.* **54,** 255–67.

WELLINGTON, W. G., 1964. Qualitative changes in populations in unstable environments. *Canad. Ent.* **96,** 436–51.

WEST, A. S., 1950. The precipitin test as an entomological tool. *Canad. Ent.* **82,** 241–4.

WHITE, J. E., 1964. An index of the range of activity. *Amer. midl. Nat.* **71,** 369–73.

WILBUR, D. A. and FRITZ, R., 1939. Use of shoebox emergence cages in the collection of insects inhabiting grasses. *J. econ. Ent.* **32,** 571–3.

WITTIG, G., 1963. Techniques in insect pathology. *In* Steinhaus, E. A. (ed.), *Insect pathology, an advanced treatise* **2,** 591–636.

WOLFENBARGER, D. O., 1946. Dispersion of small organisms. *Amer. midl. Nat.* **35,** 1–152.

WRIGHT, D. W., HUGHES, R. D. and WORRALL, J., 1960. The effect of certain predators on the numbers of cabbage root fly (*Erioischia brassicae* (Bouché)) and on the subsequent damage caused by the pest. *Ann. appl. Biol.* **48,** 756–63.

CHAPTER 10

The Construction, Description and Analysis
of Age-specific Life-tables

TYPES OF LIFE-TABLE AND THE BUDGET

The construction of a number of life-tables is vital to the description and understanding of the population dynamics of a species, and the present chapter may be regarded as the culmination of the previous nine. Although some animal ecologists, such as Richards (1940), had expressed their results showing the successive reductions in the population of an insect throughout a single generation, Deevey (1947) was really the first to focus attention on the importance of this approach. Life-tables have long been used by actuaries for determining the expectation of life of an applicant for insurance and thus the column indicating the expectation of life at a given age (the e_x column) is an essential feature of human life-tables. However, the fundamental interests of the ecologist and, even more so, of the economic entomologist are essentially different from those of the actuary and it is a mistake to believe that these approaches and parameters of primary interest in the study of human populations are also those of greatest significance to the animal ecologist. Because many insects have discrete generations and their populations are not stationary, the age-specific life-table is more widely applicable than the time-specific life-table. The differences between these two types are as follows:

An age-specific (or horizontal) life-table is based on the fate of a real cohort; conveniently the members of a population belonging to a single generation. The population may be stationary or fluctuating.

A time-specific (or vertical) life-table is based on the fate of an imaginary cohort found by determining the age structure, at a point of time, of a sample of individuals from what is assumed to be a stationary population with considerable overlapping of generations, i.e. a multi-stage population. As age determination is a prerequisite for time-specific life-tables, these will be described further in chapter 11.

The data in age-specific life-tables may be corrected so as to start with a fixed number of individuals, e.g. 1000; however, this practice, that simplifies the calculation of life expectancy, causes the very important information on actual population size to be lost. It will be seen in this chapter that the variations in population size, from generation to generation, provide the frame of reference against which the roles of the various factors are analysed; therefore, in much work on insect populations, the type of table required lists the actual absolute populations at different stages and records the action of mortality factors where these are known (see table 18, p. 302). Such a table, giving just the observed data, is well described by the term *budget* proposed by Richards (1961), which also has the advantage that it emphasizes the distinction between this approach and that of the actuary.

THE CONSTRUCTION OF A BUDGET

The ideal budget will contain absolute estimates of the total population of as many stages as possible. At some points in the generation it may be possible to determine the total number entering a stage directly, as described in chapter 9 (see also p. 233). For other stages there will be a series of estimates, made on successive sampling days, using methods based on the numbers per unit area (chapters 4–6) or from mark and recapture (chapter 3), nearest neighbour (p. 39) or removal trapping (p. 181) techniques. The problem now arises as to how to determine from these estimates the total number of individuals that pass through a particular stage in one generation.

The degree of synchronization in the life-cycle is an important factor affecting the ease or difficulty of this step. The ideal situation is when there is a point of time when all the individuals of a generation are in a given stage; a census at this time will provide a 'peak estimate' that may be used in a life-table. As the overlap in time of successive stages increases, it will be necessary to integrate a number of estimates to obtain the total population; four techniques for doing this are given below. It will be noted that all these methods make special assumptions about mortality, assuming that it is frequently constant within a stage. When there is complete overlap of all stages, methods based on the age structure of the population are most appropriate (see chapter 11). Once the series of estimates of total population at each stage have been developed it can be assumed that the differences between these represent mortality and/or dispersal. It may be possible to check this assumption by direct measurement of these factors (chapter 9.)

A budget is to some extent self-checking; erroneous population measurements may be exposed by increases in numbers at a stage when immigration is impossible or by other inconsistencies. Thus, the more terms in a budget the greater the confidence that can be placed in it (Richards, 1959); this confidence is additional to and independent of that obtained from the statistical confidence limits of the individual estimates. The latter are based solely on the information gathered by the given method for that particular stage and mean that the true value is likely (to the extent of the chosen probability level) to lie within them. Although a precise mathematical evaluation is impossible, it is reasonable to claim that when there is agreement with other estimates, made simultaneously (p. 4) or sequentially, this substantially increases the probability that the true value lies close to the estimate.

Graphical methods

1. To determine the total population of a stage

This is the crudest and simplest of the methods of integration; assuming the mortality rate is constant throughout the life of an individual (whilst in this stage), it gives a value that approximates to the total population at the median age of the stage. If mortality is both constant and heavy, then this value will differ markedly from that for the total number of individuals

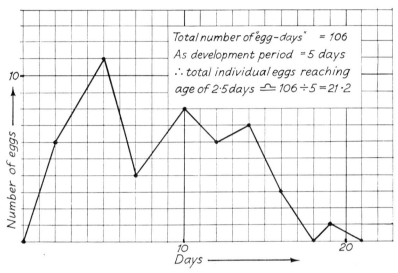

Fig. 79. The determination of the total number of individuals in a stage from series of estimates by graphical summation (hypothetical example with unrealistically small numbers for simplicity).

entering the stage. But if the mortality, although heavy, occurs entirely at the end of the stage, then the population estimate given by this method will approach the value for the total population. Successive estimates are plotted on graph paper, most conveniently allowing one square per individual and per day (fig. 79). The points are joined up and the number of squares under the line counted; this total is then divided by the mean developmental time under field conditions. This method was used by Southwood & Jepson (1962), who compared it with another method in which the total time, during which the stage was found, was divided arbitrarily into periods each corresponding to the developmental time of an individual; the mean population was calculated for each of these arbitrary periods and these means summed. The two methods are essentially similar and give similar results: both tend to underestimate the population, as individuals that are destroyed, for example by predators, are present for less than the full developmental time.

2. To determine the total change in population

Waloff & Bakker (1963) used an ingenious, partly graphical method to determine the total population change due to migration in a population of mirids.
Their approach could be applied to other situations where a stage with a well-
marked peak (fig. 80a) is divided into three phases and migration or a particular mortality factor is restricted to the second. The following points in time
must be established (fig. 80a): a=the date immediately before adult (or other
stage) appearance, the number of the previous stage (larvae) on this day being
N; b=the date of adult appearance; c=the date when all the larvae had be-

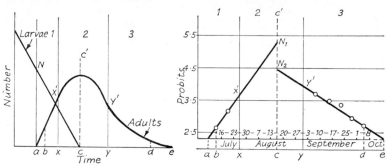

Fig. 80. The graphical determination of the population change due to a factor acting only
in the middle of a stage with a well-marked peak (after Waloff & Bakker, 1963): *a*. the actual
estimates of the stage in question (adult in this case) and the previous stage (larva); *b*. the
rise and fall of the stage as a percentage of N plotted as probits and projected to determine
the change which is expressed between N_1 and N_2.

come adults; d=the date when the last adult is recorded; x=the date of the
onset of migration; y=the date of the termination of migration. Then bx is
the pre-migration period and yd is the post-migration period.

The actual population estimates along bx' are transformed into percentages
of N and then into probit values and these will form a straight line which cuts
cc' at N_1 (fig. 80b). Similarly, the estimates along $y'd$ are transformed and a
second straight line drawn which will cut cc' at N_2. The slope of this line will
be shallower than of that based on bx', because all these estimates were from
populations that had been exposed to the loss factor (e.g. migration) in the
period xy. (Of course the line could be steeper – this would imply that immigration had exceeded emigration.)

Now, the probit value of N_1 may be converted to a percentage which
represents the percentage of N that actually became adults. If N is known, N_1
may be calculated in terms of actual individuals. Similarly N_2 may be found:
this is the total number after migration. The difference between N_1 and N_2 will
be the number of individuals that migrated.

Richards & Waloff's first method
to determine the number entering a stage

This method is applicable to a stage with a well-marked peak and an approximately steady mortality rate. In essence it consists of plotting the regression of the fall-off of numbers with time after the peak and then extending this

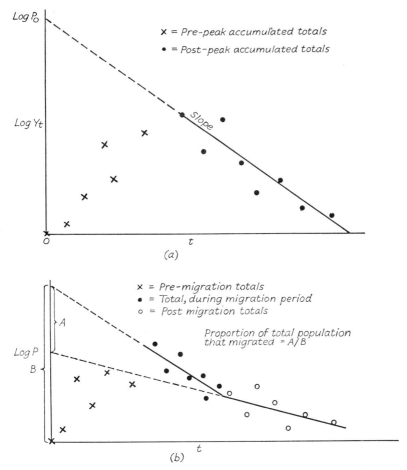

Fig. 81. *a.* A graphical representation of the principles of Richard & Waloff's first method to determine the number entering a stage. *b.* Graphical representation of the principle of Waloff & Bakker's use of the regression method to determine the change due to migration.

back to the time when the stage was first found (t_0); the 'population' corresponding to t_0 will be the total number of individuals that entered that stage (fig. 81) (Richards & Waloff, 1954).

A population exposed to a steady mortality will be expressed:

$$Y_t = P_0 S^t$$

where Y_t = population on day t, P_0 is the peak population (ideally the number hatched) and S = the fraction of the population which survives to the end of a unit of time (e.g. a day). Hence:

$$\log Y_t = \log P_0 + t \log S$$

and after the peak this will describe a straight line which is conveniently obtained from the regression of $\log Y_t$ on t: the regression coefficient will be $\log S$, the logarithm of the average, and supposedly constant, survival rate. The number entering the stage will then be given by the value of Y_t, found by inserting into the equation a value of t corresponding to the start of the stage. Alternatively, if t is numbered from the start of the stage in question, $\log P_0$ will equal the number entering the stage.

The estimates were checked against the actual population, when this method was tested in the laboratory by Dempster (1956), who concluded that reasonable results were obtained if Y_t was taken as the accumulated population. That is, after the peak of a particular instar, the values of Y_t are the total of that instar, plus any individuals that have passed through that instar and are in subsequent ones. For example, Y_{tx} for the second instar would consist of the populations of second instar, third instar and fourth instar, etc. as estimated for day tx, but Y_{tx} for the third instar would consist only of the populations of the third and subsequent instars. Dempster found that if Y_t was based solely on the numbers of the particular instar the estimates of population were too high, the slope of the line being too steep due to the confusion of moulting with mortality; the use of accumulated totals avoids this.

Waloff & Bakker (1963) used a modification of this method to determine the total change in population due to migration. Basically, separate regressions were calculated for the migration and post-migration period and the slopes ($\log S$) compared. The value of $\log S$ for the migration period represents migration and mortality, for the post-migration period just mortality. Therefore, if the difference between these is expressed as a percentage of the larger, this will be the percentage of the initial population that was lost during the migratory period.

Richards & Waloff's second method
to determine the number entering a stage

When there is no well-marked peak, but recruitment and mortality overlap widely, the regression method (above) cannot be used; however, the total number of any stage taken in all the samples (N) will be given by:

$$N = P_0 \int_0^a S^t \, dt = \frac{P_0(S^a - 1)}{\log_e S}$$

where P_0 = the total number entering the stage, S = the fraction of the population that survives per unit of time and a = the duration of the stage (Richards, 1959; Richards, Waloff & Spradbery, 1960; Richards & Waloff, 1961). Now if the number of eggs laid (P_0) and duration of the egg stage (a) are known and N obtained from samples, then the equation can be solved for S. The percentage mortality is $100(1 - S^a)$, and this may be used to calculate the number surviving the egg stage and entering the first larval instar. Thus P_0, a and N will again be known values in the equation for the first instar so that the percentage mortality for this instar and the numbers entering the next may be found. The process can be repeated to the end of the life-cycle.

It is most convenient to carry out these calculations by substituting the term U for S^a, then:

$$N = aP_0\frac{U-1}{\log_e U} \quad \text{or} \quad \frac{N}{aP_0} = \frac{U-1}{\log_e U}$$

A table $(U-1)/\log_e U$ may be constructed for values of U from 0·01 to 0·99; as the value of N/aP_0 is known, the corresponding value of U may be read off and as a is known, S may be calculated.

In order to apply this method one must have an accurate estimate for the initial P_0; Richards & Waloff (1961) obtained this from the population of adult females assessed independently and the oviposition rate measured under the field conditions. It is also necessary to determine the duration of the stage (a) experimentally and, as Richards *et al.* (1960) pointed out, differences, of as little as half a day, in the estimate of the duration of an instar can make a large difference in the estimated mortality. It is clear, therefore, that inaccuracies in these independent estimates of a and P_0, or discrepancies between the actual and assumed field conditions, which will influence the values assigned to a and P_0, are potential sources of error with this method.

Dempster's method
for the estimation of natality, mortality and migration

This method may be used with any animal where the same stages of successive generations do not overlap (Dempster, 1961). It is necessary to have a series of estimates of population, at least two more, ideally several more, than the number of stages and an independent estimate of the total natality of the first stage. The latter can be obtained from some form of emergence trap; where the eggs are laid in plant tissue, part of the plant is enclosed and the emerging larvae counted and removed. As with the previous methods, the mortality rate (μ) is assumed to be a constant, then:

$$Y_0 - Y_t = P\alpha_{(0\to t)} - \frac{(I_0 + I_t)}{2}t\mu_1 - \frac{(II_0 + II_t)}{2}t\mu_2 \dots - \frac{(Ad_0 + Ad_t)}{2}t\mu_a$$

where Y_0 and Y_t=total populations at days 0 and t (successive sampling dates), P=the total number hatching (or emerging) which found independently; $\alpha_{(0\to t)}$=the proportion of the total hatch that occurs between days 0 and t; I_0 and I_t=the total numbers of first instar larvae on the first and second sampling dates respectively, II_0 and II_t are the numbers of the second instar larvae; further terms are inserted, as appropriate, until the adult (Ad_0 and Ad_t) stage is reached; t is the time interval between day 0 and day t (the two sampling occasions) and $\mu_1, \mu_2 \ldots \mu_a$ are the average daily mortality of first and second stage larvae and adults.

The values $\mu_1 \ldots \mu_a$ are unknown, but may be found from a series of simultaneous equations, provided there is one more equation than unknown. These equations are reduced by the method of least squares and then solved by a standard mathematical procedure, such as the Doolittle Technique (see also p. 268).

Where there is migration a further term needs to be inserted into the equation; let $M=$ the net result of migration in terms of increase or decrease of population. A measure of the amount of migration may be obtained from one or more suction, rotary or interception traps placed close to the population and from this data the statistic x calculated:

$$x = \frac{\text{no. trapped between days 0 and } t}{\text{total number trapped}}$$

x is thus the migratory analogue of α. The following term is then inserted in the equation: $Mx_{(0 \rightarrow t)}$ the value of M and its sign being unknown; if M is positive migration has resulted in a gain (immigration), if negative in a loss (emigration). Estimates obtained in this way should, where possible, be compared with others obtained from directional interception traps and other approaches (pp. 260, 268).

This is a method capable of wide application; however, in order to obtain reliable estimates, a large number of accurate population samples are required, that is, it is not a 'robust' method (Dempster, pers. comm.).

THE DESCRIPTION OF BUDGETS AND LIFE-TABLES

Survivorship curves

The simplest description of a budget is the graphical representation of the fall-off of numbers with time – the survivorship curve. The number living at a given age (l_x) are plotted against the age (x); the shape of curve will describe the distribution of mortality with age. Slobodkin (1962) shows four basic types of curve (fig. 82); in type I mortality acts most heavily on the old individuals, in type II (a straight line when the l_x scale is arithmetic) a constant number die per unit of time; in type III (a straight line when the l_x scale is logarithmic) the mortality rate is constant and in type IV mortality acts most heavily on the young stages. Deevey (1947) also drew attention to these different types, but only recognized three and, in order to avoid confusion between his classification and Slobodkin's, it should be noted that Deevey plotted survivors (l_x) on a log scale and thus type II of Slobodkin was not recognized by him; type II of Deevey=type III of Slobodkin and type III of Deevey=type IV of Slobodkin.

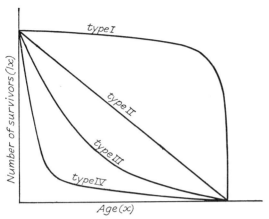

Fig. 82. Types of survivorship curves (after Slobodkin, 1962).

In insects mortality often occurs in distinct stages so that the survivorship curves show a number of distinct steps (Itô, 1961).

The life-table and life expectancy

For the further description of the data collected in the form of a budget or any type of life-table (chapter 11) it is most convenient if these are corrected so as to commence with a fixed number, usually 1000.

A table may then be constructed with the following columns (Deevey, 1947):

x the pivotal age for the age class in units of time (days, weeks, etc.)
l_x the number surviving at the beginning of age class x (out of a thousand originally born)
d_x the number dying during the age interval x
e_x the expectation of life remaining for individuals of age x

Table 15. A life-table (hypothetical)

x	l_x	d_x	L_x	T_x	e_x	$1000q_x$
1	1000	300	850	1880	1·88	300
2	700	200	600	1330	1·90	285
3	500	200	400	730	1·46	400
4	300	200	200	330	1·10	666
5	100	50	75	130	1·30	500
6	50	30	35	55	1·10	600
7	20	10	15	20	1·00	500
8	10	10	5	5	0·50	1000

In practice the table may have two further columns (table 15) to facilitate the calculation of the expectation of life as follows:

(*i*) The number of animals alive between age x and $x+1$ is found. Precisely this is:

$$L_x = \int_x^{x+1} l_x d_x$$

but if the age intervals are reasonably small it may be found from:

$$L_x = \frac{l_x + l_{x+1}}{2}$$

(*ii*) The total number of animal x age units beyond the age x, which is given by:

$$T_x = L_x + L_{x+1} + L_{x+2} \ldots L_w$$

where w=the last age. In practice it is found by summing the L_x column from the bottom upwards.

(*iii*) The expectation of life which is theoretically:

$$e_x = \frac{\int_x^w l_x d_x}{l_x}$$

and is therefore given by:

$$e_x = \frac{T_x}{l_x}$$

When the survivorship curve is of type I (fig. 82) e_x will increase with age; it will be constant for type II and decrease for types III and IV.

A further column is sometimes added to life-tables: the mortality rate per age interval (q_x), usually expressed as the rate per thousand alive at the start of that interval:

$$1000 q_x = 1000 \frac{d_x}{l_x}$$

Life and fertility tables and the net reproductive rate

In the two sections above we have been concerned solely with the description of one of the pathways of population change – mortality. In this section and the next methods of describing natality and its interaction with mortality in the population will be discussed.

A life and fertility table (or fecundity schedule) may be constructed by preparing a life-table with x and l_x columns as before, except that the l_x column refers entirely to females and should represent the number of females alive, during a given age interval, as a fraction of an initial population of one. Or, expressed another way, the life expectancy at birth to age x as a fraction of one (Birch, 1948) (table 16).

A new column is then added on the basis of observations, this is the m_x or age-specific fertility* column that records the number of living females born per female in each age interval. In practice it is frequently necessary to assume

Table 16. Life and fertility table for the beetle, *Phyllopertha horticola* (modified from Laughlin, 1965)

x (in weeks)	l_x	m_x	$l_x m_x$ $(= V_x)$
0	1·00	·—	Immature stages
49	0·46	—	
50	0·45	—	
51	0·42	1·0	0·42
52	0·31	6·9	2·13
53	0·05	7·5	0·38
54	0·01	0·9	0·01

a 50 : 50 sex ratio when $m_x = N_x/2$, N_x being the total natality per female of age x.

Columns l_x and m_x are then multiplied together to give the total number of female births (female eggs laid) in each age interval (the pivotal age being x); this is $l_x m_x$ column.

The number of times a population will multiply per generation is described by the net reproductive rate R_0, which is:

$$R_0 = \int_0^\infty l_x m_x d_x$$

$$R_0 = \Sigma \, l_x m_x$$

Thus from table 16 $R_0 = 2·94$; this net reproductive rate may be expressed in another way as the ratio of individuals in a population at the end of a generation to the numbers at the beginning of that generation. Thus,

$$R_0 = \frac{N_T}{N_0}$$

where T = generation time.

Clearly, values of R_0 in excess of one imply an increasing population, of less than one a decreasing population; when $R_0 = 1$ the population will be stationary.

Where the generation limits are obscured the value of R_0 as a description is limited and this led A. J. Lotka, a student of human demography, to propose the consideration of the growth rates of populations.

* This is often termed the fecundity column, but as it refers to live births, 'fertility' is a more appropriate term.

Population growth rates

As A. J. Lotka pointed out, the growth rate of a population is r in the equation:

$$\frac{dN}{dt} = rN$$

where N is the number of individuals at any given time (t); which may be expressed as:

$$N_t = N_0 e^{rt}$$

where e = the base of natural logarithms. The parameter r in this equation describes population growth (Paris, 1963); under conditions of an unlimited environment and with a stable age distribution this parameter becomes a constant. This has generally been considered to represent the intrinsic rate of natural increase, the maximum value of r possible for the species under the given physical and biotic environment and is denoted as r_m (Leslie & Ranson, 1940; Birch, 1948; Andrewartha & Birch, 1954). However, the studies of Lefkovitch (1963) suggest that this may not be the maximum (see below and p. 319).

The calculation of growth rate statistics is of value as a means of description of growth potential of a population under given conditions and for the comparison of various species (Smith, 1954); in connection with such comparisons it is important to remember that a range of climatic and biotic (e.g. food type) factors will influence the value of r_m (Messenger, 1964; Watson, 1964); indeed Messenger suggested that, because of this variation with climatic conditions, r_m could be used as a bioclimatic index in assessing the pest potentialities of an insect when introduced into a new area.

1. The capacity for increase (r_c)

Andrewartha & Birch (1954) described two methods of calculating r_m, one approximate, the other accurate. Laughlin (1965) has proposed that the statistic calculated by the approximate method be distinguished as the capacity for increase (r_c) and has shown that it is a valuable description of an animal's speed of multiplication. It is given by:

$$r_c = \frac{\log_e R_0}{T_c}$$

where R_0 = the net reproductive rate (see above) and T_c = cohort generation time (the mean age of the mothers in a cohort at the birth of female offspring). When as with most insects, generations are distinct, the values of R_0 and T_c can easily be determined from life and fecundity tables (see above).

Antilog$_e$ r_c, the finite capacity for increase, will give the number of times a population multiplies itself per time unit.

A species capacity for increase will approximate very closely to its intrinsic rate of natural increase when the generations are distinct, but if the generations overlap and the reproductive period (n) is long or R_0 high, then the intrinsic rate will be greater than the capacity for increase. Laughlin (1965) has made approximate comparisons of the two and shows that, where the $l_x m_x$ curve is

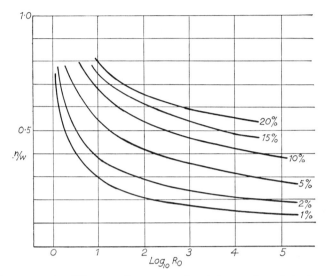

Fig. 83. The percentage difference of r_m over r_c in relation to the relative length of the reproductive period and the net reproductive rate (after Laughlin, 1965).

negatively skewed, the last 5–10% of the eggs can be disregarded when determining the end point of effective reproduction. When this has been done, the ratio n/w (i.e. the reproductive period (n) as a fraction of the oldest reproductive age (w)) is calculated and should be plotted against log R_0 on fig. 83, and this will show the approximate percentage difference of r_m over r_c and thus the extent of the additional information to be gained by the more tedious calculation of r_m.

2. The intrinsic rate of natural increase (r_m)
This is the instantaneous growth coefficient expressed when the population is growing in an unlimited environment and the age structure has become stable. Under these conditions:

$$\int_0^\infty e^{-r_m x} l_x m_x \, dx = 1$$

In solving this equation for r_m it is assumed that the developmental rates of the different individuals are normally distributed (i.e. Gaussian variates) around the mean; however, Lefkovitch (1963) suggests that this assumption may not be justified and that for this reason the actual rate of increase of the beetle *Lasioderma serricorne*, as measured by him, was greater than the r_m

calculated from age-specific life and fertility tables, and Messenger (1964) noted a similar anomaly with an aphid. However, until further studies are made, r_m must be regarded as the best available single description of the population growth potential of a species under given conditions.

The equation above can be approximated to:

$$\Sigma e^{-r_m x} l_x m_x = 1$$

Because of the construction of mathematical tables for powers of e the equation is most easily solved if both sides are multiplied by e^k. The method is described by Birch (1948) and, more recently, in detail by Watson (1964); both these authors used e^7.

Then:

$$e^7 \Sigma e^{-r_m x} l_x m_x = e^7$$

$$\Sigma e^{7 - r_m x} l_x m_x = 1096 \cdot 6$$

The value of r_c, approximately corrected from fig. 83, is taken as a possible value of r_m and then two trial values arbitrarily selected on either side of it, differing in the second decimal place. Watson (1964) used trial values of $0 \cdot 20$ and $0 \cdot 21$ and the following explanation is based on his paper. A table is constructed with columns x, l_x, m_x and $l_x m_x$; developed as above, and for each trial r_m columns:

(1) $r_m x$ the trial r_m multiplied by the pivotal age

(2) $7 - r_m x$ 7 minus column 1

(3) $e^{7 - r_m x}$ found from tables by looking up the exponential function
                         of column 2

(4) $e^{7 - r_m x} l_x m_x$ column 3 multiplied by the entry in the $l_x m_x$ column

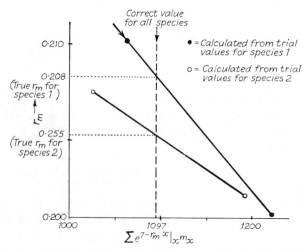

Fig. 84. The calculation of true r_m's graphically from two trial values (modified from Watson, 1964).

Column 4 is then summed and this gives a value for $\Sigma\, e^{7-r_m x} l_x m_x$ which will depart from 1096·6 by an extent depending on how close the trial r_m is to the true value. The true r_m can then be found graphically by plotting the two trial r_m's against their sums of column 4 (fig. 84).

The finite rate of natural increase, the number of times the population increases per unit of time is:

$$\lambda = \frac{N_t + 1}{N_t} = e^{r_m} = \text{antilog}_e\, r_m$$

As
$$\frac{N_T}{N_0} = e^{r_m T}$$

where T = generation time; the latter may be defined as

$$T = \frac{\log_e R_0}{r_m}$$

which although mathematically precise, is not easily expressed biologically (Slobodkin, 1962). Laughlin (1965) discusses the uses and meanings of T compared with T_c.

THE ANALYSIS OF LIFE-TABLE DATA

In the previous section we were concerned with the description of a life-table by a single parameter; the present section will discuss the methods of 'taking the life-table apart' so as to determine the role of each factor. Several life-tables are necessary; ideally these will be a series for a number of generations of the same population, but some information can be obtained from life-tables from different populations or by measuring density, mortality and the associated factors in different parts of the habitat. Such analysis is not only of considerable theoretical interest, but will eventually provide a rational and predictive basis for pest control: enabling both the forecasting of climatically induced outbreaks, and also the making of prognoses of the effects of changes in cultural or control practices.

The comparison of mortality factors within a generation (table 17)

1. Apparent mortality
This is the measured mortality, the numbers dying as a percentage of the numbers entering that stage, i.e. d_x as a % of l_x (see also p. 248). Its main value is for simultaneous comparison cither with independent factors or with the same factor in different parts of the habitat (see 5 below).

2. Real mortality
This is calculated on the basis of the population density at the beginning of the generation, i.e. $100 \times d_i / l_c$ where d_i = the deaths in the ith age interval and

Table 17. Various measures for the comparison of mortality factors

Stage	l_x	d_x	% apparent mortality	% real mortality	% indispensable mortality	Mortality/survivor ratio
Eggs	1000	500	50	50	3	1·00
Larvae	500	200	40	20	2	0·66
Pupae	300	270	90	27	27	9·00
Adult	30					

l_c the size of the cohort at the commencement of the generation. The real mortality column in table 17 is the only % column that is additive and is useful for comparing the role of population factors within the same generation.

3. Indispensable (or irreplaceable) mortality

This is that part of the generation mortality that would not occur, should the mortality factor in question be removed from the life system, after allowance is made for the action of subsequent mortality factors. It is often assumed that these will still destroy the same percentage independent of the change in prey density; clearly this assumption will not always be justified. To take an example of the calculation of the indispensable mortality from the table, consider the egg stage mortality: if there is no egg mortality 1000 individuals enter larval stage where a 40% mortality leaves 600 survivors to pupate; in the pupal stage a 90% mortality leaves 60 survivors, that is 30 more than when egg mortality occurs, and thus its indispensable mortality

$$= 30/1000 \times 100 = 3\%.$$

When it is known that the subsequent mortalities are unrelated to density the indispensable component of a factor may be used for assessing its value in control programmes (e.g. Huffaker & Kennet, 1965). If the exact density relationship of subsequent factors is known then a corrected, and more realistic, indispensable mortality can be calculated.

Factors acting contemporaneously will also affect the indispensable component of a mortality factor. In an important paper, to which reference should be made for further details, Morris (1965) shows that the interaction of two contemporaneous mortality factors will be expressed by:

$$S = 1 - (m_1 + m_2) + v(m_1 m_2)$$

where S=proportion surviving, $m_1 = M_1/N$, M_1=the numbers killed by factor 1 and N=the numbers alive at the beginning of the age interval, similarly $m_2 = M_2/N$, and v=the interaction coefficient, an index of vulnerability. If $v = 1 \cdot 0$, animals affected by one factor will be as vulnerable as those unaffected; $v < 1 \cdot 0$ will imply that vulnerability to one factor decreases vulnerability to the other and $v > 1 \cdot 0$ that vulnerability to one increases vulnerability to the other. Morris has suggested that the interaction coefficient could be determined by statistical inference, e.g. multivariate analysis (see Morris 1963a), ideally combined with experimental evidence of the mode of interaction.

The relations between changes in the various terms in the equation may be seen by plotting S against m_2, when the intercept on the S axis will represent $1-m_1$, that on the m_2 axis $(1-m_1)/(1-vm_1)$ and the slope vm_1-1. From hypothetical examples Morris demonstrates that factors may be important even if their apparent mortality is low, but they operate contemporaneously with large apparent mortalities and have vulnerability coefficients of less than one. In control work, when immediate population reduction is desired a factor with the two last mentioned properties would be ideal.

4. Mortality – survivor ratio

Introduced by Bess (1945) this measure represents the increase in population that would have occurred if the factor in question had been absent. If the final population is multiplied by this ratio then the resulting value represents, in individuals, the indispensable mortality due to that factor.

5. The response of a natural enemy to the density of the prey

The response of a predator (or parasite) to variations in the density of its prey (or host) in different parts of the habitat may be investigated by determining the regression of apparent mortality (as a percentage) in different areas (e.g. trees) of the habitat on the prey density in these areas. If the regression is significant the action of the natural enemy is density-dependent, either directly ($b*$ positive) or inversely (b negative). Solomon (1949) pointed out that this response had two components: functional and numerical. Holling (1959) elaborated these terms and defined a functional response as when there are changes in the number of prey taken or killed by each predator (or parasite) and a numerical response when the number of predators (or parasites) per unit area changes with a change in prey density. Others have used these terms differently, and Hassell (1966) has suggested that where a density-dependent response is shown by an enemy *within one generation* this is well described as a 'behavioural response'; and considered as 'superproportional' when the proportion (conveniently a percentage) of predation or parasitism is greater in regions of higher host density (i.e. a direct density-dependent factor) or as 'subproportional' when the percentage of predation is smaller in regions of higher host density (i.e. an inverse density-dependent factor).

If the population density (i.e. intensity, p. 2) of the predator or parasite (adult parasite in the case of parasitic insects) and that of the prey are known from different regions of the habitat as well as the mortality, it is possible to distinguish between what Hassell (1966) terms the 'individual response' (corresponding to Holling's functional response), and the 'aggregative response' (corresponding to Holling's numerical response). Hassell defines these

* $b=$ the regression coefficient.

in terms of the proportion of the prey killed (rather than the numbers, so that the effect on the prey is easily inferred). An individual response will be recognized by obtaining a significant regression when the percentage mortality divided by the density of enemy is plotted against prey density. An aggregative response can be demonstrated by plotting the number of enemies in each sample, expressed as a percentage of the total enemies in all samples, against the host density (Hassell, 1966).

The simple statistical relationship of population size to a factor

If the size of the population of a certain stage is measured over a number of generations, straightforward statistical correlation or regression analysis methods may be used to test the relationship of the variations in population with some other factor, e.g. climate, the numbers of natural enemies, the quantity of food available. Williams (1961) used this method extensively to demonstrate relationships between light-trap catch and immediate and previous climate; he was able to demonstrate that the relationships held, over many years and in two different areas, and that it would be possible to forecast the size of the catch if the weather conditions could be forecast. It is of course an elementary statistical principle that correlation is not causation; as G. C. Varley has pointed out, there is a good correlation between his own increasing age and the increase in the population of Ceylon, and I believe one has been shown in a Dutch village between the number of babies and the number of storks! Such correlations can easily be dismissed as meaningless, but in other instances although the relationship may appear reasonable it is difficult to be sure that it is not equally fallacious. Where there is extensive data, as in Williams's work, it seems likely that there is a causal link, but the mechanism through which previous weather influences the catch remains obscure (Varley, 1963). The strongest evidence for the validity of a relationship established in this way will come from direct experiments; often, however, the ecologist has to be content with an apparently sound biological link that holds under a variety of conditions, which are such that possible 'common causes' have varied independently and so been eliminated.

This problem is very germane to the present chapter, for although the simple correlation of population size and an independent measure of a factor is of comparatively limited use, the major techniques outlined below are largely based on correlation and regression methods. When the aim is prediction rather than interpretation it does not matter whether correlation is causal or not provided it is consistent. However, prediction will be based on the development of adequate models and, as Watt (1961, 1962) has pointed out, in addition to the disadvantages implicit from the above, linear regression equations cannot adequately express many biological processes. Watt concludes that 'the main advantage of multiple regression analysis is that its procedures are mathematically straightforward rather than that the fitted equations bear close correspondence to events in biological reality' and that increasing use is being made of reasonably realistic differential equations.

Survival analysis and model construction

The work of Watt (1961, 1963*a*, 1964) represents a great advance in population ecology in bridging the gap between the mathematical model constructed on *a priori* assumptions and the description of actual changes in field populations. Watt describes in detail both the theory and practice for the development of inductive and mixed deductive-inductive models; in the former the survival of a particular stage is related to the magnitude of various factors that might affect it. The mixed model also requires information on the actual (apparent) mortality caused by these factors (appropriate methods for determining these are given in chapter 9). The data are first grouped and then expressed graphically, from the form of the graphs the type of equation best expressing the relationship is inferred. In the mixed model the expected mortality due to the factor, calculated from the equation, is compared with the actual mortality. Such comparisons may lead to a revision of the form of the equation. The eventual model will describe the index of population trend in terms of the survival of the different stages as related to the various factors.

The Index of Population trend (I) was proposed by Balch & Bird (1944) and is:

$$I = \frac{P_{n+1}}{P_n}$$

where P = total population of a particular stage and n = any given generation. The stage chosen for the determination of I is important (see also p. 299). Watt (1961) recommends the adult stage, but as Morris (1963) points out, the egg stage is preferable as this is probably the most uniform stage with respect to quality. If the same number of females survive to adulthood in two generations, but conditions of stress in one have led to an adult population with only half the normal fecundity, this should be shown by the model and this can only be done if I is taken from egg to egg. Therefore, following Morris (1963):

$$I = \frac{P_{En+1}}{P_{En}} = S_E \times S_L \times S_P \times S_A \times p_{\female} \times p_F \pm \frac{P_{Dn}}{P_{En}}$$

where S_E = survival of eggs, S_L = survival of larvae, S_P = survival of pupae, S_A = survival of adults up to and including the period of oviposition; $p_{\female}$ = the proportion of adults that are females, p_F = the proportion of mean maximal fecundity that can be obtained by population of females because of their quality (e.g. fecundity as indicated by size), P_{Dn} = population of eggs lost or added to the population as a result of migration during generation n and P_{En} = the population of eggs of generation n.

This represents the form of the model and then following Watt's (1961) approach a series of sub-models, one for each age interval, is built up, as was done by Morris and co-workers (1963). In this way the values of S_E, S_L, etc. can be replaced by expressions from the sub-models; survival in each age interval will be expressed as functions of other factors, e.g.:

$$S_E = f(_EX_1, \ _EX_2, \ _EX_3, \ \ldots \ _EX_i$$

where $f_EX_1, \ldots$ etc. represent the level of a certain factor and its influence on this equation, the egg stage. The ecologist will need to decide what are the possible factors, for example the abundance of various parasites and predators and the level of different climatic factors, e.g. temperature, rainfall, wind gust index. It is most important that the meterological measurements be those most applicable to the stage and behaviour in question; e.g. in relating migration and temperature, it is probably only the temperature during the actual hours of migration that is significant. The records are then ranked according to the level of the particular factor, the independent variable, e.g. rainfall, and divided in n groups.* The mean rainfall or other variable and the mean survival of the stage in each group are obtained and plotted against each other.

The resulting graph will indicate the relationship of survival to the independent variable. It may show that it will be necessary to transform the independent variable to logs or reciprocals in order to make the relationship approximately linear. The values of S (the dependent variable) should not be transformed as these must remain in the arithmetic form to allow multiple regression analysis with the total S_G equation (e.g. Mott, 1963b).

The appropriate function to describe the relationship can then be computed by calculating the regression line. Then the difference between the observed S and the calculated S is found for the relationship that shows the greatest correlation and, with these differences as the dependent variable, the above processes repeated with the other variables to determine if a higher correlation could be obtained by including them (viz. could the proportion of the variance explained by the main factor (variable) alone be increased by taking another factor into the sub-model). As a result of such a process a sub-model is constructed. Mott (1963a) developed a sub-model for the survival of young larvae (S_s) of the spruce budworm:

$$S_s = 0{\cdot}448 - 0{\cdot}0245 F_d + \frac{1{\cdot}1123}{P_s} - 0{\cdot}0533 \log D_{cc}$$

where F_d = tree diameter, P_s = larval density and D_{cc} = cumulative defoliation.

A multiple regression analysis, with the partitioning of the variance, is carried out with the final equation. With the above, which accounted for 49·2% of the total variance, the tree diameter was responsible for 25·6%, the

---

* As each group should consist of 10, preferably nearer 50, records, extensive data is required for this type of analysis; with limited material the grouping may be omitted, but far more difficulty will be experienced in interpreting the graphs as they will be very irregular, each survival reflecting the influence of variables other than the one being plotted.

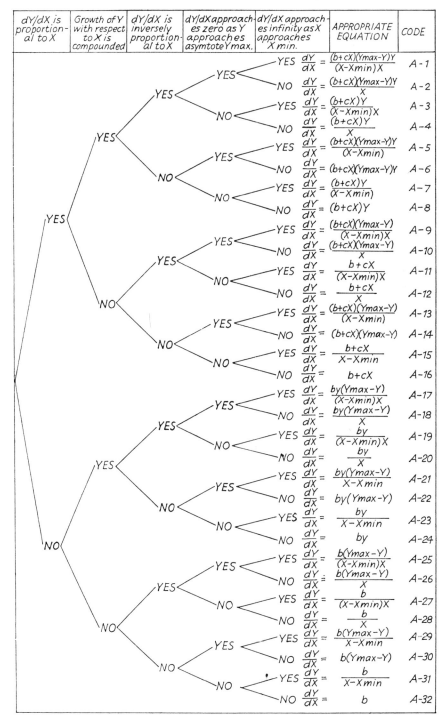

Fig. 85. The logical tree diagram for deducing which equation is most appropriate to describe a phenomenon (after Watt, 1961).

competition effect of larval density for 16·0% and cumulative defoliation for 7·6%.

A complete model for generation survival can be built up based on similar regression, correlation and multiple regression techniques, and the process is described in detail in Morris (1963a). In this instance the sub-models accounted for between 44% and 85% of the variation in survival in the particular age interval, and it was concluded that only variables that had effects of some magnitude on the survival would be mimicked by the model.

It may be desired to develop a deductive–inductive model along the lines described by Watt (1961), expressing the phenomenon in terms of differential equations. For this it will be necessary to have information on the actual predation or parasitism. Initially, the data may be grouped and graphed as before. Then the appropriate equation must be determined and for this reference should be made to Watt's logical tree diagram reproduced as fig. 85 and the investigator asking himself the series of appropriate questions set out along the top of the table, e.g. 'Is dy/dx proportional to x?' If the answer is 'Yes' the upper line is followed, if 'No' the lower one.

Once the elementary equation has been picked it is integrated and transformed to a form suitable for testing against the observed results graphically (or, if necessary, statistically). The original equation may be found inappropriate and a new one have to be selected. It is then necessary to see if another variable also influences the mortality (M) or survival ($S = 1 - M$) of the stage. A series of cycles of calculations will be made as described by Watt (1961). On one hand these models are of predictive value and on the other, because of the analysis of the roles of various factors in the survival, they offer an insight into the dynamics of the population.

Regression analysis to determine the main variables affecting the index of population trend – Morris's key factor analysis

This method is less demanding on the mathematical facility of the worker than survival analysis. Precise population measurements are necessary for only one stage in each generation, but information on the proportion destroyed by parasites and predators and on the level of the food supply and weather are also needed. Morris (1959) put forward the idea that although many variables contributed to mortality in a population, the main fluctuations are due to only a few factors; the measurement of these few would provide the key to the prediction of population in the next generation and he called these 'key factors'. This method of analysis is designed to develop simple, predictive equations containing these key factors.

The concept of key factor has been adopted by many ecologists and it appears that there may often be one factor that is responsible for the majority of the fluctuations in a particular index of population trend (Varley & Gradwell, 1960; Watt, 1963*b*); this has been referred to as 'the key factor'. It must be stressed that this is the key factor for prediction, the factor that accounts for the main fluctuations in population size and *not* the principal regulating or density-dependent factor or factors. In general one would not expect the same factor to be both key and regulatory (Varley, 1963). The present method, however, not only allows the key factor or factors to be recognized, but also the extent of density-dependent regulation and the factors responsible for it together with other significant parameters. It has the advantages over survival analysis that more limited budgets are acceptable and the computations are considerably simpler.

As Varley & Gradwell (1965) have shown, the stage selected as the basis of *I* may influence which factor appears to be the key one for prediction; that is, if the generation base is taken from egg to egg the 'key factor' may be different from that disclosed when the generation is taken from late larva to late larva. Therefore, for pest outbreak prediction the generation base should be from one damage-causing stage (generally the larva) to the same stage in the next generation, and the key factor will then be that variable that causes the major fluctuations in numbers of larva from generation to generation.

Morris's method is based on simple regression analysis and involves the determination of the influence of the size of the previous generation and of the various density-dependent factors. Then the key factor or factors are recognized as the factors responsible for the majority of the deviations from the regression line of population size on survivors from the previous population (Morris, 1963*c*). The method may be explained step by step with reference to fig. 86. The data from different areas should be analysed separately as the level of the population and the roles of the different factors may vary from locality to locality, and Solomon (1964) has suggested that it may be instructive to consider periods of population increase separately from periods of decline.

(1) The data, from a life-table or budget, are converted into logarithms; this stabilizes the variance and provides linearity: if the untransformed data are used a curved plot will result (fig. 86*a*). The linear regression of log population of the chosen stage (see above) of generation $n+1$ on log population of generation n is calculated (fig. 86*b*). This shows the extent to which the size of the previous generation influences the size of the next; in this case (fig. 86*b*) the coefficient of determination (r^2, where $r=$correlation coefficient) of 0·3 indicates that 30% of the variation in log P_{n+1} is explained by log P_n. That is, r^2 may be taken as a measure of stability, showing the extent to which population size fluctuates from generation to generation. The lower the r^2 the more fluctuating the population; r^2 describes the interaction of the net reproductive rate (R_0) of the species with the environmental factors of the particular population. The regression coefficient (b) describes the extent to which the rate of population increase falls off with density; a coefficient of 1·0 implies that there is no density dependence in the population, while low values of b

indicate a very high level of density dependence. Another meaningful ecological parameter is F in the equation:

$$\log P_{n+1} = \log F + b \log P_n$$

F is the effective rate of increase = antilog of the intercept on the $\log P_{n+1}$ axis

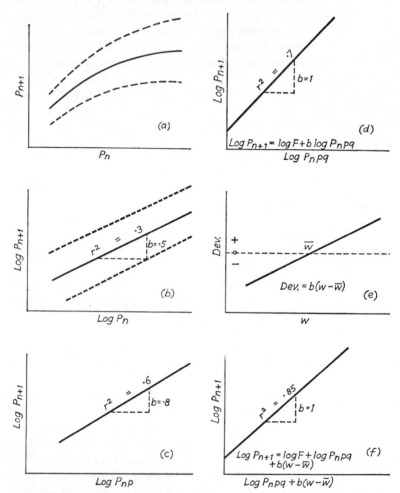

Fig. 86. The steps in a Morris-type key factor analysis (after Morris, 1963c).

when $\log P_n = 0$, i.e. when $P_n = 1$. Populations in different habitats will often
be found to differ in their F values (Morris, 1963b and c).

(2) The next step involves the recognition of the density-dependent factor
or factors and their incorporation into the independent variable of the regression equation. Thus, in the example (fig. 86c), the previous population is multiplied by proportion surviving parasitism (p) and although this increases the

value of b to 0·8, there is a further density-dependent factor. The addition of the proportion of the population surviving predation (q) (fig. 86d) raises the value of b to approximately 1·0 and allows one to claim that the density-dependent factors have been recognized. With field data b may still fall short of 1 after all observed factors have been added; b must then be retained in the predictive equation.

(3) In this step factors such as weather, that do not generally act in a density-dependent manner, are tested against the deviations of the actual points from the expected points calculated from:

$$\log P_{n+1} = \log F + b \log P_n pq$$

From such a graph (fig. 86e) the value for the weather index, at zero deviation from the expected values, may be read off and is referred to as $\bar{w}$. If the plot is linear a regression may be calculated, but in other instances it will be necessary to draw a curve.

(4) The regression derived from the last step is added to the previous equation and the change in the value of r^2 will give a measure of the extent to which this factor accounts for fluctuations in the population.

(5) Further factors may be tested as in 3 and 4 and added to the equation until the residual variation around the regression line is not much greater than the sampling error. Then a final equation of the form:

$$\log P_{n+1} = \log F + b \log P_n pq + b(w - \bar{w}) + \dots$$

may be used to predict the population size of generation $n+1$.

In conclusion then, the Morris analysis provides the following:

(*i*) A predictive equation for the fluctuations in the index of population trend of the selected stage (age class); this will incorporate the key factors.

(*ii*) The extent of density-dependence in the population trend given by $1·0 - b$, where b is the coefficient in the regression of population size in one generation on that in the previous generation (fig. 86b).

(*iii*) A measure of the population fluctuations (of the chosen stage) from generation to generation given by r^2 of the correlation of P_{n+1} with P_n (fig. 86b).

(*iv*) The extent to which various factors contribute to the fluctuations in the size of the population of the selected stage given by the change in r^2 as each is incorporated in the regression equations (figs. 86c, d and f).

(*v*) The extent to which various factors act in a density-dependent manner given by the change in b as each is incorporated in the regression equation (figs. 86c and d).

(*vi*) The effective rate of increase of the population given by F in the regression equations, i.e. antilog of the intercept in figs. 86b, c, d and f. This is the average number of times generation $n+1$ will be greater than the survivors from the density-dependent processes in generation n. The value of F may be expected to vary from habitat to habitat and is, in a way, a measure of habitat favourability. However, as Morris (1963b) has pointed out, in order to obtain a reliable value of F it is necessary to analyse data over a long period and for more than one population oscillation.

Analysis to recognize the roles of factors in a series of successive life-tables –. Varley & Gradwell's method

These methods developed by Varley & Gradwell (1960, 1963*a* and *b*, 1965; and Varley, 1963), relying heavily as they do on graphical correlation, are easier to use than either Morris's key factor or Watt's survival analysis, furthermore they give slightly different information. Like these methods they demand the data from a series of successive life-tables.

Varley & Gradwell's method differs from Morris's in that the whole genera-tion is considered and thus it is immediately apparent in which age interval the density-dependent and key factors lie, rather than having to select factors from biological knowledge and correlate each in turn with the generation mortality. It is also the most direct method of testing the role of changes in natality from generation to generation.

Varley & Gradwell's method may be outlined as follows:

(1) The maximum potential natality is found by multiplying the number of females of reproductive age by the maximum mean fecundity/female and this figure is entered in the budget (table 18).

(2) The values in the budget are converted to logarithms.

(3) A convenient generation basis in this method is adult to adult; the base

Table 18. A budget prepared for Varley & Gradwell's analysis

	Nos/10 sq m (observed, unless marked *)	Log nos/10 sq m	k's
Maximum potential natality (no. reprod. ♀ × maximum natality)	$\frac{1}{2}$ × 30 × 100 = 1500	3·176	
k_0 (variation in natality)			0·076
Eggs laid	1260	3·100	
k_1 (egg loss)			0·171
Eggs hatching	850	2·929	
k_2 (predation, etc.)			0·498
3rd stage larvae	270	2·431	
k_3 (apparent parasitism of larvae)	100		0·201
[Larvae surviving parasitism]	170*	2·230	
k_4 (predation and other larval mortality)			0·276
Pupae	90	1·954	
k_5 (overwintering loss)			0·301
Adults emerging	45	1·653	
k_6 (dispersal, etc.)			0·352
Adults reproducing	20	1·301	
		K =	1·875

chosen will affect the recognition of key factors (Varley & Gradwell, 1965) (see p. 299). The total generation 'mortality' is given by subtracting the log of the population of adults entering the reproductive stage from the log maximum potential natality of the previous generation – this value is referred to as K (table 18).

(4) The series of age-specific mortalities are calculated by subtracting each log population from the previous one (table 18); these are referred to as k's, so that:

$$K = k_0 + k_1 + k_2 + \ldots k_i$$

Where precise estimates of mortality and migration (see chapter 9) are available these are also incorporated into the equation. These series of k's – one series for each generation – provide a complete picture of population change. In the subsequent steps of this analysis the role of each k factor is examined separately, but it must be remembered that sampling errors are 'hidden' in each k and may be responsible for spurious results. The identification of the k value with a specific factor presents no problem when it is based on an apparent mortality, but when it is the difference of successive estimates it should, strictly, be referred to as 'overwintering loss' or 'loss of young adults'. It may be possible from other knowledge to indicate the major components of these losses; such assumptions could be checked by testing the correlation between the k value and an independent measure of the loss factor, e.g. the abundance of a predator, over a number of generations. k_0, the difference between the log maximum potential natality and log actual natality, has a special significance, for it does not represent mortality in the strict sense, but the variation in natality. This is compounded of two separate causes: death of the reproducing females before the end of the reproductive life and variations in the fertility of the females. The two could be separated by determining the form of survival curve of the reproducing female (chapter 11).

(5) The next step involves the recognition of the key factor for the index of population trend from adult to adult. This is done by visual correlation, K and k_0 to k_i are plotted against generation and it may easily be seen which k is most closely correlated with K (fig. 87). Alternatively the correlation coefficients may be calculated.

(6) The various k's are then tested for direct density dependence. Firstly each k is plotted against the numbers entering the stage (age interval) on which it acts (fig. 88); if the regression is significant then density dependence may be suspected. However, the two variables are not independent (they are actually $\log P_1$ and $\log P_1 - \log P_2$) and so the regression could be spurious, due to sampling errors. The second step therefore is to plot the log numbers entering the stage ($\log P_1$) against the log number of survivors ($\log P_2$). The regressions of $\log P_2$ on $\log P_1$ and of $\log P_1$ on $\log P_2$ should be calculated, and if both the regression coefficients depart significantly from $1 \cdot 0$, then the density dependence may be taken as real (see also Watt, 1964).

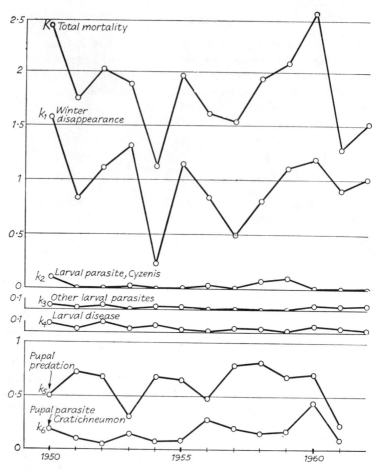

Fig. 87. The recognition of the key factor by the visual correlation of various k's with K (after Varley & Gradwell, 1960).

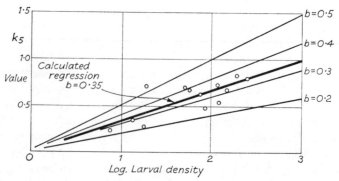

Fig. 88. The recognition of density dependence of a k factor by plotting the value of this factor against the log density at the start of the stage on which it acts (after Varley & Gradwell, 1963a).

(7) If density dependence is shown to be real, attention may now be re-focused on the plot of k_x against the numbers entering the stage (fig. 88). The slope of the line, the regression coefficient, should be determined as this will give a measure of how the factor will act; the closer the regression co-efficient is to 1·0, the greater the stabilizing effect of that regulatory factor. If the coefficient is exactly 1·0 the factor will compensate completely for any changes in density; if the coefficient is less than 1·0 the factor will be unable to compensate completely for the changes in density caused by other disturbing factors; whilst a coefficient of more than 1·0 implies overcompensation.

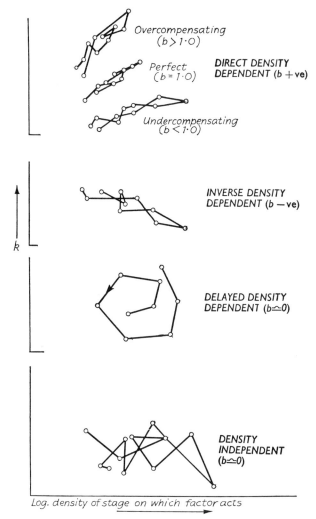

Fig. 89. Time sequence plots showing how the different density relationships may be recognized from the patterns produced.

(8) Further insight into the mode of action of population factors may be obtained by plotting the k value against log initial density (as in fig. 88) and then joining the points up in a time sequence plot (Varley, 1947, 1953; Morris, 1959; Varley & Gradwell, 1965). The different types of factor will trace different patterns (fig. 89): direct density-dependent factors will trace a more or less straight line or narrow band of points, delayed density factors circles or spirals; density-independent factors irregular or zigzag plots, whose amplitude reflects the extent to which they fluctuate. Solomon (1964) discusses how the order in which various factors act will influence the magnitude of their effect. This type of plot, the linking of consecutive points serially, is of particular value in investigating what Hassell (1966) has appropriately termed 'intergeneration relationships', and it is the only method by which a delayed relationship (a delayed density-dependent factor) can be recognized. As a factor that is directly density-dependent over several generations, will kill a higher proportion of prey in years of greater prey density, Hassell describes such a relationship as 'superproportional', whilst the relationship between an inverse density-dependent factor and its 'victim' will be 'subproportional'.

In conclusion Varley & Gradwell's method allows:

(*i*) The recognition of the key factor (or factors) or the period in which it acts.

(*ii*) The investigation of the role of natality in population dynamics.

(*iii*) The consideration of the role of mortality factors at every stage of the life-cycle, the recognition of the different density relationships of these factors and an indication of their mode of operation: direct density-dependent factors tend to stabilize, delayed density-dependent factors lead to oscillations, density-independent factors lead to fluctuations and inverse density-dependent factors will tend to accentuate the fluctuations.

The investigation of the roles of different factors in single-generation budgets

The above methods can be used with continuous populations for which a series of estimates have been made in successive generations, but with many pests of arable crops or extremely migratory insects continuous populations do not exist and therefore it is not possible to calculate a meaningful population trend from generation to generation. It is, however, possible to obtain a number of incomplete budgets from egg to late immature stage or to the emerging adult. Such data may be used to determine the relative importance of natality compared with mortality in determining the size of the final or economic population. In other words to answer the question: is the size of the population of a caterpillar in a field determined mostly by the number of eggs laid, or by the level of egg parasitism or by the amount of early larval mortality? The data may be examined initially by graphical methods (2 below), or statistical analysis alone used (3 below).

The procedure is as follows:

(1) The various population estimates are converted to logarithms: if P_E = number (absolute density of eggs laid and P_R = number of the resulting population (late larvae, pupae or emerging adults), then

$$\log P_E - \log P_R = \kappa$$

κ being the total mortality over that part of the life-cycle studied. (The symbol κ (kappa) is used to distinguish this from K, which is the total mortality including variation in natality over the whole life-cycle.)

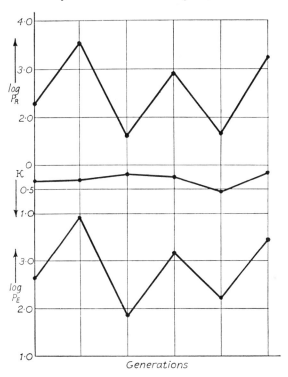

Fig. 90. The graphical investigation of the roles of natality (P_E) and mortality (κ) in determining the size of the resulting population (P_R). Data on the frit fly from Southwood & Jepson (1962) showing the dominant role of natality.

If apparent parasitism or other mortality factors are known, appropriate k values are calculated as in Varley & Gradwell's method (p. 302). Then a residual mortality k_r is found:

$$k_r = \kappa - (k_1 + k_2 + \ldots k_n)$$

(2) The correlation of the different values may be examined by a graphical method (fig. 90). P_E and P_R are plotted normally, but κ or the series of k's are plotted on an inverted scale so that high levels of mortality will be represented by dips that will correspond with low values in P_E. In some cases it will be found that fluctuations in P_R are obviously accounted for almost entirely by

variations in natality (P_E). As P_E and P_R are statistically independent this conclusion need not be questioned. However, reliance cannot be placed on the correlation of κ with P_R as these are not independent (see Watt, 1964).

(3) A more precise evaluation of the role of natality may be obtained by calculating the value of the coefficient of determination (r^2) for P_R plotted against P_E. This is a measure, as a percentage, of the amount of the variance of P_R accounted for by P_E, i.e. of the role of natality.

This method allows the relative importance of different pathways of population change to be assessed in crop insects and others where there is a 'gap' in the budget data for part or all of the adult stage and successive generations are not part of the same population. It differs from the other methods in that the comparative basis is not total mortality or the index of population trend, but the actual size of the population of a certain stage. It will probably be useful in ecological investigations, in connection with integrated pest control programmes, to determine the role in population fluctuation of predator and parasite induced mortality compared with that due to variations in the number of eggs laid, which stems from the numbers of females invading the field and their survival and fertility.

The mode of action of individual mortality factors may be investigated by comparing the intensity of their action in different parts of the habitat where the host's (or prey's) densities differ (see p. 293).

REFERENCES

ANDREWARTHA, H. G. and BIRCH, L. C., 1954. *The distribution and abundance of animals.* Chicago, 782 pp.

BALCH, R. E. and BIRD, F. T., 1944. A disease of the european spruce sawfly, *Gilpinia hercyniae* (Htg.), and its place in natural control. *Sci. Agr.* **25**, 65–80.

BESS, H. A., 1945. A measure of the influence of natural mortality factors on insect survival. *Ann. ent. Soc. Amer.* **38**, 472–82.

BIRCH, L. C., 1948. The intrinsic rate of natural increase of an insect population. *J. anim. Ecol.* **17**, 15–26.

DEEVEY, E. S., 1947. Life tables for natural populations of animals. *Quart. Rev. Biol.* **22**, 283–314.

DEMPSTER, J. P., 1956. The estimation of the numbers of individuals entering each stage during the development of one generation of an insect population. *J. anim. Ecol.* **25**, 1–5.

DEMPSTER, J. P., 1961. The analysis of data obtained by regular sampling of an insect population. *J. anim. Ecol.* **30**, 429–32.

HASSELL, M. P., 1966. Evaluation of parasite or predator responses. *J. anim. Ecol.* **35**, 65–75.

HOLLING, C. S., 1959. The components of predation as revealed by a study of small mammal predation on the European pine sawfly. *Canad. Ent.* **91**, 293–320.

HUFFAKER, C. B. and KENNET, C. E., 1965. Ecological aspects of control of olive scale *Parlatoria oleae* (Colvee) by natural enemies in California. *Proc. XII int. Congr. Ent.* 585–6.

ITÔ, Y., 1961. Factors that affect the fluctuations of animal numbers, with special reference to insect outbreaks. *Bull. Nat. Inst. Agric. Sci. C* **13**, 57–89.

LAUGHLIN, R., 1965. Capacity for increase: a useful population statistic. *J. anim. Ecol.* **34**, 77–91.

LEFKOVITCH, L. P., 1963. Census studies on unrestricted populations of *Lasioderma serricorne* (F.) (Coleoptera: Anobiidae). *J. anim. Ecol.* **32**, 221–31.

LESLIE, P. H. and RANSON, R. M., 1940. The mortality, fertility and rate of natural increase of the vole (*Microtus agrestis*) as observed in the laboratory. *J. anim. Ecol.* **9**, 27–52.

MESSENGER, P. S., 1964. Use of life tables in a bioclimatic study of an experimental aphid-braconid wasp host–parasite system. *Ecology* **45**, 119–31.

MORRIS, R. F., 1959. Single-factor analysis in population dynamics. *Ecology* **40**, 580–8.

MORRIS, R. F. (ed.), 1963a. The dynamics of epidemic spruce budworm populations. *Mem. ent. Soc. Can.* **31**, 1–332.

MORRIS, R. F., 1963b. Chapters 6, 7 and 18 in 'The dynamics of epidemic spruce budworm populations'. *Mem. ent. Soc. Can.* **31**, 30–7, 116–29.

MORRIS, R. F., 1963c. Predictive population equations based on key factors. *Mem. ent. Soc. Can.* **32**, 16–21.

MORRIS, R. F., 1965. Contemporaneous mortality factors in population dynamics. *Canad. Ent.* **97**, 1173–84.

MOTT, D. G., 1963a. The analysis of the survival of small larvae in the unsprayed area. *Mem. ent. Soc. Can.* **31**, 42–52.

MOTT, D. G., 1963b. The population model for the unsprayed area. *Mem. ent. Soc. Can.* **31**, 99–109.

PARIS, O. H., 1963. The ecology of *Armadillidium vulgare* (Isopoda: Oniscoidea) in California Grassland: Food, Enemies and weather. *Ecol. Monogr.* **33**, 1–22.

RICHARDS, O. W., 1940. The biology of the small white butterfly (*Pieris rapae*), with special reference to the factors controlling abundance. *J. anim. Ecol.* **9**, 243–88.

RICHARDS, O. W., 1959. The study of natural populations of insects. *Proc. R. ent. Soc. Lond. C* **23**, 75–9.

RICHARDS, O. W., 1961. The theoretical and practical study of natural insect populations. *A. Rev. Ent.* **6**, 147–62.

RICHARDS, O. W. and WALOFF, N., 1954. Studies on the biology and population dynamics of British grasshoppers. *Anti-Locust Bull.* **17**, 182 pp.

RICHARDS, O. W. and WALOFF, N., 1961. A study of a natural population of *Phytodecta olivacea* (Forster) (Coleoptera: Chrysomeloidea). *Phil. Trans. B* **244**, 205–57.

RICHARDS, O. W., WALOFF, N. and SPRADBERY, J. P., 1960. The measurement of mortality in an insect population in which recruitment and mortality widely overlap. *Oikos* **11**, 306–10.

SLOBODKIN, L. B., 1962. *Growth and regulation of animal populations.* New York, 184 pp.

SMITH, F. E., 1954. Quantitative aspects of population growth. *In* Boell, E. (ed.), *Dynamic of growth processes.*

SOLOMON, M. E., 1949. The natural control of animal population. *J. anim. Ecol.* **18**, 1–35.

SOLOMON, M. E., 1964. Analysis of processes involved in the natural control of insects. *Adv. Ecol. Res.* **2**, 1–58.

SOUTHWOOD, T. R. E. and JEPSON, W. F., 1962. Studies on the populations of *Oscinella frit* L. (Dipt.: Chloropidae) in the oat crop. *J. anim. Ecol.* **31**, 481–95.

VARLEY, G. C., 1947. The natural control of population balance in the knapweed gallfly (*Urophora jaceana*). *J. anim. Ecol.* **16**, 139–87.

VARLEY, G. C., 1953. Ecological aspects of population regulation. *Trans. IX int. Congr. Ent.* **2**, 210–14.

VARLEY, G. C., 1963. The interpretation of change and stability in insect populations. *Proc. R. ent. Soc. Lond. C* **27**, 52–7.

VARLEY, G. C. and GRADWELL, G. R., 1960. Key factors in population studies. *J. anim. Ecol.* **29,** 399–401.

VARLEY, G. C. and GRADWELL, G. R., 1963a. The interpretation of insect population changes. *Proc. Ceylon Assoc. Adv. Sci.* **18** (D), 142–56.

VARLEY, G. C. and GRADWELL, G. R., 1963b. Predatory insects as density dependent mortality factors. *Proc. XVI int. zoo. Congr.* **1,** 240.

VARLEY, G. C. and GRADWELL, G. R., 1965. Interpreting winter moth population changes. *Proc. XII int. Congr. Ent.* 377–78.

WALOFF, N. and BAKKER, K., 1963. The flight activity of Miridae (Heteroptera) living on broom, *Sarothamnus scoparius* (L.) Wimn. *J. anim. Ecol.* **32,** 461–80.

WATSON, T. F., 1964. Influence of host plant condition on population increase of *Tetranychus telarius* (Linnaeus) (Acarina: Tetranychidae). *Hilgardia* **35** (11), 273–322.

WATT, K. E. F., 1961. Mathematical models for use in insect pest control. *Canad. Ent.* **93,** suppl. 19, 62 pp.

WATT, K. E. F., 1962. Use of mathematics in population ecology. *A. Rev. Ent.* **7,** 243–260.

WATT, K. E. F., 1963a. Mathematical population models for five agricultural crop pests. *Mem. ent. Soc. Can.* **32,** 83–91.

WATT, K. E. F., 1963b. [Discussion.] *Mem. ent. Soc. Can.* **32,** 98–9.

WATT, K. E. F., 1964. Density dependence in population fluctuations. *Canad. Ent.* **96,** 1147–8.

WILLIAMS, C. B., 1961. Studies in the effect of weather conditions on the activity and abundance of insect populations. *Phil. Trans.* B **244,** 331–78.

CHAPTER 11

Age-grouping of Insects and Time-specific Life-tables

This chapter is concerned with techniques for animals whose generations overlap widely; age-grouping is a prerequisite for these methods which have been most widely applied with vertebrate populations. Analysis is easiest with two extreme types of population – the stationary and the expanding. If the population can be assumed to be stationary, then the fall-off in numbers in successive age groups will reflect the survivorship curve and thus a time-specific (or vertical) life-table can be constructed on this basis (p. 316). If the population is expanding, the age structure may become stabilized and then mortality can be estimated from the difference between expected and actual growth rates (p. 317). Age-grouping may also provide useful information on the fertility or potential fertility of the population (see p. 240).

AGE-GROUPING OF INSECTS*

The methods of age-grouping (or age-grading) insects will be referred to only in outline, as the details will vary from species to species. The immature stages of most insects are easily aged, larval instars being distinguished by the diameter of the head, the length of the appendages and other structural features. It is possible to age-group within the instars of some Heteropterous larvae as the number of eye facets increases for some time after moulting; this was noted in lace-bugs (Tingidae) (Southwood & Scudder, 1956) and in Corixidae, where it is even more marked; the interocular distance decreases throughout the instar (E. C. Young, unpub.). In the last larval instar of Exopterygota the wing pads frequently darken shortly before the final moult.

Different ages of the pupal stage may often be determined by dissection, particularly in the Diptera, where various categories based on pigmentation can be recognized: e.g. unpigmented, eyes of pharate adult pigmented, head pigmented, pharate adult fully pigmented (Schneider & Vogel, 1950; van Emden *et al.*, 1961).

Most ageing methods have, however, been concerned with the adult insect; some of the types of criteria used are indicated below. Age-grouping of mosquitoes is reviewed by Hamon *et al.* (1961) and by Muirhead-Thomson

---

* Strictly it is not correct to equate age with stage; the age (in time units) of a given stage will vary with environmental condition and between individuals.

(1963) and for Diptera of medical importance as a whole by Detinova (1962); Russian workers have contributed greatly to this subject. Most methods rely on criteria that are indications of some physiological process, particularly reproduction and excretion, or on general wear and tear; therefore the precise chronological equivalent of a given condition may vary from habitat to habitat or even between individuals.

1. Daily growth layers in the cuticle

The demonstration by Neville (1963*a*) that there are daily growth layers present in some areas of the cuticle of certain insects opened up the possibility of an ageing criteria for insects as precise as that available from fish scales. The bands are most easily seen if the hind tibia is sectioned (hand-sectioning with fresh razor-blades may be adequate for large insects) and the sections examined under a microscope with crossed polaroids. A pair of cuticular layers (one dark and one light in polarized light) is laid down every 24 hours; this process commences in the pharate adult (in the last larval instar) and continues for the first few days of adult life. In order to age adults it is therefore necessary to section the tibia of newly moulted adults to determine the number of layers laid down before adult life (Neville, 1963*b*). Adult age is therefore calculated as:

$$A = \frac{T-l}{2} \text{ days}$$

where T = total number of rings and l = number of rings in the newly moulted adult (i.e. laid down during 'larval life'). Neville stresses that it is necessary to count the maximum numbers of layers visible, as various parts of the cuticle grow for a longer time than others.

The limitations of the method are: that deposition of new cuticular rings occurs only in the early part of adult life, usually ending during the second week, and that this phenomenon does not appear to occur in Endopterygota. Neville (1963*b*) found cuticular rings in a variety of orthopteroids, the earwig, a dragonfly and a homopteron (*Aphrophora*). They have also been demonstrated and figured in Heteroptera (Dingle, 1965).

2. Sclerotization and colour changes in the cuticle and wings

In all insects the newly emerged adult is pale and the cuticle untanned – in most species the major part of tanning is completed during a short teneral period.

However, complete sclerotization may not occur for a considerable time, especially if a period of diapause or aestivation intervenes; e.g. Lagace & van den Bosch (1964) found in the weevil, *Hypera*, that the elytra remained thin and almost teneral for much of the summer diapause. During teneral development in the Corixidae and Notonectidae the cuticle is pigmented at different rates; the sequence of pigmentation of the mesotergum is remarkably constant, proceeding forwards, in a number of stages, from the posterior region (Young, 1965). The wings of young dragonflies are milky, becoming clear when mature (Corbet, 1962a and b).

Various excretory pigments are accumulated throughout adult life and especially during diapause; some of these occur in the cuticle and may cause progressive colour changes. In other instances cuticular colour change is a product of the sclerotization process. Dunn (1951) showed that the region of the discal cell and the associated veins of the hind wing of the Colorado beetle (*Leptinotarsa*) change from yellowish, in the newly emerged individual, to reddish after hibernation, and the green shieldbug, *Palomena prasina*, becomes redder, often a dark bonze, during hibernation (Schiemenz, 1953); in contrast, the pink colouring of another pentatomid, *Piezodorus lituratus*, disappears while overwintering. Many Miridae change colour during or after hibernation and yellows on the forewings of various Heteroptera often darken with age becoming orange or even reddish (Southwood & Leston, 1959). The coloration of the bodies of adult dragonflies changes with age (Corbet, 1962a and b).

3. Developmental changes in the male genitalia

The males of many insects have a period of immaturity during which they may be recognized by the condition of the male genitalia. In most Nematocera the male hypogydium rotates soon after emergence; Rosay (1961) found in mosquitoes that the time for rotation was similar in the species of *Aedes* and *Culex* studied, but was strongly influenced by temperature (at 17°C – 58 hours, at 28°C – 12 hours). The aedaegus of the weevil, *Hypera*, remains relatively unsclerotized throughout the period of aestivation lasting several months (Lagace & van den Bosch, 1964).

4. Changes in the internal non-reproductive organs

The fat-body is perhaps the most variable of these; in some insects it is large at the start of adult life, gradually waning (e.g. in the moth, *Argyroploce* (Waloff, 1958)), and in others it is slowly built up prior to diapause. The availability and quality of food affect the condition of the fat-body and other organs (Fedetov, 1947, 1955, 1960; Haydak, 1957), as does parasitism.

The deposition of coloured excretory products in various internal organs, especially the malpighian tubules, provides another measure of age. Haydak (1957) found in worker honey-bees that the malpighian tubules are clear for the first three days of life, milky from three to ten and in older bees generally (not always) yellowish-green.

In newly emerged mosquitoes, bees, moths and other endopterygote insects part of the gut is filled with the brightly coloured meconium; this is usually voided within a day or two, at the most (Haydak, 1957; Rosay, 1961).

The detailed studies of Haydak (1957) and others on the honey-bee have shown that a range of organs, especially various glands, change their appearance with age.

5. The condition of the ovaries and associated structures

Criteria associated with changes in the female reproductive system have been used widely in ageing studies; they are valuable for even when they do not provide a precise chronological age, they do give information on the extent of egg laying, which is for some purposes more useful. The principal characters that have been used may be summarized under the following headings.

i. Egg rudiments. In those insects that do not develop additional egg follicles during adult life, a count of the number of egg rudiments will indicate the potential fecundity; at the start of adult life the count will be high, gradually falling off, though a large number of rudiments may still remain at the end of life (Waloff, 1958; Corbet, 1962*b*).

ii. Follicular relics. After an egg has been laid, the relics of the follicle, which are often pigmented, will remain in bases of the ovariole pedicels or in the oviducts for a variable period enabling a parous female to be recognized (Lineva, 1953; Gillies, 1958; Lebied, 1959; Corbet, 1960, 1961; Hamon *et al.*, 1961; Saunders, 1962, 1964; Anderson, 1964). In some insects the total amount of relics accumulates with an increasing number of cycles (Anderson, 1964), in others they are eventually lost. V. P. Polovodova demonstrated in *Anopheles* that each time an egg develops it causes local stretching of the stalk of the oviduct. These dilations contain the remains of the follicles and if the ovaries are carefully stretched and examined (see Giglioli, 1963) the number of dilations may be counted. In certain mosquitoes the maximum number of bead-like dilations in any ovariole can be taken as equal to the number of ovarian cycles; with other species difficulties have been encountered (Muirhead-Thomson, 1963).

iii. Ovarian tracheoles. The tracheoles supplying the ovaries of nulliparous females are tightly coiled ('tracheal skeins'); as the eggs mature these become stretched, so that they do not resume their previous form, even in interovular periods. These changes have been observed and used for ageing in mosquitoes (Hamon *et al.*, 1961; Detinova, 1962; Kardos & Bellamy, 1962), in dragonflies (Corbet, 1961) and in calypterate flies (Anderson, 1964).

iv. Ovariole cycles and combined evidence. In many insects the ovaries pass through a series of cycles; the stage in any given cycle may be easily recognized by the size of the most mature egg rudiments. Kunitskaya (1960) recognized six phases in the growth and maturation of oocytes in fleas. Taken in conjunction with other evidence that indicates whether the female is nulliparous or parous, the age may be determined over two ovarian cycles. In vivaparous insects and others (e.g. Schizopteridae) where one large egg is laid at a time, the ovaries develop alternatively and this may allow a larger number of reproductive cycles to be recognized (Saunders, 1962, 1964). In some insects the number of functional ovarioles decreases after the first two cycles and this may be used as an index of age.

6. Indices of copulation

Although frequency of copulation is not a reliable index of chronological age, it may be 'calibrated' for a particular population and gives *per se* information of ecological significance. The presence of sperms in the spermatheca will provide evidence of pairing; in some mosquitoes a gelatinous mating plug remains in the oviduct for a short period (Muirhead-Thomson, 1963). In insects where the sperms are deposited in a spermatophore the remains of these in the spermatheca will give a cumulative measure of copulation (Waloff, 1958).

In many dragonflies the appendages of the male will leave characteristic 'copulation marks' on the compound eyes or occipital triangle of the female; in Zygoptera some sticky secretion may remain on the sides of the female's thorax (Corbet, 1962a). In Cimicidae with a broad spermalege, every pairing will leave a characteristic groove (Usinger, 1966).

7. Changes in weight

Insects that feed little or not at all during adult life will become progressively lighter; Waloff (1958) showed that individual variation due to size differences could be reduced if a weight/length ratio was used. With Lepidoptera weight/ wing length is a convenient measure and Waloff found in a number of species that this falls off strikingly with age, e.g. male *Argyroploce* with an expectation of life of 10 days had a ratio of 1·93, but when the expectation of life was 2·5 days the ratio was 1·13.

In other insects, the adult weight will fluctuate, reflecting ovarian cycles (Waloff, 1958; see also p. 241) or changes associated with diapause. In Crustacea, Mollusca and those few insects (e.g. Collembola) that continue to grow after the onset of reproduction, size and weight will be positively, but perhaps not precisely, correlated with age.

8. 'Wear and tear'

As an adult insect becomes older its cuticle and appendages become damaged by contact with the environment and this 'wear and tear' may be used as an index of age. Kosminskii (1960) has found that fleas may be age-graded by the extent to which the ctenidal (genal comb) bristles are broken; whilst Michener *et al.* (1955) and Daly (1961) used the wear on the mandibles of wild bees. However, the most widely applicable index of this type is provided by the tearing or tattering of the wings, e.g. in Lepidoptera, Diptera (Saunders, 1962) and Hymenoptera (Michener *et al.*, 1955). Although apparently crude, the number of tears ('nicks') in the wings has been found to correlate well with other indices of ageing (Michener & Lange, 1959; Saunders, 1962).

THE TIME-SPECIFIC LIFE-TABLE AND SURVIVAL RATES

If it is justified to assume that population size and time-specific survival (i.e. survival of the total population in one time period compared with the next) are constant, then a time-specific life-table may be easily constructed, for these assumptions will imply that the various age groups were equal in numbers at birth and that the differences between them reflect the mortality they have suffered.

In contrast to the age-specific life-tables, where successive estimates need to be compared, the time-specific life-table is based solély on the age-grouping

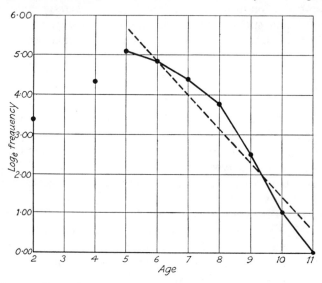

Fig. 91. A time-specific survivorship curve. The logarithms of the frequencies plotted against age groups in a season's sample of the fish, *Leucichthys sardinella* (after Wohlschlag, 1954).

of the individuals collected at a single instant of time. Thus, a relative method (chapter 7) may be used for sampling the population, provided that it samples at random with respect to the different age groups. The youngest age group may be equated with a convenient number* (e.g. 1; 100; 1000), and the other values corrected accordingly to give the l_x column. The remaining columns of the table can then be calculated as described in chapter 10 (p. 285). An example of this type of life-table and its calculation is that given by Paris and Pitelka (1962) for the woodlouse, *Armadillidium*.

An extensive collection of age-grouping data is provided by the 'catch curves' obtained in fishing, and their analysis has been described by Ricker (1944, 1948), Wohlschlag (1954), Beverton & Holt (1957) and others. An

---

* There is no reason to retain the actual number, for this is entirely arbitrary, depending on sample size; in age-specific life-tables it represents the size or density of an actual cohort.

approach to the analysis is provided when log numbers are plotted against age, by the comparison of actual shape of the plot and the straight line that would result from a Slobodkin type III constant survival rate (fig. 91). Variations in the rate of recruitment and in both the age- and time-specific survival rates will affect the shape of the curve. Age-specific survival rates may be obtained from mark and recapture data (chapter 3) and a measure of recruitment can sometimes be obtained from another source, e.g. with insects from emergence traps. By obtaining information from other sources in this way the departures of the time-specific survivorship curve (fig. 91) from linearity can often be interpreted; if recruitment and time-specific survival rates are constant then the fall-off with age in fig. 91 implies increasing mortality with increasing age (Wohlschlag, 1954).

Another source of extensive age-grouped data is the hunting records of terrestrial vertebrates. Surveys of the proportions of various ages and sexes are made before and after hunting and the numbers of the different groups killed are also known; from this information it is possible to calculate natality (referred to as production), survival rates and absolute population. The methods of computation have been reviewed by Hanson (1963) and some of these might be combined with the 'removal-sampling' approach and used with insects. Some of the methods do not require hunting returns; of these the equation for the calculation of differential survival of age classes is of particular potential interest to insect ecologists (Hanson, 1963; Kelker & Hanson, 1964). It could be applied to a situation where generations overlapped, but each was comparatively well synchronized; from biological knowledge we must select three times: t_1 shortly before generation II becomes adult, t_2 just after generation II has become adult and t_3 a subsequent occasion. Assuming that the mortality of both sexes is equal, then the ratio of the survival of generation I to that of generation II during the period t_2 to t_3 is given by:

$$\frac{S_{\mathrm{II}}}{S_{\mathrm{I}}} = \frac{(\male t_2 - \female t_2)(\male t_3 \female t_1 - \male t_1 \female t_3)}{(\male t_3 - \female t_3)(\male t_2 \female t_1 - \male t_1 \female t_2)}$$

where the symbols represent the number of males and females in the samples on dates t_1, t_2 and t_3 as defined above.

The use, in entomology, of age-grouping, time-specific life-tables and survivorship curve analysis of this type will probably prove most important in attempts to investigate the dynamics of the adult population. Detailed studies of this type will be necessary if the full meaning of k_0 (p. 303) is to be investigated.

THE POTENTIAL RATE OF INCREASE AND THE ESTIMATION OF
MORTALITY IN AN ANIMAL WITH OVERLAPPING GENERATIONS

It is difficult to apply the age-specific life-table approach (chapter 11) to aphids and other insects where the generations overlap considerably. Arguing from A. J. Lotka's equation, for the growth rate of a population with a stable age distribution, Hughes (1962, 1963) proposed that mortality could be measured by comparing the actual with the expected population size; the latter being calculated from the rate of increase which itself is determined from the size of various age groups.

If the age distribution is stable then the frequencies of the age groups will be found to correspond to a geometric progression (Williams, 1961); Hughes (1962) found that such distributions occurred commonly in expanding aphid populations. To use the method, information on the developmental rates and times and on prevailing environmental conditions must be obtained independently. The steps in the method are outlined:

1. The potential rate of increase (λ) is calculated:

$$e^\lambda = \frac{\text{I} + \text{II}}{\text{II} + \text{III}}$$

where e = base of natural logarithms and I to III represents the numbers of instars I to III respectively.

2. On the assumption that the numbers should form a geometric progression, the expected frequencies of the different instars are calculated from λ and a χ^2 test applied. Further analysis is undertaken only where a low value of χ^2 indicated that there was a stable age distribution.

3. The observed rate of increase was obtained graphically by plotting the population per instar period against 'time'; however, as Hughes (1962) pointed out, for a poikiothermic animal in a fluctuating environment a physiological time scale should be used, e.g. the accumulated day-degrees above the temperature threshold. The value on the ordinate corresponding to one developmental period (prior to the sampling date) is taken as an estimate of e^p where

$$p = \lambda - \mu$$

μ = overall mortality rate. Where e^p is greater than e^λ further analysis is discontinued, otherwise μ is found.

Hughes (1962, 1963) also describes how the number emigrating may be determined from the number of alate fourth instar larvae and the adult reproductive rate (γ):

$$\gamma = \frac{1 - e^{-\lambda}}{e^{-\beta\lambda} - e^{-w\lambda}}$$

where β = mean age at start of reproduction and w is the mean age death, both expressed in terms of instar periods. If selective mortality is operating a corrected value for the reproductive rate must be calculated from:

$$\gamma_c = \frac{\gamma}{P_s}$$

where P_s = the probability that a last instar larva will survive the selective mortalities and not emigrate, but reproduce in the local population.

Thus
$$P_s = (1 - \mu_s)(1 - E)$$
where μ_s = selective mortality rate and E = emigration.

THE ESTIMATION OF THE RATE OF INCREASE IN POPULATIONS USING MATRICES

Lefkovitch (1965) has pointed out that grouping animals by stage is not exactly equivalent to ageing them and he has developed a model using stage-grouping. In this a series of equations is obtained, one for each stage, expressing the relationship of the numbers in other stages at time t to those in that stage at time $t + 1$ (i.e. the next census occasion). This series of equations can be expressed as a matrix and the latent roots determined by standard mathematical procedure. The values for the matrix are obtained by regression analysis and Lefkovitch discusses the appropriateness of the classical regression through the mean compared to regression through the origin; if there are no density (crowding) effects the latter method will provide the correct values. When the population is growing in an unlimited environment the dominant root of the matrix (M) is equal to e^{rm}. In order to use this method it is necessary to have a large number of census observations on a population growing or declining at a constant rate.

REFERENCES

ANDERSON, J. R., 1964. Methods for distinguishing nulliparous from parous flies and for estimating the ages of *Fannia canicularis* and some other cyclorrophous Diptera. *Ann. ent. Soc. Amer.* **57**, 226–36.

BEVERTON, R. J. H. and HOLT, S. J., 1957. On the dynamics of exploited fish populations. *Fishery investigations, ser. 2.* **19**, 533 pp. Min. Agric. Fish. Food Gt Britain, London, H.M.S.O.

CORBET, P. S., 1960. Recognition of nulliparous mosquitoes without dissection. *Nature, Lond.* **187**, 525–6.

CORBET, P. S., 1961. The recognition of parous dragonflies (Odonata) by the presence of follicular relics. *Entomologist* **94**, 35–7.

CORBET, P. S., 1962a. Age-determination of adult dragonflies (Odonata). *Proc. XI int. Congr. Ent.* **3**, 287–9.

CORBET, P. S., 1962b. *A biology of dragonflies.* London, 247 pp.

DALY, H. V., 1961. Biological observations on *Hemihalictus lustrans*, with a description of the larva (Hymenoptera: Halictidae). *J. Kansas ent. Soc.* **34**, 134–41.

DETINOVA, T. S., 1962. Age-grouping methods in Diptera of medical importance with special reference to some vectors of malaria. *Monogr. Ser. World Hlth Org.* **47**, 216 pp.

DINGLE, H., 1965. The relation between age and flight activity in the milkweed bug, *Oncopeltus. J. exp. Biol.* **42**, 269–83.

DUNN, E., 1951. Wing coloration as a means of determining the age of the Colorado beetle (*Leptinotarsa decemlineta* Say). *Ann. appl. Biol.* **38**, 433–4.

EMDEN, H. F. VAN, JEPSON, W. F. and SOUTHWOOD, T. R. E., 1961. The occurrence of a partial fourth generation of *Oscinella frit* L. (Diptera: Chloropidae) in southern England. *Ent. exp. appl.* **4**, 220–5.

FEDETOV, D. M., 1947, 1955, 1960. The noxious little tortoise, *Eurygaster integriceps* Put. [In Russian.] **1** (272 pp.) and **2** (271 pp.) (1947); **3** (278 pp.) (1955); **4** (239 pp.) (1960).

GIGLIOLI, M. E. C., 1963. Aids to ovarian dissection for age determination in mosquitoes. *Mosq. News* **23**, 156–9.

GILLIES, M. T., 1958. A review of some recent Russian publications on the technique of age determination in *Anopheles*. *Trop. Dis. Bull.* **55**, 713–21.

HAMON, J., GRJEBINE, A., ADAM, J. P., CHAUVET, G., COZ, J. and GRUCHET, H., 1961. Les méthodes d'évaluation de l'âge physiologique des moustiques. *Bull. Soc. ent. Fr.* **66**, 137–61.

HANSON, W. R., 1963. Calculation of productivity, survival, and abundance of selected vertebrates from sex and age ratios. *Wildl. Monogr.* **9**, 1–60.

HAYDAK, M. H., 1957. Changes with age in the appearance of some internal organs of the honeybee. *Bee World* **38**, 197–207.

HUGHES, R. D., 1962. A method for estimating the effects of mortality on aphid populations. *J. anim. Ecol.* **31**, 389–96.

HUGHES, R. D., 1963. Population dynamics of the cabbage aphid, *Brevicoryne brassicae* (L.). *J. anim. Ecol.* **32**, 393–424.

KARDOS, E. H. and BELLAMY, R. E., 1962. Distinguishing nulliparous from parous female *Culex tarsalis* by examination of the ovarian tracheation. *Ann. ent. Soc Amer.* **54**, 448–51.

KELKER, G. H. and HANSON, W. R., 1964. Simplifying the calculation of differential survival of age-classes. *J. Wildl. Mgmt* **28** (2), 411.

KOSMINSKII, R. B., 1960. The method of determining the age of the fleas *Leptopsylla segnis* Schönh. 1811 and *L. taschenbergi* Wagn. 1898 (Suctoria-Aphaniptera) and an experiment on the age analysis of a population of *L. segnis*. [In Russian.] *Med. Parazitol.* **29**, 590–4.

KUNITSKAYA, N. T., 1960. On the reproductive organs of female fleas and determination of their physiological age. [In Russian.] *Med. Parazitol.* **29**, 688–701.

LAGACE, C. F. and VAN DEN BOSCH, R., 1964. Progressive sclerotization and melanization of certain structures in males of a field population of *Hypera brunneipennis* (Coleoptera: Curculionidae). *Ann. ent. Soc. Amer.* **57**, 247–52.

LEBIED, B., 1959. Détermination de l'âge physiologique des diptères. Nouvelle méthode basée sur la recherche des vestiges du processus de l'ovulation. *Riv. Parassit.* **20**, 91–106.

LEFKOVITCH, L. P., 1965. The study of population growth in organisms grouped by stages. *Biometrics* **21**, 1–18.

LINEVA, V. A., 1953. Physiological age of females of *Musca domestica* L. (Diptera: Muscidae). [In Russian.] *Ent. Obozr.* **33**, 161–73.

MICHENER, C. D., CROSS, E. A., DALY, H. V., RETTENMEYER, C. W. and WILLE, A., 1955. Additional techniques for studying the behaviour of wild bees. *Insectes Sociaux* **2**, 237–46.

MICHENER, C. D. and LANGE, R. B., 1959. Observations on the behaviour of Brazilian Halictid bees (Hymenoptera, Apoidea). IV. *Augochloropsis*, with notes on extralimital forms. *Amer. Mus. Novitates* **1924**, 1–41.

MUIRHEAD-THOMSON, R. C., 1963. *Practical entomology in malaria eradication.* WHO (MHO/PA/62.63). Part 1: 64–71.

NEVILLE, A. C., 1963a. Daily growth layers in locust rubber-like cuticle, influenced by an external rhythm. *J. Ins. Physiol.* **9**, 177–86.

NEVILLE, A. C., 1963b. Daily growth layers for determining the age of grasshopper populations. *Oikos* **14**, 1–8.

PARIS, O. H. and PITELKA, F. A., 1962. Population characteristics of the terrestrial isopod *Armadillidium vulgare* in California grassland. *Ecology* **43**, 229–48.

RICKER, W. E., 1944. Further notes on fishing mortality and effort. *Copeia* **1944**, 23–44.

RICKER, W. E., 1948. Methods of estimating vital statistics of fish populations. *Indiana Univ. Publ. Sci. Ser.* **15,** 101 pp.

ROSAY, B., 1961. Anatomical indicators for assessing the age of mosquitoes: the teneral adult (Diptera: Culicidae). *Ann. ent. Soc. Amer.* **54,** 526–9.

SAUNDERS, D. S., 1962. Age determination for female tsetse flies and the age composition of samples of *Glossina pallidipes* Aust., *G. palpalis fuscipes* Newst. and *G. brevipalpis* Newst. *Bull. ent. Res.* **53,** 579–95.

SAUNDERS, D. S., 1964. Age-changes in the ovaries of the sheep ked, *Melophagus ovinus* (L.) (Diptera: Hippoboscidae). *Proc. R. ent. Soc. Lond. A* **39,** 68–72.

SCHIEMENZ, H., 1953. Zum Farbwechsel bei heimischen Heteropteren unter besonderer Berücksichtigung von *Palomena* Muls. & Rey. *Beitr. Ent.* **3,** 359–71.

SCHNEIDER, F. and VOGEL, W., 1950. Neuere Erfahrungen in der Bekämpfung der Kirschenfliege (*Rhagoletis cerasi*) Schweiz. *Z. Obst-Weinbau* **59,** 37–47.

SOUTHWOOD, T. R. E. and LESTON, D., 1959. *Land and water bugs of the British Isles.* London, **436** pp.

SOUTHWOOD, T. R. E. and SCUDDER, G. G. E., 1956. The bionomics and immature stages of the thistle lace bugs (*Tingis ampliata* H.-S. and *T. cardui* L.; Hem., Tingidae). *Trans. Soc. Brit. Ent.* **12,** 93–112.

USINGER, R. L., 1966. *Monograph of Cimicidae.* The Thomas Say Foundation, Ent. Soc. Amer. (in press).

WALOFF, N., 1958. Some methods of interpreting trends in field populations. *Proc. X int. Congr. Ent.* **2,** 675–6.

WILLIAMS, E. J., 1961. Fitting a geometric progression to frequencies. *Biometrics* **17,** 584–606.

WOHLSCHLAG, D. E., 1954. Mortality rates of whitefish in an arctic lake. *Ecology* **35,** 388–96.

YOUNG, E. C., 1965. Teneral development in British Corixidae. *Proc. R. ent. Soc. Lond. A.* **40,** 159–68.

CHAPTER 12

Experimental Component Analysis of Population Processes

Experimental component analysis is an important new approach to the study of population processes, such as predation or parasitism, that has been developed by Holling (1963, 1964, 1965, 1966). It is based on the philosophy that the apparent complexity and diversity of population dynamics is due to the action and interaction of a relatively small number of components. Therefore a particular process is broken down into all its components. These components are investigated experimentally and their actions and interactions expressed in a series of fragmented equations. These equations can then be synthesized into a single systems model of the process. Holling (1963, 1966) points out that the model must have four properties: wholeness, realism, precision and generality. The wholeness must stem from a consideration of all the components that influence the process; its realism must be tested by the comparison of the predictions from the model with data from actual observations (e.g. Holling, 1966); precision will automatically follow if the model is expressed in mathematical terms. The generality or the breadth of application will depend on each component being assessed in general terms and the basic features of the process being distinguished from those that are specific; ultimately the extent to which this has been successful will need to be tested by a broad comparative survey (Holling, 1966). A satisfactory model may be used for the prediction of the effects of changes in the environment on population processes, in fact for the simulation of Nature.

It will be seen therefore that whereas in life-table analysis (chapters 10 and 11) an attempt is made to break down the changes in population size that result from the processes (predation, competition, natality, etc.), in component analysis one works from the experimental determination of the action and interaction of the process up to the complete model of population change. As Holling (in LeRoux, 1963) suggests component analysis should theoretically precede life-table studies as it will indicate which features – e.g. the amount of food the stomach holds – need to be measured in conjunction with the measurements of population size, and on the other hand the life-table will be necessary to indicate which of the processes is the key one.

The components of the process of predation have mostly been analysed by Holling) 1965, 1966). In the first place the distinction must be made between the functional response of a predator to increased prey density, that is the consumption of more prey per predator and the numerical response, due to the increase in numbers of predators (Solomon, 1949; see also p. 293). To date Holling's study has been concerned with the functional response. The first step in component analysis is to decide the actual factors that are possible components of the process; those for predation are shown in fig. 92. For a valid model, with both breadth and depth, it is most important that these components be expressed in general terms and that all components be included.

It is then necessary to decide which of these components are basic to all predators and the word 'Yes' (fig. 92) indicates that there are actual components of all situations. Others will be subsidiary, present in some situations, absent in other, and the words 'Yes' and 'No' are entered for them. Holling (1966) points out that as there are 5 dichotomies in the figure, 2^5 or 32 different types of functional response to prey and predator density are possible.

The third step involves the selection of a suitable predator–prey system,

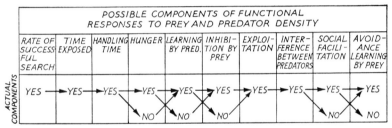

Fig. 92. The basic and subsidiary components in the functional response of a predator to a prey density (after Holling, 1966).

with which to determine experimentally the quantitative action and interaction of the component, and the experimentation with this system. Such studies are described in detail by Holling (1964, 1965, 1966); initially the basic components must be identified and expanded (or subdivided), then the subsidiary components and lastly the interaction of the different components. These steps are set out diagrammatically in fig. 93; the equations for each sub-component or interaction are established experimentally.

The final step in building the model is the synthesis of the numerous equations for the action and interaction of the different sub-components into a single functional response model. The complexity of the model is so great that if the language of differential calculus is used it soon becomes intractable. Three salient features of biological processes are that they have thresholds and a historical aspect (the influence of past events) and are discontinuous, due for example to periods of sleep. Holling found that the model could be constructed in the form of difference equations (Goldberg, 1961) which, unlike calculus, are appropriate for describing the discontinuous nature of the processes, and that the historical aspect and the role of the thresholds could well be expressed in Fortran, one of the languages of digital computers (McCracken, 1961).

The computer may then be used to simulate Nature, to determine the effect of a process, after any number of cycles, given certain conditions. The pre-

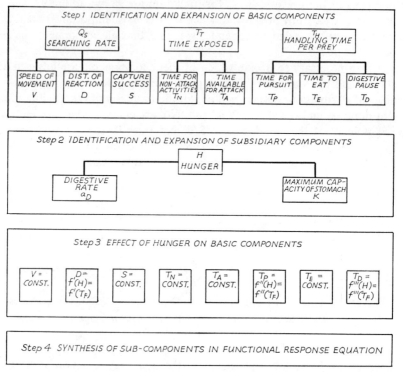

Fig. 93. The steps taken in the component analysis of the response of predators to prey density – the roles of rate of successful search, time exposed, handling time and hunger (after Holling, 1963).

dictions of the model should be tested against observations and if it appears to be true it may be used to predict other characteristics and phenomenon (Holling, 1965).

The ecologist may use component analysis in two ways; he may attempt to build up models for processes that have not hitherto been analysed or he may apply Holling's models for predation to other predator–prey systems.

REFERENCES

GOLDBERG, s., 1961. *Introduction to difference equations.* New York.
HOLLING, C. S., 1963. An experimental component analysis of population processes. *Mem. Ent. Soc. Can.* **32**, 22–32.

HOLLING, C. S., 1964. The analysis of complex population processes. *Canad. Ent.* **96,** 335–47.

HOLLING, C. S., 1965. The functional response of predators to prey density and its role in mimicry and population regulation. *Mem. ent. Soc. Can.* **45,** 5–60.

HOLLING, C. S., 1966. The functional response of invertebrate predators to prey density. *Mem. ent. Soc. Can.* (in press).

LEROUX, E. J. (ed.), 1963. Population dynamics of agricultural and forest insect pests. Discussion. *Mem. ent. Soc. Can.* **32,** 92–102.

MCCRACKEN, D. D., 1961. *A guide to Fortran programming.* New York and London, 88 pp.

SOLOMON, M. E., 1949. The natural control of animal population. *J. anim. Ecol.* **18,** 1–35.

CHAPTER 13

The Measurement of Association between
Species and the Description of a Fauna

<hr />

The methods described in this chapter may be used in both autecological and synecological studies, although they have hitherto been mainly restricted to the latter. The simplest type of index, and the one that is of value in autecology, is based on the comparison of the distribution of two species. There are two main approaches: one founded on the assumption that both species have an equal opportunity to occur in all the samples, and so the degree of association is measured by comparing the difference between the actual and the expected number of joint occurrences. The second approach considers only the number of joint occurrences as a proportion of the total number of occurrences, and so describes the frequency with which two species occur together (index of affinity). Both these methods are based on the presence or absence of the species in the samples and do not take account of the numbers found. An index may be based on these by treating the number of individuals, that occur in the samples where both species are found, as a percentage of the total individuals.

The comparison of two faunas may be made on similar lines; a quotient (or coefficient) of similarity (or community) may be derived based on the number of species common to both faunas (or samples). This is analogous to the index of affinity, but, when used with faunas, rare species may be over-emphasized as they are given the same weight as the abundant ones. A second approach, the percentage of similarity, is based on the similarity of the samples in terms of individuals and thus may stress the dominant species. A third approach is based on the concept that the relation of the number of individuals to the number of species in a habitat can be related to certain mathematical, notably logarithmic, distributions; the index that describes the relationship for a particular habitat should be a constant whatever the sample size. The indices of diversity and similarity are based on this approach, but they have certain practical shortcomings.

Communities may be recognized in general qualitative terms related to their flora and physical features; more detailed studies based on the composition of the fauna may use the indices or coefficients derived for the comparison of species or samples, considering each pair in turn, or utilize multivariate methods, which allow the comparison of a series of measurements simultaneously either in terms of their similarities (component and factor analysis)

326

or differences (discriminatory analysis). Recently, information theory has been used in an attempt to obtain descriptive measures of communities and investigate their stability (Margalef, 1957; Fager, 1962; Watt, 1964).

Each of these aspects will now be considered in detail.

THE MEASUREMENT OF ASSOCIATION BETWEEN SPECIES

In many types of ecological work it is desirable to examine and express quantitatively the degree of association between two species; this may be positive if the species require similar conditions and/or if there is some mutualism or predator–prey relationship between them, or negative if they require different conditions or actively compete with each other. It is clear, therefore, that such measurements would be of value, for example, in assessing the extent of interspecific effects between various ectoparasites on mammals (Evans & Freeman, 1950) or the amount of mutualism, prey specificity or competition between species of aphids and their various predators and attendant ants. (Rank correlation methods (p. 337) may also be applicable here.) Changes in the amount of association between species at different seasons or under different conditions can be used to show a change in the relationship. For example Murdoch (1963) showed, in cogeneric marsh carabid beetles, that during the winter months there was a positive association of high value, but during the summer the association became negative; it was concluded that competition was minimal in the winter months, but increased in the summer breeding season.

Besides the great utility of a measure of association in autecological studies as outlined above, a measure of association can be used as an initial step in the delimitation of communities (e.g. Fager, 1957; Davis, 1963).

The departure of the distribution of presence or absence from independence

These methods measure the departure from independence of the distribution of the two species and *assume that the probability of occurrence of the species is constant for all samples*. Thus if the distribution of two aphid predators were being compared it would only be legitimate to include samples that also contained the prey. A good example of the use of these indices is given by Evans & Freeman (1950), who measured the interspecific association of two species of flea on two different rodents (*Apodemus* and *Clethrionomys*); they found that there was a strong negative association on *Apodemus* and a moderate positive one on *Clethrionomys* and suggested that the coarse and longer fur of *Clethrionomys* allowed the two fleas to avoid competition and exist together on that host. However, when applied to habitats whose uniformity is doubtful, these methods may give results of uncertain value, as was found by Macan (1954) in a study of the associations of various species of corixid bug in different ponds. In such a situation some samples may be from habitats that are outside the environmental ranges of the species; this will have the effect of inflating the value for *d* in the table below and so lead to too many positive associations.

Fager (1957) has demonstrated, by examples, that if two species are rare and therefore both are absent from most of the samples (this could, as just indicated, be due to unsuitable samples being included), a high level of association will be found. Conversely, if two species occur in most of the samples and so are nearly always found together, no association will be shown with these methods. (Although a biological association is obvious, it is equally correct to say that this does not depart significantly from an association that is due to chance and therefore does not necessarily imply any inter-specific relationship.)

1. The contingency table

The basic feature of these methods is the 2×2 contingency table.

Species B	Species A Present	Absent	
Present	a	b	$a+b$
Absent	c	d	$c+d$
	$a+c$	$b+d$	$n=a+b+c+d$

Such a table should always be drawn up so that A is more abundant than B, i.e. $(a+b) < (a+c)$. A number of statistics are available for analysis of such a table, but the corrected chi-square (χ^2) makes fewest assumptions about the type of distribution, and the significance of the value obtained can be determined from tables available in standard statistical textbooks. It is calculated:

$$\chi^2 = \frac{n[|ad-bc|-(n/2)]^2}{(a+c)(b+d)(a+b)(c+d)}$$

where the letters are as in the contingency table above and $|ad-bc|$ signifies placing the term in the positive form. If *ad* is greater than *bc* then the association is positive (affinity); if *bc* is greater than *ad* then the association is negative (repulsion). The test in this form is only valid if the expected numbers (if the distribution was random) are not less than 5; there is only one degree of freedom and so the 5% point is 3·84. Therefore, if a χ^2 of less than this is obtained, any apparent association could well be due to chance and further analysis should be abandoned. If the smallest expected number is less than 5 the exact test should be used and the relevant tables are available (e.g. Fisher & Yates, 1960).

2. Coefficients of association

If χ^2 is significant then one of the coefficients of association may be used to give an actual quantitative value for comparison with other species. They are designed so that the coefficient has the same range as the correlation coefficient (r), i.e. $+1$ = complete positive association, -1 = complete negative association and 0 = no association. Cole (1949) reviews a number of coefficients and points out how, if the above interpretations of values from $+1$ to -1 are to hold for comparative purposes, the plot of the value of the coefficient against the possible number of joint occurrences should be linear; for several of the coefficients it is not, and for those in which it is the plot does not pass through the zero. Cole devised an index that was linear and so allowed direct comparison. Some coefficients are:

i. Coefficient of mean square contingency. This coefficient makes no assumption about distribution, but it cannot give a·value of $+1$ unless $a = d$ and b and $c = 0$. For less extreme forms of association it is useful and easily calculated:

$$C_{AB} = \sqrt{\frac{\chi^2}{n + \chi^2}}$$

where C_{AB} = coefficient of association between A and B, n = total number of occurrences, and the χ^2 value is obtained as above.

This coefficient is recommended by Debauche (1962) and was used by Davis (1963).

ii. Yule's coefficient. Yule's coefficient puts greater weight on a joint occurrence when the two species occur nearly independently than when they show a degree of association. It is not really applicable to species comparison though easily calculated.

$$C_{AB} = \frac{ad - bc}{ad + bc}$$

iii. Coefficient of interspecific association. This measure was devised by Cole (1949) to overcome some of the objections of the above and other coefficients. Different formulae must be used, depending on the sizes of the figures in the table, to give the coefficient and its standard error:

When $ad \geq bc$:

$$C_{AB} = \frac{ad - bc}{(a+b)(b+d)} \pm \sqrt{\frac{(a+c)(c+d)}{n(a+b)(b+d)}}$$

When $bc > ad$ and $d \geq a$:

$$C_{AB} = \frac{ad - bc}{(a+b)(a+c)} \pm \sqrt{\frac{(b+d)(c+d)}{n(a+b)(a+c)}}$$

When $bc > ad$ and $a > d$:

$$C_{AB} = \frac{ad - bc}{(b+d)(c+d)} \pm \sqrt{\frac{(a+b)(a+d)}{n(b+d)(c+d)}}$$

These formulae have been used by Evans & Freeman (1950), Macan (1954), Hale (1955) and others.

iv. Coefficient of partial interspecific association. This coefficient was also developed by Cole (1957) and is basically similar to his earlier index (above), but it allows the comparison of species A and B, both in the presence and in the absence of C, which may be another species or an environmental factor. The relevant formulae are given in table 19.

Table 19. Formulae for the coefficients of partial association (after Cole, 1957)

Coefficient	x	Value of coefficient $x > 0$	Value of coefficient $x < 0$
$C_{AB}.C+$	$\dfrac{a_1d_1-b_1c_1}{N_{C+}}$	$\dfrac{x}{z_2+x}$	$\dfrac{x}{z_1-x}$
$C_{AB}.B+$	$\dfrac{a_1c_2-a_2c_1}{N_{B+}}$	,,	,,
$C_{BC}.A+$	$\dfrac{a_1b_2-a_2b_1}{N_{A+}}$	,,	,,
$C_{AB}.C-$	$\dfrac{a_2d_2-d_2c_2}{N_{C-}}$	$\dfrac{x}{z_1+x}$	$\dfrac{x}{z_2-x}$
$C_{AC}.B-$	$\dfrac{b_1d_2-b_2d_1}{N_{B-}}$	,,	,,
$C_{BC}.A-$	$\dfrac{c_1d_2-c_2d_1}{N_{A-}}$	,,	,,

Where the appropriate $2\times2\times2$ tables are

$C+$

	$B+$	$B-$	
$A+$	a_1	b_1	
$A-$	c_1	d_1	N_{C+}

$C-$

	$B+$	$B-$	
$A+$	a_2	b_2	
$A-$	c_2	d_2	N_{C-}

$B+$

	$C+$	$C-$	
$A+$	a_1	a_2	
$A-$	c_1	c_2	N_{B+}

$B-$

	$C+$	$C-$	
$A+$	b_1	b_2	
$A-$	d_1	d_2	N_{B-}

$A+$

	$C+$	$C-$	
$B+$	a_1	a_2	
$B-$	b_1	b_2	N_{A+}

$A-$

	$C+$	$C-$	
$B+$	c_1	c_2	
$B-$	d_1	d_2	N_{A-}

and z_1=either a_1 or d_1 or b_2 or c_2, whichever is smaller.
z_2=either b_1 or c_1 or a_2 or d_2, whichever is smaller.

Frequency of occurrence together – Index of affinity

In order to overcome some of the objections to the above indices when considering habitats that may be heterogeneous, Fager (1957) suggested this index which relates the probabilities of the joint occurrence of the two species to the sum of their occurrences. It does not consider negative association, for, as Fager says, failure to find a species may be due to many causes.

As samples from which the species are absent are excluded, this technique is basically sounder as a preliminary step for the delimitation of communities than the indices given above, for in such work it is clearly impossible to assume that 'the probability of occurrence of the two species is constant for all samples'.

The number of occurrences of A must lie between half and equality to those of B. Fager does not actually give a formula for calculating the index, for he works on the number of significant joint occurrences; however the index could be taken as:

$$I_{AB} = \frac{2J}{nA + nB}$$

where J=number of joint occurrences nA=number of occurrences of A, nB=number of occurrences of B.

It provides a measure of the frequency with which species occur together.

Minimum values of joint occurrence that are significant are given in table 20.

Table 20. Minimum values of J (joint occurrences) which are significant at the 0·5 level (after Fager, 1957)

n_A	1·0	n_B/n_A 1·5	2·0
5	5	5	—
6	5	6	6
7	6	7	7
8	7	8	8
9	7	8	9
10	8	9	10
20	14	16	17
30	19	22	24
40	25	29	32
50	29	35	39
60	36	42	46
70	41	48	53
80	46	55	59
90	52	61	67
100	57	67	74

Significance may be tested for intermediate values by simple proportion e.g. if $nA=25$ and $nB=35$ then $nB/nA=1\cdot4$ and the minimum significant J can be estimated as:

$$16+\frac{22-16}{2}-\frac{1}{5}\left[\left(16+\frac{22-16}{2}\right)-\left(14+\frac{19-14}{2}\right)\right] = 18\cdot5$$

For other values a one-tailed '*t*-test' is used:

$$t = \left[\frac{(nA+nB)(2J-1)}{2nAnB}-1\right]\left[\sqrt{nA+nB-1}\right]$$

The minimum significant value for t being $1\cdot645$ (at 5% probability level).

Proportion of individuals occurring together

The above methods take no account of the numbers of individuals involved, and it is possible to imagine a situation where large numbers of individuals occurred in the samples where both species were found (joint occurrences) and only singletons or a few individuals in the other samples – yet because of the large number of the latter, little association was demonstrated by the indices described above.

In such extreme cases, and perhaps in others, an index based on the total number of individuals of both species occurring together in samples as a proportion of the total individuals could be used. If the equation of Whittaker & Fairbanks (1958) is modified, in order to get the normal range of -1 (no association) to $+1$ (complete association), the index of association of individuals is:

$$Iai = 2\left[\frac{Ji}{A+B}-0\cdot5\right]$$

where $Ji=$no. of individuals of A and B in samples where both species are found, and A and $B=$total number of individuals of A and B in all samples.

THE COMPARISON OF FAUNA IN SPACE OR TIME

Discussion

It is often desirable to compare the fauna of two habitats, say of oak trees on basic and acid soils; many of the species collected will be the same, but as the samples are likely to be of a different size direct comparison is not possible (even if the samples were of the same size there would be no way of assessing whether any differences that did occur were due to chance or whether they were real). Another type of situation where comparison is desirable is in the assessment of faunal change in the same habitat over a period of time, associated with either natural succession or with the influence of man – a comparison that is important in conservation work.

The basis of all comparisons is the assumption that the proportion of the number of species (S) to the number of individuals (N) is a characteristic parameter of the fauna of a habitat. In view of the fluctuations in the population level of individual species from year to year and from place to place this cannot actually be true except for a given habitat at a given time. Nevertheless, minor fluctuations are not likely to alter the parameter greatly and their effects will fall within the 'error' where this is calculated. Much of the work in this field has been done by botanists who have used their indices as a basis for the separation of various communities (Greig-Smith, 1964). The earliest index was that of Jaccard (1912), whose formula was:

$$\frac{j}{(a+b-j)}$$

where $a=$ the number of species in habitat A, $b=$ the same for habitat B and $j=$ the number of species found in both habitats.

Kulezyński (1928) proposed another index:

$$\frac{j}{2}\left(\frac{1}{a}+\frac{1}{b}\right)$$

More recently Sørensen (1948) devised a third that he called the *quotient of similarity*; in this the number of species found in both habitats (j) is emphasized more than in earlier indices and is given by:

$$QS = \frac{2j}{a+b}$$

These indices (collectively referred to as coefficients of community) all measure the relative similarity of two habitats in terms of species composition and so, as Whittaker & Fairbanks (1958) have pointed out, they may overvalue the rare species relative to the dominant ones.

The other simple approach is the *percentage of similarity* which is based on a comparison of the make-up of the two samples in terms of individuals of the various species; as such, it places the emphasis on the dominant species (Raabe, 1952). The value of the percentage of similarity for a pair of samples is given by the summation of the smaller values of the percentage of the total individuals, i.e.

$$\% \, S = \Sigma \min (a, b, \ldots x)$$

Thus in two habitats A and B with % compositions of their fauna:

Species	a	b	c	d
A	25	42	10	23
B	9	58	1	32
$\% \, S =$		$9+42+1+23 = 75$		

Kontkanen (1950) and Whittaker & Fairbanks (1958) have compared these two approaches: Kontkanen, working with leafhoppers (Homoptera: Auchenorrhyncha), found the coefficient of community most satisfactory, and Whittaker & Fairbanks, who were studying freshwater plankton, the percentage of similarity.

Williams (1949, 1950) and Mountford (1962) have shown, on theoretical grounds, that the values of these indices alter with sample size. This is due to the fact that at first species are collected as rapidly as individuals (the first six moths to enter a light-trap are likely to be different species), but subsequently new species will be found much less frequently, although many individuals will be taken. Fisher, Corbet & Williams (1943) proposed that such a process was best described by the logarithmic series and this was used to describe a number of situations by Williams (1944, 1945, 1947, 1964). Their index of diversity (α) is given by the formula:

$$S = \alpha \log_e \left(1 + \frac{N}{\alpha}\right)$$

where S = number of groups (species), N = number of individuals.

Margalef (1951) has proposed a simpler index of diversity, being

$$\alpha = \frac{S-1}{\log_e N}$$

Preston (1948) suggested that the log normal distribution would describe the relationship between groups and individuals better, as it did not demand the large number of species represented by a single individual which is a feature of the logarithmic series and yet is clearly incorrect in terms of world or continental fauna. Subsequently (1960, 1962) he has developed this idea suggesting that it must be regarded as a truncated log normal, ending at the crest. This simplifies its use as it relates two of the parameters. Williams (1953, 1960, 1964) accepted that the log normal was preferable and Grundy (1951) has provided tables from which it is theoretically possible to calculate for a sample, or series of samples, the number of species that will be represented by singletons and the proportion of the total number of species in the habitat that will be collected. The median number of individuals per species (a) and the variance (σ^2) of the abundance of the species in natural logarithms must first be calculated, and Grundy's solutions to these problems were not published before his death.

Although the distinction between these mathematical models is important when describing the fauna of whole continents and more particularly in the inferences that can be drawn from the model, if it is accepted as correct, this distinction is not so significant in making more limited comparisons between habitats, or rather between samples. The Williams's index of diversity was used successfully by him (1951) to compare catches, of Lepidoptera in light-traps, in different situations; Banks (1959) and Southwood (1960) also used it to make similar comparisons. These trap catches are drawn more or less at random from a mixture of habitats and niches and, as Clark *et al.* (1964) have suggested, such random sampling is a condition for the use of the log series.

However, if the logarithmic indices are applied to collections from natural habitats, it is found that they too are influenced by the size of the sample (Hairston & Byers, 1954), although on mathematical grounds this should not happen if the samples are all from the same habitat. Hairston & Byers suggested that this was due to the species in the habitat being differently distributed; the rare species being more clumped than the commoner ones, because their habitat demands are more exacting than those of the more ubiquitous species; thus the index of diversity would increase as larger samples were taken and more niches of these rarer species were included in them. Subsequently, Hairston (1959) demonstrated that this hypothesis, in so far as it referred to clumping (measured by 'k', see p. 25), was correct – the least abundant species were the most clumped (i.e. had the lowest k values).

An index of similarity (I) has been devised by Mountford (1962), this is in fact the reciprocal of the index of diversity (i.e. $1/\alpha$) and allows a direct quantitative and qualitative comparison between two sites. Although used successfully by Mountford for the comparison of the soil communities of various woodlands, Davis (1963), also working with soil invertebrates, found that it was only slightly more satisfactory than Sørensen's similarity quotient which is much easier to calculate.

Darwin (1960) has suggested that the B-distribution, which is related to the logarithmic series, might be used to describe a flora or fauna when the number of species, but not the number of individuals found in each sample, is known.

Another distinct approach is the use of rank correlation methods. As has been shown by Ghent (1963), the rank coefficient τ of Kendall (1962) may be used to compare communities in terms of the relative abundance of the constituents. The comparison is fairly simple if the animals are ranked in relatively few groups of high taxonomic level (e.g. orders), but the ecological significance of such comparisons is limited. The calculation of τ between the species components of two communities is far more complex, for many species will tie for rank. It would seem that τ would be of most value in measuring succession or change with time of the fauna (or flora) of a single habitat or related adjacent habitats.

Summary

1. Quotient of similarity – Sørensen

This is the simplest of the indices and, like those of Williams and Mountford, because of the clumping of rare species, it is affected by sample size. Sørensen's quotient has been found useful by Kontkanen (1957), Looman & Campbell (1960), Davis (1963) and Moritz (1963) and is given by:

$$QS = \frac{2j}{a+b}$$

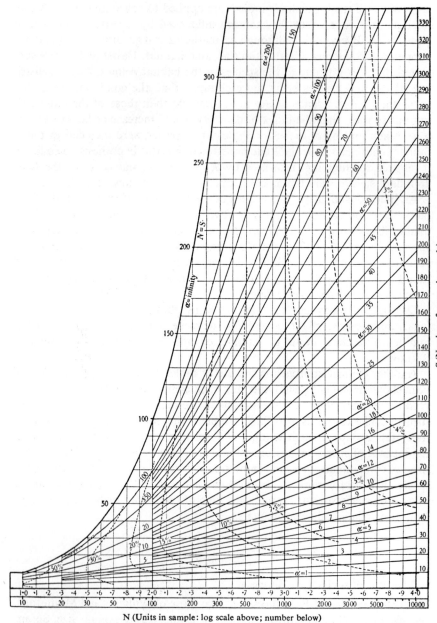

N (Units in sample: log scale above; number below)

Fig. 94. Nomogram for determining the Index of Diversity (α) for the number of species (S) and the number of individuals (N) in a random sample of a fauna (after Williams, 1947).

2. Index of diversity – Williams

This index allows comparison of faunas, provided sampling was sufficiently random. It is useful, for example, with light-trap catches from different areas or from the same habitat in successive years. Identical indices could, however, be obtained from distinct faunas and this point should be checked by pooling catches; if the faunas are identical the index will not change.

The index of diversity (α) is most conveniently read off from Williams's nomogram (fig. 94).

3. Index of similarity – Mountford

Based on the same theoretical principles as Williams's index and probably subject to the same shortcomings, this index is designed to facilitate the direct comparison of a number of samples with a view to delimiting communities (see below).

The approximate formula is:

$$I = \frac{2j}{2ab - (a+b)j}$$

or *I* can be evaluated graphically from fig. 95.

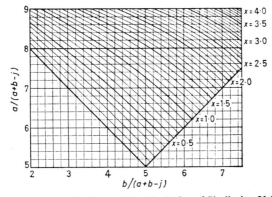

Fig. 95. Nomogram for determining the Index of Similarity. Values of $(a + b - j) \times I = x; a > b$ (after Mountford, 1962).

4. Rank correlation – Kendall's tau

The value of τ is computed from the comparison of the ranks, in terms of abundance, of different taxonomic groups in two samples from two faunas. Kendall (1962) and Ghent (1963) give accounts of its calculation.

5. Measures of 'organization'

The measures detailed for the description of community organization (p. 345) may also be used to compare faunas in space and time.

DELIMITATION OF COMMUNITIES

Qualitative

Zoologists frequently delimit their communities by reference to plants or environmental factors. The most universal classification of habitats is that of Elton & Miller (1954):

(*i*) Terrestrial system
    Formations: Open-ground type – if any dominant plants, these not more than 15 cm (6 in.) high.
                Field type – dominant life form coincides with field layer, usually not more than 2 m in height.
                Scrub type – dominant life form does not exceed a shrub layer, height generally not over 7·6 m (25 ft).
                Woodland type – trees dominant life form.

    Vertical layers: Subsoil and rock.
                Topsoil.
                Ground zone, including low-growing vegetation, less than 15 cm (6 in.).
                Low canopy – up to about 7·6 m (25 ft).
                High canopy.
                Air above vegetation.

(*ii*) Aquatic system.
    Formation types: these are shown in table below.

	A Very small	B Small	C Medium	D Large	E Very large
1 Still	Tree hole	Small pond 17 m²	Pond 0·4 hect.	Large pool or Tarn 40 hect.	Lake or Sea
2 Slow	Trickle Gutter	Ditch Field dyke	Canal River bank Water		
3 Medium	Trickle	Lowland brook Small stream	Lowland river	Lowland large river	River estuary
4 Fast	Spring	Upland weir Small torrent stream	Large torrent stream		
5 Vertical or steep	Water drip Pipe outlet	Small weir Water-fall	Large weir Medium waterfall	Large waterfall	

Vertical layer: Bottom, light, dark zones, water mass, light and dark zones –
free water not among vegetation.
Submerged vegetation.
Water surface – upper and under surface of film of floating
leaves.
Emergent vegetation – reed swamp and similar vegetation, the
bases of which are in the water.
Air above vegetation.

(*iii*) Aquatic – terrestrial transition system – defined further by body type with
which it occurs and by vegetational systems corresponding to the terrestrial
system.

(*iv*) Subterranean system – caves and underground waters.

(*v*) Domestic system.

(*vi*) General system: Dying and dead wood.
Macro-fungi.
Dung.
Carrion.
Animal artefacts – nests, etc.
Human artefacts – fence posts, straw stacks, etc.

Further division of the habitat into communities may be made on the type
of plant, but in soil (Macfadyen, 1952, 1954; Davis, 1963) and freshwater
studies (Whittaker & Fairbanks, 1958), divisions have been based on the
fauna itself; these techniques (see below) have been used in few other situations (Kontkanan 1957), but their use could undoubtedly be extended.

Quantitative

There are two main approaches to delimitation based on either:

(i) Species by species.
(ii) Sample by sample.

1. Species by species

a. Recurrent groups – Fager (1957)

A measure of the association between various abundant species (all species if
they are not too numerous) is obtained as described above. Fager has defined
a recurrent group as one that satisfies the following conditions:

i. The evidence for affinity is significant at 0·05 level for all pairs of species
within the group.

ii. The group includes the greatest possible number of species.

iii. If several groups with the same number of members are possible, those
are selected which will give the greatest number of groups without
members in common.

iv. If two or more groups with the same number of species and with
members in common are possible, then the one that occurs as a unit in
the greatest number of samples is chosen.

Faunal Studies

A set of data is analysed against these tests in turn. A table is drawn up with the species arranged in order from that with the greatest number of affinities to that with least (table 21).

Table 21. An example of the affinity between pairs of species, based on the significance of the number of joint occurrences (table 20) (after Fager, 1957) ($+$ = significant affinity)

	A	B	C	D	E	F	G	H	J	K	L	M	N	P	Q	Number of affinities
A		+	+	+	+	+	+	+	+	+	+	+	−	−	+	12
B	+		+	+	+	−	+	+	+	−	+	−	−	−	+	9
C	+	+		+	+	+	−	+	+	+	+	−	−	−	−	9
D	+	+	+		+	−	+	+	+	+	−	+	−	−	−	9
E	+	+	+	+		−	−	−	+	−	+	−	+	−	+	8
F	+	−	+	−	−		+	+	−	+	−	−	+	+	−	7
G	+	+	−	+	−	+		−	−	−	−	+	+	+	−	7
H	+	+	+	+	−	+	−		−	−	−	−	−	+	−	6
J	+	+	+	+	+	−	−	−		−	−	−	−	−	−	5
K	+	−	+	+	−	+	−	−	−		−	−	−	+	−	5
L	+	+	+	−	+	−	−	−	−	−		−	−	−	−	4
M	+	−	−	+	−	−	+	−	−	−	−		+	−	−	4
N	−	−	−	−	+	+	+	−	−	−	−	+		−	−	4
P	−	−	−	−	−	+	+	+	−	+	−	−	−		−	4
Q	+	+	−	−	+	−	−	−	−	−	−	−	−	−		3

Fager outlines the steps as follows:

(1) Count down until the number of species exceeds the number of affinities, e.g. at species H, where no. of species $(X)=8$, and number of affinities $(Y)=6$.

(2) Now if X is equal to, or less than, $Y+2$, the largest potential group will contain $X-1$ species.

(3) To form an actual group of Z members from this potential group of V members, at least Z of them must have $Z-2$ affinities with others of the potential group. In the example (table 21) let $Z=7$ from (2) above:

Species	A	B	C	D	E	F	G	H		
Affinities	7	6	6	6	4	4	4	5	$V=8$	$Z=7$

As there are only 4 species, with more than 5 affinities, a group of 7 cannot be formed.

(4) If this test is negative let $Z=$ one less than in previous test and add in all species with $Z-1$ affinities: in example J and K tabulate as below:

Species	A	B	C	D	E	F	G	H	J	K		
Affinities	9	7	8	8	5	5	4	5	5	4	$V=10$	$Z=6$

There are now over 6 species with more than 4 affinities.

(5) A second test at this stage to ensure that requirement I is met – in order to

form a group of Z members from V potential members, the following inequality must hold:

$$(V-1)(2Z-V) < 1 + \Sigma \, Z \text{ largest affinities } - \Sigma \text{ rest of the affinities}$$

In the example this is:

$$(10-1)(2 \times 6-10) < 1 + (9+8+8+7+5+5) - (5+5+4+4)$$

(6) Further elimination: eliminate those species which do not have *more than* $Z-2$ affinities, i.e. G and K, and repeat tabulation:

	A	B	C	D	E	F	H	J	$V = 8$
	7	6	7	6	5	3	5	5	$Z = 6$

(7) Repeat until no more species can be eliminated:

1st	A	B	C	D	E	H	J	$V = 7$
	6	6	6	6	5	4	5	$Z = 6$

2nd	A	B	C	D	E	J	$V = 6$
	5	5	5	5	5	5	$Z = 6$

(8) Now apply test 5 from above

$$(6-1)(2 \times 6-6) < 1 + 6 \times 5 - 0$$

Therefore species A–E, J constitute the group

(9) Examine species not included in group and eliminate species which only have affinities with group. In example L and Q – these are associates of group.

(10) Proceed as before with remaining species, omitting affinities with members of first group. With example this would lead to five possible groups: FGN, FGP, FKP, GMN, FHP.

(11) Criterion *iii* will be satisfied if GMN or FHP or FKP are selected.

(12) Choice between FHP and FKP depends on the original sampling results, criterion *iv*.

The final result can be expressed as:

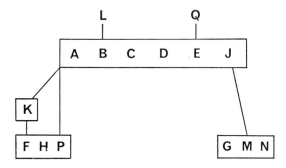

If this analysis was carried out on a large number of species, the three groups and their associates could be considered as three communities.

b. Trellis diagram

Here the individual form comparisons are grouped into a table, like table 21, and the communities delimited, more or less, by eye. Such methods have been more frequently used to compare samples (see below).

2. Sample by sample

Here the basic indices are those given above, although some other methods are being used by plant ecologists, for example Williams & Lambert (1959, 1960), in which the recording of presence or absence of species, rather than counting individuals, is an adequate assessment of the sample.

a. Trellis diagram

This old method has been extensively used. An index, such as Sørensen's (1948) (see above), is applied to the data and the sample localities are arranged in an order so that the highest values come on the diagonal, i.e. the samples with the highest similarities are placed together (see fig. 96). A subjective

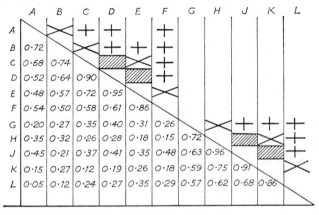

Fig. 96. An example of a trellis diagram. The shading of the squares (+ = 0·50 − 0·70, × = 0·70 − 0·90, cross-hatching = 0·90 − 1·0) helps with the interpretation, which in this straight-forward case, is that there are two communities (A–F & G–L).

assessment is then made of the groups on the basis of discontinuity. Kontkanen (1957) has discussed the value of various indices for this method and Davis (1963) and Macfadyen (1954) give examples of their use.

b. Index of similarity – Mountford (1962)

This index is versatile and may be calculated (see above) for actual samples or for the pooled results of a series of samples from the same site; however, as pointed out earlier, in the latter case the same number and size of sample should be taken from the different sites. An index may also be derived for the comparison of several sites with another site; for example, that for the comparison of two sites A and B with a third C would be:

$$I(AB:C) = \frac{I(AC) + I(BC)}{2}$$

The general formula for the comparison of a group of m sites with another (C) is:

$$I(A_1A_2A_3 \ldots A_m : C) = \frac{I(A_1C) + I(A_2C) + I(A_3C) + \ldots I(A_mC)}{m}$$

Its use can be further extended to compare groups, say between A_1 and A_2 and B_1 and B_2:

$$I(A_1A_2 : B_1B_2) = \frac{I(A_1B_1) + I(A_1B_2) + I(A_2B_1) + I(A_2B_2)}{4}$$

The general formula for this type of comparison between $A_1, A_2 \ldots A_m$ and $B_1, B_2 \ldots B_n$ is defined as:

$$\frac{1}{mn} \sum_{i=1}^{m} \sum_{j=1}^{n} I(A_iB_j)$$

Mountford (1962) gives the following example which shows how the series of indices between sites is determined and from which a final classification can be derived:

Let sites be A, B, C, D, and E with indices of similarity:

	B	C	D	E
A	0·074	0·113	0·095	0·103
B		0·136	0·144	0·117
C			0·135	0·119
D				0·068

The highest index is that between sites B and D, i.e. 0·144, therefore B and D are grouped together and the indices of similarity worked out between this group and the remaining sites using the formula given above. Thus the index between E and the group is:

$$I(BD:E) = \frac{I(BE) + I(DE)}{2}$$
$$= \frac{0·117 + 0·068}{2}$$
$$= 0·0925$$

A new table is formed:

	BD	C	E
A	0·0845	0·113	0·103
BD		0·1355	0·0925
C			0·119

The highest value being between BD and C these are combined to form a new group and indices between this group and A and E found. For example:

$$I(BCD:A) = \frac{I(BA) + I(CA) + I(DA)}{3}$$
$$= \frac{0·074 + 0·113 + 0·095}{3}$$
$$= 0·094$$

Giving table:

	BCD	E
A	0·094	0·103
BCD		0·1013

This time one of the original indices, that between A and E, is the highest and so these form a second group and therefore the final stage is a comparison of the two groups given by:

$$I(\text{AE: BCD}) = \frac{1}{2 \times 3}(0{\cdot}074 + 0{\cdot}113 + 0{\cdot}095 + 0{\cdot}117 + 0{\cdot}119 + 0{\cdot}068)$$

$$= 0{\cdot}0976$$

Now for the final classification (fig. 97) B and D are the first species taken out, C is arranged on apex line next to B because the index of similarity between B and C (0·136) is just greater than that between D and C (0·135); similar considerations govern the positions of A and E, the index between C and E being higher than that between C and A.

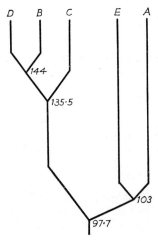

Fig. 97. The classification of five hypothetical sampling sites based on the indices of similarity between them (after Mountford, 1962).

A diagram like fig. 97 is limited by the restriction to two dimensions and an alternative method, eliminating calculation of all but the first step, would be to build a model representing each site, for instance by golf balls and the indices by pieces of wire of exactly the right length to correspond with the indices.

Although this process is completely objective the level of division into communities must still be determined. The question posed is: are all the sites distinct communities or are, for example, B and D representatives of the same one? Such a decision must be based largely on biological considerations, but some of the measures of community structure (see below) could provide additional evidence.

c. Cluster analysis

A simple index, such as that of Sørensen, may be used to compare samples and then the relationships illustrated by models or diagrams devised by cluster analysis methods, already described briefly for Mountford's method. Davis (1963) has used this method in a study of soil invertebrates.

d. Multivariate methods

Undoubtedly the most logical approach to the delimitation of communities, or more strictly speaking, to the comparison of a series of samples, is the use of multivariate methods which allow a series of measurements to be compared simultaneously (Blackith, 1962). Further details of these methods may be found in Greig-Smith (1964), Lambert & Dale (1964) and Seal (1964).

e. Changes in the diversity line

As has been shown by Fisher, Corbet & Williams (1943), if the cumulative species total is plotted against the log of the number of individuals counted, a straight line is produced. On theoretical grounds and from studies of arctic flora, Odum, Cantlon & Kornicker (1960) have postulated that a break in this implies passing from one community to another. It might be possible, if a series of samples were taken along a transect and these added in sequence, to detect a shift in the line where the community changed. It is difficult to visualize a situation where this technique would provide information that was not already apparent from biological considerations.

ANALYSIS AND DESCRIPTION OF COMMUNITIES OR GROUPS

Having established groupings of species or samples by the above methods it is often desirable to analyse their organization or relationships further.

Relation of different species

These types of comparison can only properly be made within communities; standard statistical tests may be used and Fager (1957) has discussed their use in this context.

Dominance – whether one species is constantly dominant over the other. The various species are ranked in all the samples and the concordance among the rankings are tested by the statistic W (Kendall, 1962, pp. 94–106).

Relative abundance of two species over all samples can be compared with the U-test (Rao, 1952, pp. 236–57; Hoel, 1954, pp. 291–3) which, unlike the '*t*-test', is applicable to non-normal distributions.

Concordance between species as to what is a 'good' habitat may be tested by taking the total individuals/species as a measure of 'goodness' of each sample and then samples ranked for number of species and statistic W (Kendall, 1962, pp. 94–106) used.

Correlations between species are particularly appropriate in more detailed analysis of predator–prey relations or other associations between species. Rank correlation coefficients, e.g. Kendall's (1962, pp. 34–8) Tb are appropriate.

Organization

It has been shown above that the delimitation of areas with more or less similar faunas is a practical possibility, but whether the habitats so recognized represent discrete communities with a definite structure and organization, is more difficult to determine. Indeed, the extent to which communities exist as discrete, structured entities is a matter of speculation and dispute among ecologists. As a step towards determining how a community is organized

MacArthur (1957) devised three models of the relationship of numbers of individuals to numbers of species, each based on a different arrangement of the niches: non-overlapping, overlapping* and particulate (or separate). The first model is often referred to as the 'broken-stick model', as the habitat can be likened to a stick broken into a number of pieces – the niches – and this model was the only one found to fit his data for birds. In it the abundance of

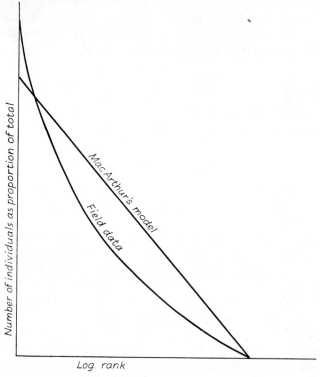

Fig. 98. Comparison of the plot of the number of individuals against log rank for Mac-Arthur's model and some types of field data (modified from Lloyd & Ghelardi, 1964).

the rth rarest species, as a proportion of the total individuals, is given by:

$$\frac{N}{S} \sum_{i=1}^{r} \left(\frac{1}{S-i+1}\right)$$

If the number of individuals (as a proportion of the total) is plotted against the log of the rank (in terms of abundance), data conforming to this model will describe a straight line (fig. 98). Although Hutchinson (1957) found some other sets of data could be fitted to the model, most workers have found that

* A reformation of the model for overlapping niches is given by Vandermeer, J. H. & MacArthur, R. H. (1966, *Ecology* **47**, 139–40).

the resulting plots are too steep and curved (Hairston, 1964; Lloyd & Ghelardi, 1964). MacArthur's models have not, therefore, provided a means of determining the type of organization in a community; however, the 'broken-stick model' has been used as a 'standard' against which the parameters of faunas can be compared either in terms of the moments or an information function.

Lloyd & Ghelardi (1964) have pointed out that the diversity of a fauna stems from two components: the actual number of species and the 'equitability', the extent of the numerical equality between the species. They provide a measure of equitability based on the use of information theory; another possible way of measuring it is also suggested here.

1. The description of the species–abundance curve in terms of its moments

Preston (1948) pointed out the number of individuals per species in a natural population will describe a log normal curve (i.e. a normal curve when the number of individuals is plotted on a log scale). Hairston (1959, 1964) has shown that a useful description of the shape of this curve for any habitat may be obtained by comparing the observed variance with that expected on the basis of MacArthur's model and that the larger the ratio the greater the homogeneity or organization in the community. He demonstrated the validity of this conclusion by comparing the effect on the ratio of the inclusion of samples from other habitats with the effect of further samples from the same habitat. The former caused the ratio to increase linearly, but samples from other habitats, which increased the heterogeneity of the sample, reduced the ratio, i.e. reduced the variance towards that expected on the MacArthur model. Hairston found that if the observed variance is divided by the square of the mean, virtually the same results are obtained and, as this is simpler than the calculation of the expected variance, it is the most practical way of applying this test for the degree of homogeneity in a community. It may be used: (*i*) to compare samples from different habitats, provided the samples are the same size and the same taxonomic group is being studied, (*ii*) to describe and analyse changes within the same habitat with time and (*iii*) to help determine which of a series of samples belongs to a given habitat (or community).

2. The description of the species–abundance curve using information theory

MacArthur (1955) proposed that information theory, developed during the Second World War (Yockey *et al.*, 1956), could be used to advantage in ecology; the more complex a community the greater its information content and stability. MacArthur & MacArthur (1961) and Watt (1964) have used the Shannon–Wiener function to express the information content of a community. This is given by:

$$H(S) = - \sum_{i=1}^{S} p_i \log_2 p_i$$

where S=total number of species in the sample, p_i=the observed proportion of individuals that belong to the ith species (i=1, 2, 3, ... 5).

The value of I (I=$H(S)$) is another expression of the diversity of the fauna, as well as its stability. Following their suggestion that the equitability component of animal diversity should be separated from the effect of the number of species, Lloyd & Ghelardi (1964) proposed that the Shannon–Wiener function of the MacArthur model be taken as a 'yardstick' for maximum equitability of a habitat with a given number of species, as in practice this appears to represent the maximum ecological diversity attainable (Hairston, 1959; see above). They made the comparison by calculating the number (S') of hypothetical, equitably distributed species (i.e. on the MacArthur model) that would be needed to produce a species diversity equivalent to the observed one; the equitability measure was given by the ratio:

$$\varepsilon = \frac{S'}{S}$$

where S=the actual number of species.

The information content of a given sample can be calculated from the modified equation:

$$H(S) = c\left\{\log_{10} N - \frac{1}{N}\sum_{r=1}^{s} n_r \log_{10} n_r\right\}$$

where n_r are the numbers found in the r species, N is total number of individuals, S the total number of species and c=3·321928 (the conversion factor to change the base of logarithms from 10 to 2). The values of $n_r \log_{10} n_r$ for each species can be read off from a table (which can easily be constructed for n_r=1 to 200) and the total sum ($\Sigma\, n_r \log_{10} n_r$) found.

S' is the number of species in a habitat with 'maximum' equitability, the information function of which is represented by $M(S')$. Therefore, in order to calculate ε, one needs to find S' corresponding to $M(S')$ when $M(S')=H(S)$, and this may be done from table 22. The value of $H(S)$ for the particular habitat is entered in the $M(S')$ column and the corresponding value of S' read off; this is then divided by the actual total number of species to give the equitability component (ε).

The use of the information function $H(S)$ as a measure of stability implies that the values for the relative abundance of each species, indicated by the sample, reflect the probability of occurrence of the different species. But as Preston (1962) pointed out, in random sampling the rate of accumulation of new species falls as sampling proceeds, eventually levelling off (see also p. 334); thus the initial values of S will be too high, relative to the number of individuals. On the other hand, the heterogeneous nature of many habitats will tend to introduce a bias, in the opposite direction, into data from most sampling methods; the diversity of the initial samples being too low (Hairston, 1959). Because these two effects cannot be assumed to cancel each other out,

Table 22. The diversity in terms of species, $M(S')$, characteristic of MacArthur's model for various numbers of hypothetical species (S') (after Lloyd & Ghelardi, 1964)

S'	$M(S')$	S'	$M(S')$	S'	$M(S')$	S'	$M(S')$
1	0·0000	51	5·0941	102	6·0792	205	7·0783
2	0·8113	52	5·1215	104	6·1069	210	7·1128
3	1·2997	53	5·1485	106	6·1341	215	7·1466
4	1·6556	54	5·1749	108	6·1608	220	7·1796
5	1·9374	55	5·2009	110	6·1870	225	7·2118
6	2·1712	56	5·2264	112	6·2128	230	7·2434
7	2·3714	57	5·2515	114	6·2380	235	7·2743
8	2·5465	58	5·2761	116	6·2629	240	7·3045
9	2·7022	59	5·3004	118	6·2873	245	7·3341
10	2·8425	60	5·3242	120	6·3113	250	7·3631
11	2·9701	61	5·3476	122	6·3350	255	7·3915
12	3·0872	62	5·3707	124	6·3582	260	7·4194
13	3·1954	63	5·3934	126	6·3811	265	7·4468
14	3·2960	64	5·4157	128	6·4036	270	7·4736
15	3·3899	65	5·4378	130	6·4258	275	7·5000
16	3·4780	66	5·4594	132	6·4476	280	7·5259
17	3·5611	67	5·4808	134	6·4691	285	7·5513
18	3·6395	68	5·5018	136	6·4903	290	7·5763
19	3·7139	69	5·5226	138	6·5112	295	7·6008
20	3·7846	70	5·5430	140	6·5318	300	7·6250
21	3·8520	71	5·5632	142	6·5521	310	7·6721
22	3·9163	72	5·5830	144	6·5721	320	7·7177
23	3·9779	73	5·6027	146	6·5919	330	7·7620
24	4·0369	74	5·6220	148	6·6114	340	7·8049
25	4·0937	75	5·6411	150	6·6306	350	7·8465
26	4·1482	76	5·6599	152	6·6495	360	7·8870
27	4·2008	77	5·6785	154	6·6683	370	7·9264
28	4·2515	78	5·6969	156	6·6867	380	7·9648
29	4·3004	79	5·7150	158	6·7050	390	8·0022
30	4·3478	80	5·7329	160	6·7230	400	8·0386
31	4·3936	81	5·7506	162	6·7408	410	8·0741
32	4·4381	82	5·7681	164	6·7584	420	8·1087
33	4·4812	83	5·7853	166	6·7757	430	8·1426
34	4·5230	84	5·8024	168	6·7929	440	8·1757
35	4·5637	85	5·8192	170	6·8099	450	8·2080
36	4·6032	86	5·8359	172	6·8266	460	8·2396
37	4·6417	87	5·8524	174	6·8432	470	8·2706
38	4·6792	88	5·8687	176	6·8596	480	8·3009
39	4·7157	89	5·8848	178	6·8758	490	8·3305
40	4·7513	90	5·9007	180	6·8918	500	8·3596
41	4·7861	91	5·9164	182	6·9076	550	8·4968
42	4·8200	92	5·9320	184	6·9233	600	8·6220
43	4·8532	93	5·9474	186	6·9388	650	8·7373
44	4·8856	94	5·9627	188	6·9541	700	8·8440
45	4·9173	95	5·9778	190	6·9693	750	8·9434
46	4·9483	96	5·9927	192	6·9843	800	9·0363
47	4·9787	97	6·0075	194	6·9992	850	9·1236
48	5·0084	98	6·0221	196	7·0139	900	9·2060
49	5·0375	99	6·0366	198	7·0284	950	9·2839
50	5·0661	100	6·0510	200	7·0429	1000	9·3578

Lloyd & Ghelardi (1964) proposed that the use of their equitability measure be restricted to 'local situations', where the collection can be considered complete. The application of the information function to larger habitats may perhaps be achieved by using the log normal distribution to give a measure of the true probability of occurrence of a given species (R. L. Dalleske, unpublished).

It should, perhaps, be mentioned that MacArthur, Lloyd & Ghelardi and

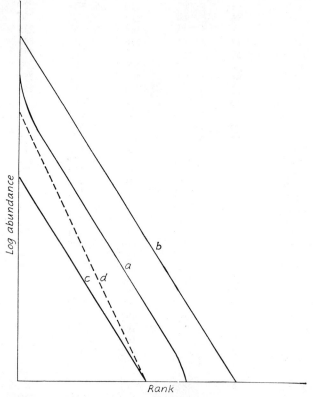

Fig. 99. The plot of log abundance against rank: *a.* typical field data; *b, c* and *d.* hypothetical regressions for habitats with different diversity; *b* and *c* have the same equitability, but different numbers of species, *c* and *d* the same numbers of species, but differ in the equitability component.

others have mainly considered the information content of a habitat as it is given by the distribution of individuals between species, and have implied that the greater number of species, the greater the number of different paths for the energy to flow through and hence the greater the stability. Watt (1964), on the other hand, has considered the information content as given by the distribution of types of food eaten among the species. Therefore his conclusion, that genera containing numbers of polyphagous species have a lower information content and hence less stability than those containing mono-phagous species, is not necessarily at variance with the previously held notion, that habitats with a large number of species are more stable than those with smaller numbers. Indeed, in general the greater the diversity of the fauna in a habitat the fewer the species with polyphagous or generalized feeding habits.

3. The description of the equitability of the species–abundance curve in terms of its slope

If a measure of the abundance of a species – either individuals, biomass or production – is plotted on a log scale against the rank, the resulting graph is frequently a straight line, with or without inflections at the top and bottom (e.g. Whittaker, 1965). The slopes of the lines are a measure of the equita-bility of the distribution of abundance between species; parallel lines will represent faunas with different numbers of species, but similar equitability. The slope of line can be conveniently expressed by the coefficient b of the regression of log abundance on rank. This is a measure of equitability for descriptive and comparative purposes and unlike ε is unrelated to any par-ticular model. It should not of course be computed for any fauna that would produce a strongly sigmoid plot on fig. 99.

REFERENCES

BANKS, C. J., 1959. Experiments with suction traps to assess the abundance of Syrphidae (Diptera), with special reference to aphidophagous species. *Ent. exp. appl.* **2**, 110–24.

BLACKITH, R. E., 1962. The handling of multiple measurements. *In* Murphy, P. W. (ed.), *Progress in Soil Zoology* 37–42.

CLARK, P. J., ECKSTROM, P. T. and LINDEN, L. C., 1964. On the number of individuals per occupation in a human society. *Ecology* **45**, 367–72.

COLE, L. C., 1949. The measurement of interspecific association. *Ecology* **30**, 411–24.

COLE, L. C., 1957. The measurement of partial interspecific association. *Ecology* **38**, 226–233.

DARWIN, J. H., 1960. An ecological distribution akin to Fisher's logarithmic distribution. *Biometrics* **16**, 51–60.

DAVIS, B. N. K., 1963. A study of micro-arthropod communities in mineral soils near Corby, Northants. *J. anim. Ecol.* **32**, 49–71.

DEBAUCHE, H. R., 1962. The structural analysis of animal communities of the soil. *In* Murphy, P. W. (ed.), *Progress in Soil Zoology*, 10–25.

ELTON, C. S. and MILLER, R. S., 1954. The ecological survey of animal communities with a practical system of classifying habitats by structural characters. *J. Ecol.* **42**, 460–96.

EVANS, F. C. and FREEMAN, R. B., 1950. On the relationship of some mammal fleas to their hosts. *Ann. ent. Soc. Amer.* **43**, 320–33.

FAGER, E. W., 1957. Determination and analysis of recurrent groups. *Ecology* **38**, 586–95.

FAGER, E. W., 1962. Communities of organisms. *In* Hill, M. N. (ed.), *The Sea* **2**, 415–37.

FISHER, R. A., CORBET, A. S. and WILLIAMS, C. B., 1943. The relation between the number of species and the number of individuals in a random sample of an animal population. *J. anim. Ecol.* **12**, 42–58.

FISHER, R. A. and YATES, F., 1960. *Statistical tables for biological, agricultural and medical research.* Edinburgh and London, 138 pp.

GHENT, A. W., 1963. Kendall's 'Tau' coefficient as an Index of similarity in comparisons of plant or animal communities. *Canad. Ent.* **95**, 568–75.

GREIG-SMITH, P., 1964. *Quantitative plant ecology.* London, 256 pp.

GRUNDY, P. M., 1951. The expected frequencies in a sample of an animal population in which the abundancies of species are log-normally distributed. Part 1. *Biometrika* **38**, 427–34.

HAIRSTON, N. G., 1959. Species abundance and community organization. *Ecology* **40**, 404–16.

HAIRSTON, N. G., 1964. Studies on the organisation of animal communities. *J. anim. Ecol.* **33** (suppl.), 227–239.

HAIRSTON, N. G. and BYERS, G. W., 1954. The soil arthropods of a field in southern Michigan. A study in community ecology. *Contrib. Lab. Vert. Biol. Univ. Mich.* **64**, 1–37.

HALE, M. E., 1955. Phytosociology of corticolous cryptograms in the upland forests of southern Wisconsin. *Ecology* **36**, 45–63.

HOEL, P. G., 1954. *Introduction to mathematical statistics.* 2nd ed. New York.

HUTCHINSON, G. E., 1957. Concluding remarks. *In* Demerec, M. (ed.), *Population Studies: Animal Ecology and Demography. Cold Spring Harb. Sym. quant. Biol.* **22**, 415–27.

JACCARD, P., 1912. The distribution of the flora in the alpine zone. *New Phytol.* **11**, 37–50.

KENDALL, M. G., 1962. *Rank correlation methods.* London, 199 pp.

KONTKANEN, P., 1950. Quantitative and seasonal studies on the leafhopper fauna of the field stratum on open areas in North Karelia. *Soc. Zool. Bot. Fenn. Vanamo Ann. Zool.* **13** (8), 1–91.

KONTKANEN, P., 1957. On the delimitation of communities in research on animal bio-coenotics. *In* Demerec, M. (ed.), *Population Studies: Animal Ecology and Demography. Cold Spring Harb. Sym. quant. Biol.* **22**, 373–8.

KULEZYŃSKI, S., 1928. Die Pflanzenassoziationen der Pieninen. *Bull. int. Acad. Pol. Sci. Lett., B* Suppl. **2**, 57–203.

LAMBERT, J. M. and DALE, M. B., 1964. The use of statistics in phytosociology. *Adv. Ecol. Res.* **2**, 59–99.

LLOYD, M. and GHELARDI, R. J., 1964. A table for calculating the 'equitability' component of species diversity. *J. anim. Ecol.* **33**, 217–25.

LOOMAN, J. and CAMPBELL, J. B., 1960. Adaptation of Sørensen's K (1948) for estimating unit affinities in prairie vegetation. *Ecology* **41**, 409–16.

MACAN, T. T., 1954. A contribution to the study of the ecology of the Corixidae (Hemipt.). *J. anim. Ecol.* **23**, 115–41.

MACARTHUR, R. H., 1955. Fluctuations of animal populations and a measure of community stability. *Ecology* **36**, 533–36.

MACARTHUR, R. H., 1957. On the relative abundance of bird species. *Proc. Nat. Acad. Sci.* **43**, 293–5.

MACARTHUR, R. H. and MACARTHUR, J. W., 1961. On bird species diversity. *Ecology* **42**, 594–8.

MACFADYEN, A., 1952. The small Arthropods of a *Mólinia* fen at Cothill. *J. anim Ecol.* **21**, 87–117.

MACFADYEN, A., 1954. The invertebrate fauna of Jan Meyen Island (East Greenland). *J. anim. Ecol.* **23**, 261–98.

MARGALEF, R., 1951. Diversidad de especies en las comunidades naturales. *Publnes. Inst. Biol. apl., Barcelona* **6**, 59–72.

MARGALEF, R., 1957. La teoria de la informacion en ecologia. *Mem. R. acad. Barcelona* **32**, 373-449 (transl. by W. Hall, *Gen. System.* **3**, 36–71).

MORITZ, M., 1963. Über Oribatidengemeinschaften (Acari: Oribatei) norddeutscher

Laubwaldböden, unter besonderer Berücksichtigung der die Verteilung regelnden Milieubedingungen. *Pedobiologia* **3**, 142–243.

MOUNTFORD, M. D., 1962. An index of similarity and its application to classificatory problems. *In* Murphy, P. W. (ed.), *Progress in Soil Zoology*, 43–50.

MURDOCH, W. W., 1963. The population ecology of certain Carabid beetles living in marshes and near freshwater. *D.Phil. Thesis, Oxford Univ.*

ODUM, H. T., CANTLON, J. E. and KORNICKER, L. S., 1960. An organizational hierarchy postulate for the interpretation of species–individual distributions, species entropy, ecosystem evolution and the meaning of a species–variety index. *Ecology* **41**, 395–9.

PRESTON, F. W., 1948. The commonness and rarity of species. *Ecology* **29**, 254–83.

PRESTON, F. W., 1960. Time and space and the variation of species. *Ecology* **41**, 611–27.

PRESTON, F. W., 1962. The canonical distribution of commonness and rarity. Part I. *Ecology* **39**, 185–215. Part II. *ibid.* **39**, 410–32.

RAABE, E. W., 1952. Über den 'Affinitätswert' in der Planzensoziologie. *Vegetatio, Haag* **4**, 53–68.

RAO, C. R., 1952. *Advanced statistical methods in biometric research.* New York.

SEAL, H. L., 1964. *Multivariate statistical analysis for biologists.* London, 207 pp.

SØRENSEN, T., 1948. A method of establishing groups of equal amplitude in plant sociology based on similarity of species content and its application to analyses of the vegetation on Danish commons. *Biol. Skr.* (*K. danske vidensk. Selsk.* N.S.) **5**, 1–34.

SOUTHWOOD, T. R. E., 1960. The flight activity of Heteroptera. *Trans. R. ent. Soc. Lond.* **112**, 173–200.

WATT, K. E. F., 1964. Comments on fluctuations of animal populations and measures of community stability. *Canad. Ent.* **96**, 1434–42.

WHITTAKER, R. H., 1965. Dominance and diversity in land plant communities. *Science* **147**, 250–60.

WHITTAKER, R. H. and FAIRBANKS, C. W., 1958. A study of plankton copepod communities in the Columbia basin, south eastern Washington. *Ecology* **39**, 46–65.

WILLIAMS, C. B., 1944. The index of diversity as applied to ecological problems. *Nature, Lond.* **155**, 390–1.

WILLIAMS, C. B., 1945. Recent light-trap catches of Lepidoptera in the U.S.A., analysed in relation to the logarithmic series and the index of diversity. *Ann. ent. Soc. Amer.* **38**, 357–64.

WILLIAMS, C. B., 1947. The logarithmic series and the comparison of island floras. *Proc. Linn. Soc. Lond.* **158**, 104–8.

WILLIAMS, C. B., 1949. Jaccard's generic coefficient and coefficient of floral community in relation to the logarithmic series. *Ann. Bot. Lond. N.S.* **13** (49), 53–8.

WILLIAMS, C. B., 1950. The application of the logarithmic series to the frequency of occurrence of plant species in quadrats. *J. Ecol.* **38**, 107–38.

WILLIAMS, C. B., 1951. Diversity as a measurable character of an animal or plant population. *Année biol.* **27**, 129–41.

WILLIAMS, C. B., 1953. The relative abundance of different species in a wild animal population. *J. anim. Ecol.* **22**, 14–31.

WILLIAMS, C. B., 1960. The range and pattern of insect abundance. *Amer. Nat.* **94**, 137–51.

WILLIAMS, C. B., 1964. *Patterns in the balance of Nature and related problems in quantitative ecology.* London and New York, 324 pp.

WILLIAMS, W. T. and LAMBERT, J. M., 1959. Multivariate methods in plant ecology. I. Association-analysis in plant communities. *J. Ecol.* **47**, 83–101.

WILLIAMS, W. T. and LAMBERT, J. M., 1960. Multivariate methods in plant ecology. II. The use of an electronic digital computer for association analysis. *J. Ecol.* **48**, 689–710.

YOCKEY, H. P., PLATZMAN, R. L. and QUASTLER, H. (eds.), 1956. *Symposium on information theory in biology.* Los Angeles, 418 pp.

CHAPTER 14

The Estimation of Productivity and the Construction of an Energy Budget

The size of a population and the interactions between populations within an ecosystem may be expressed in terms of biomass (weight of living material) or energy content, as well as in numbers. Biomass and energy are useful to ecologists in that they provide a common unit for the description of populations of animals and plants of different sizes. Descriptions of the predator in these terms are often essential in studies on the effect of insect predators of varying ages on a prey population (Szalay-Marzsó, 1958), and the prey consumed by general predators, e.g. insectivorous birds, is best expressed as biomass or calories. Conversely if the energy requirements are known from metabolic measurements, they may be used to predict the food requirements in the field (Pearson, 1954; Stiven, 1961), although the quality of the food in terms of specific amino-acids, vitamins and other constituents will also be important. The energy equations for an individual may be expressed:

Gross energy = Digestible energy = Metabolizable energy = Resting energy
or (assimilation) + +
energy intake + Urinary waste ↓ Activity
(ingestion) Faecal waste ↓ +
Growth
+
Reproduction

(Note – only the upper term partakes in the equation to its right.)

The concept of energy is also useful in the consideration of the functioning of the ecosystem; Ivlev's (1939, 1945) and Lindeman's (1942) now classical papers pointed the way to this approach. Various trophic levels can be distinguished in the ecosystem; firstly there are the primary producers (i.e. plants) that build up complex substances from simple inorganic substances utilizing the energy from sunlight. The total annual energy intake of these primary producers is usually referred to as the *gross production*; and the total amount of biomass produced per year as the *net production* (i.e. gross production less losses due to respiration*). The amount of living material present at any given time is the *standing crop*. Unfortunately the use of these

* Throughout this chapter respiration is taken to include the energy lost in each chemical process; in the animal – the specific dynamic action component.

354

terms has been confused, but Macfadyen (1963) has given a useful table of synonymy. Information on primary productivity and the absorption of solar energy by plants is given by Doty (1961), Ovington (1962), Westlake (1963), Bray & Gorham (1964), Wiegert & Evans (1964), Gates (1965) and Loomis (1965). Other trophic levels are occupied by consumers and decomposers, i.e. animals and certain plants (e.g. fungi, bacteria).

The energy budget of an animal population, or a trophic level, can be expressed in several equations (Slobodkin, 1962; Wiegert, 1964):

$$A = R+N \tag{1}$$

where A =assimilation or income (that is ingestion less faecal waste, see 4 below), R =respiration and N =net production (or total yield), i.e. the weight of the animals produced plus their excretory products.

$$A = cP \tag{2}$$

where c =the maintenance cost $[(R+N)/P]$ of maintaining one calorie of the standing crop of P calories per unit time.

$$A = Y_i \div E_i \tag{3}$$

where Y_i =the specific yield of i in calories from the population and E_i =the growth efficiency, the inverse of the cost of producing yield of type i (E_i will be a decimal value) (see also Wiegert's (1964) discussion of efficiencies).

$$A = I-E \tag{4}$$

where I =energy ingested and E =energy egested, i.e. the energy content of the faeces.

These equations demonstrate the usefulness of energy, as opposed to biomass, in the description of this aspect of ecosystem or population dynamics, for calories provide the common unit of expression. The studies of Odum & Odum (1955) on a coral reef, of Odum (1957) on a hot spring and of Teal (1957) on a cold spring exemplify the value of the measurement of biomass and energy in describing and analysing the trophic structure of ecosystems.

The consideration of population processes in terms of their energies may also, when combined with evolutionary theory, provide new insights into the mechanisms of evolution (Slobodkin, 1962; Connell & Orias, 1964).

For any particular species there are two parts to the construction of an energy budget: the total number or biomass of individuals – the productivity – and the energy budget of each individual.

THE ESTIMATION OF PRODUCTIVITY

If a detailed life-table or budget has been constructed (see chapter 10) then the standing crop of the population at any given time can be determined by converting numbers to biomass (dry weight is usually the most appropriate measure). The net production consists, however, of the total amount of material synthesized by the animal and is obtained by summing:

(*i*) The increase in the standing crop during the season (or other time unit).

(*ii*) The biomass of all individuals that died or were eaten during the season.

(*iii*) The biomass of the total number of exuviae shed by all the individuals (those alive and those now dead) and of any other product, e.g. the spittle of cercopids (Wiegert, 1964), the byssus of mussels (Kuenzler, 1961), the silk of many insects, mites and spiders.

(*iv*) The biomass of any reproductive products (sperms, eggs), young individuals or adults that have left the area (i.e. emigration).

Strictly the amount of nitrogenous waste excreted should also be measured. The biomass of any individuals that immigrated into the population must be subtracted from the total obtained above.

It will be apparent that the calculation of net production from a budget, as was done by Smalley (1960), Wiegert (1964) and Golley & Gentry (1964), demands that the form of the mortality curve, the actual population at various stages and immigration and emigration are accurately known. The weights of the various products can be determined in the laboratory, but caution should be exercised in assuming that laboratory-determined rates hold under field conditions.

A somewhat different approach was developed by Neess & Dugdale (1959) for the study of the production of chironomid larvae in a lake. Instead of separating the numbers into different age categories (as in a budget) and then multiplying the age categories by their respective biomasses, Neess & Dugdale use the product of these variables as expressed in the field in terms of weight. Their method will be explained in detail.

The net production of a developing larval population is the product of two opposing processes, the increase in weight of the individual and the fall in the number of individuals due to mortality; these two may be expressed:

$$k_g Q_t = \frac{dQ_t}{dt}$$

$$-k_m N_t = \frac{dN_t}{dt}$$

where Q_t = the weight of an individual at time t, k_g = the growth rate, k_m = the mortality rate and N_t = the size of the population at time t.

From these equations the expression

$$Q_t = \frac{Q_0}{(N_0/N_t)^{-k_g/k_m}} = Q_0 \left(\frac{N_0}{N_t}\right)^{k_g/k_m}$$

may be derived, where Q_0 = the weight of a newly hatched larva and N_0 = the total natality. For given values of N_0 and Q_0 the shape of the curves describing the relationship between Q_t and N_t is determined solely by the ratio-k_g/k_m; if the ratio remains constant, the growth–survivorship curve will trace out the same path. Neess & Dugdale noted that within the range of values of the ratio up to 2, large changes occur in the area under the curve for small variations in the actual ratio. Now, the area under the curve corresponds to the actual net production. Therefore, if it can be shown that k_g/k_m is a constant, a smooth curve may be drawn of numbers on mean weight and the area beneath it found. As the above equation can be rearranged to:

$$\log Q_t = \log Q_0 + (k_g/\dot{k}_m) \log (N_0/N_t)$$

the constancy of the ratio may be tested by plotting $\log N_t$ against $\log Q_t$. A straight line will indicate that the ratio is constant.

The numbers per unit area can then be plotted against the mean weight, a smooth curve drawn and the area below it (ACDE in fig. 100) found with a planimeter. This is the actual net production in biomass per unit area (the units corresponding of course to those of Q_t and N_t).

A number of terms may be defined by reference to fig. 100:

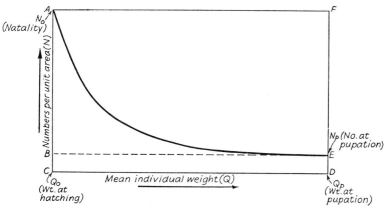

Fig. 100. The relationship between numbers and mean individual weight in an insect population during larval development; the area below the curve may be measured to give actual net production. The letters indicate areas representing other productivity terms (see text) (modified from Neess & Dugdale, 1959).

ACDE   Actual net production.

BCED   Actual net recruitment or increase in standing crop due to this cohort $= Q_p N_p$.

ABE   Directly recycled production.

ACDF   Potential net production $= N_0 Q_p$.

AEF   Lost potential net production.

ABEF   Lost potential recruitment.

This method is most appropriate when the development of the individuals of a generation is closely synchronized or where a particular cohort can be recognized and distinguished from others.

The energy budget for a population is usually derived using one or more of the equations listed in the introduction to this chapter, more especially:

$$\text{Assimilation} = \text{Respiration} + \text{Net production} \qquad (1)$$

$$\text{Assimilation} = \text{Ingestion} - \text{Egestion} \qquad (4)$$

Frequently two of the terms in the equations will be found directly and the third by calculation. For example, with a particular animal it might be difficult to determine the respiratory rate in the field, but ingestion and egestion per individual could be measured and these values would be converted to calories; knowing the numbers of individuals in the field, the total energy assimilation (the energy income) of the population could be calculated. Assuming the numbers of individuals of different ages throughout the season is known from a budget and the calorific value per individual of each age group has been found, the net production can be calculated. The difference between the assimilation and net production will be a measure of respiration.

The construction of an energy budget requires the initial development of a numerical budget or the measurement of production as indicated above (Neess & Dugdale's method), then the majority of the following must be determined: biomass, calorific value of each individual and its products, feeding, egestion and respiration. The energy budget will, perforce, contain a number of approximations and the more variables that can be determined the more reliance can be placed upon it; clearly if all the terms in any of the equations (1) to (4) are determined and their magnitudes prove compatible, when they are substituted in the equations, this provides valuable evidence as to their reliability. Thus, as with a numerical budget (p. 278) a detailed energy budget will expose its own errors. Richman's (1958) and Wiegert's (1964) studies may be taken as models for the details of the construction of an energy budget.

Measurement of biomass

Biomass is generally expressed in terms of dry weight; a known number of animals are dried until their weight is constant and this value is taken as the dry weight. Material should be dried at a low temperature (freeze-drying or at maximum of 60°C) to avoid the loss of volatile – especially lipoid – constituents, for although their contribution to the total dry weight may not be great, they may contribute significantly to the calorific value which is usually determined on the same material.

With small animals, especially plankton, it may be more convenient to work with the volume of the animals rather than the actual numbers (e.g. in Neess & Dugdale's method). A number of devices for measuring the volume of small animals have been developed (e.g. Gnanamuthu, 1952; Andrássy, 1956; Yentsch & Hebard, 1957; Frolander, 1957).

Determination of caloric value

The energy content of a material may be determined directly by oxidation either by potassium dichromate in sulphuric acid (Ivlev, 1934; Teal, 1957) or by burning in oxygen and determining the amount of heat liberated. The latter method – bomb calorimetry – is most convenient and widely used in ecology; however, it involves drying the material, and even when precautions are taken to avoid loss of volatile substances the energy content of dry plant material has been found to be about 8% less than that of the fresh (Komor, 1940).

Phillipson (1964) has described a miniature non-adiabatic bomb calorimeter that is simple and suitable for handling materials in the order of 5–100 mg dry weight. It is operated by placing the material in a platinum pan which is enclosed in the 'bomb'. The bomb is filled with oxygen until a pressure of 30 atmospheres is reached, cooled until the temperature, as indicated by a thermocouple, is steady, and then enclosed in a polystyrene insulating jacket. The sample is ignited by passing an electric current through a thin wire which presses against it. The temperature rises rapidly, and this is recorded by the deflection of a potentiometer attached to the thermocouple. The maximum deflection in a firing is a measure of the caloric content of the sample. The instrument is calibrated by burning given weights of a substance of known calorific value. The results from the Phillipson calorimeter have been found to be virtually identical with those obtained by the more complex instrument used by Slobodkin & Richman (1960, 1961).

A commercially available 'ballistic bomb calorimeter' that works on similar principles to the Phillipson model can be modified to operate with samples giving an output of about 2 kcal, i.e. 0·3–0·6 g of most biological materials (D. J. Cross, unpublished). The amount of ash present in a substance can influence its calorific value if measured in this way; magnesium and calcium carbonates may decompose at the high temperatures momentarily reached and this reaction will absorb some of the heat produced.

Westlake (1963) suggests that the approximate energy content may be determined indirectly from an analysis of a plant (or animal) as the energy contents of the constituents are available from tables (table 23).

Naturally not all the energy in an animal or plant is available to an animal that eats it, and quite frequently only a proportion of the potentially digestible energy is assimilated. The assimilation rates for various types and quantities of food need to be determined. The total energy is, however, available to the ecosystem as micro-organisms can break down almost all organic compounds.

Table 23. Energy content of various substances and living materials (from Westlake, 1963; Slobodkin & Richman, 1961; Wiegert, 1964; and others)

	Kcal/g dry wt
Monosaccharides, e.g. glucose	3·7
Disaccharides, e.g. sucrose	4·0
Polysaccharides, e.g. starch, cellulose	4·2
Protein: crude	5·7
Fat: ether extract	9·5
Crude fibre	4·5–4·7
Leaves of plants	4·2
Stems of plants	4·3
Roots of plants	4·7
Seeds	5·1
Litter	4·3
Tomato xylem sap	4·5
Mollusca: *Modiolus*	4·6
Succinea	5·4
Crustacea: *Daphnia*	4·4
Crayfish, immature	4·4
Diaptomus articus	5·5
Calanus hyperboreus	7·4
Insects: *Tenebrio molitor* – adult	5·0
T. molitor – larva	6·3
Philaenus spumarius – egg	6·3
P. spumarius – larva	5·3
P. spumarius – adult ♂	5·7
P. spumarius – adult ♀	5·9
P. spumarius – exuvia	5·2
P. spumarius – spittle	4·7

Values for the energy content of various plants have been published by Ovington & Heitkamp (1960) and Golley (1960) and of animals by Golley (1960), Slobodkin & Richman (1961), Comita & Schindler (1963) and others; some of these values, together with others for animals, are given in table 23. Cross & Southwood (unpublished) found that a large part of the variation in caloric value between different insects was attributable to differences in the fat content. The fat content of an individual varies throughout life and this may be the explanation of the seasonal change in the calorific value of the spittle bug, *Philaenus*, noted by Wiegert (in Slobodkin, 1962).

In fact the variations from individual to individual and within the same individual, with time, are major potential sources of error in energy budgets.

The measurement of feeding and assimilation

1. The quality of the food eaten

In some instances, such as with many arboreal lepidopterous larvae, the nature of an animal's food may easily be determined by observation in the field; observations in the laboratory may also be used, but with caution, for many animals will eat unnatural foods under artificial conditions. Another method, frequently used by ornithologists, is to examine the crop contents (p. 249). Such methods may be used with chewing insects and the remains of different types of plant or animal identified under the microscope (e.g. Hanna, 1957; Mulkern & Anderson, 1959). This approach can be quantified using a sedimentation technique (Brown, 1961). In plant-feeding sucking insects the actual tissue – phloem, xylem, mesophyll cells – from which the nutriment is obtained should be determined.

The identification of the meals of predators by serological techniques is discussed in chapter 9 (p. 250), where reference is also made to the use of radio-isotope tagged prey. In the pioneer study of Pendleton & Grundmann (1954) the prey were tagged in the field through their host plant; Odum & Kuenzler (1963) and Paris & Sikora (1965) have incorporated phosphorus-32 into plants and by the subsequent examination of suspected herbivores determined their food and some measure of the relative importance of different plants in the diet.

2. Feeding and assimilation rates
There are three basic approaches to the measurement of these rates and related parameters:

   a. Radiotracer – measuring the passage of radio-isotopes from the food to the animal and their subsequent loss.
   b. Gravimetric – by the direct weighing of the food, the faeces and the animal.
   c. Indicator – by marking the food with an inert non-absorbed indicator, the increase in its concentration as it passes through the alimentary canal measures the amount of matter absorbed.

a. Radiotracer techniques
Radiotracers* may be used in two different ways: the amount of radio-isotope used may be small relative to equilibrium body burden of the animal, then the rate of increase of assimilation of the isotope is linearly related to the rate of assimilation of the food, as for example in the studies of Engelmann (1961), Strong & Landes (1965) and Hubbell *et al.* (1965). Alternatively the body burden may be increased so as to reach equilibrium when the following relationship holds:

$$r = \frac{KQ_e}{a}$$

where r=feeding rate (measured in μc/day), a=proportion of ingested

* Further information on radiotracer techniques is given on pp. 63–71 and 251–3.

nuclide assimilated, K=the elimination constant*=0·693÷biological half-life (in days) and Q_e=the whole body radioactivity (in μc) in a steady state equilibrium. Therefore if the whole body radioactivity is measured and the assimilation rate and the biological half-life are known, the feeding rate may be calculated. This approach has been developed by Crossley (1963a, b and c), who worked in an environment heavily contaminated with caesium-137. This isotope is almost completely assimilated so that the term 'a' can be dropped from the above equation. Crossley (1963b and c) found that the biological half-life appeared to be linearly related to body weight, except that in the pupal stage, of course, there was no elimination. However, as Odum & Golley (1963) point out and Hubbell et al. (1965) confirm, the biological half-life of an isotope in a given animal is variable and will be influenced by temperature, activity, food and other factors, so that the half-life in the field is likely to be different from that determined in the laboratory.

Working on the isopod, *Armadillidium*, Hubbell et al. (1965) also show that the percentage of the isotope ingested that is actually assimilated will vary with the feeding rate; they used Sr[85] and, with this biologically significant element (it is utilized in the exoskeleton), its assimilation rate paralleled the actual assimilation of nutriments from the food.

In conclusion therefore, before radio-isotopes can be used to estimate feeding and assimilation rates in field populations, it is necessary to determine:

(*i*) The variability of the rate of assimilation of the isotope under field conditions.

(*ii*) The variability of the biological half-life of the isotope under field conditions.

(*iii*) Whether the level of isotope in the organism is low relative to the equilibrium level or whether it is high, a steady state having been reached. This is done from the equation

$$ra = KQ_e$$

already given, but some measure of r and a must be obtained experimentally so that the expected equilibrium body burden of radio nuclide (Q_e) can be compared with that actually observed.

Feeding or ingestion and assimilation can usually be separated, for when an animal is fed on radio-isotope tagged food and the fall-off of radioactivity with time is measured, it will be found that at first the curve is steep, reflecting the loss of the ingested but non-assimilated component; later the curve becomes shallow and this represents the elimination rate of the assimilated isotope (Odum & Golley, 1963) (fig. 101). Furthermore, Odum & Golley point out that the assimilated isotope is eliminated in different ways depend-

---

* This formula only applies to isotopes with long half-lives, so that the effective half-life= the biological half-life. Where radioactive decay is significant then this elimination rate needs to be added to that due to the biological half-life.

ing on the element, e.g. iodine mainly through the exuviae, zinc mainly by excretion, especially after moulting, or with the female, by the eggs.

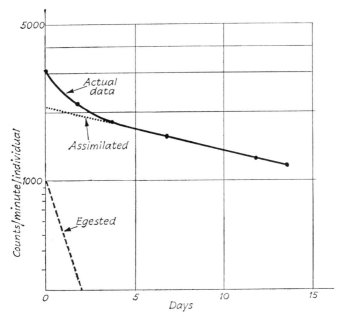

Fig. 101. The fall-off of radioactivity with time after ingestion showing the separation of the component that is assimilated from the component that is egested (from Odum & Golley, 1963; data based on marine isopod, *Idothea*, ingesting seaweed tagged with zinc-65).

b. Gravimetric techniques

The simplest approach to the measurement of ingestion and one that is frequently applicable is to weigh the food before and after the animal has fed (e.g. Smith, 1959; Phillipson, 1960; Fewkes 1960; Evans, 1962; Strong & Landes, 1965; Hubbell *et al.*, 1965); if all values are reduced to dry weight, errors due to the loss of moisture during feeding will be eliminated, otherwise this must be determined from controls. The quantity of leaf litter destroyed by soil arthropods may be determined by exposing a known quantity in mesh (e.g. nylon) bags (Crossley & Hoglund, 1962).

In the laboratory the faeces may usually be collected and their dry weight and calorific value found; the latter will, of course, differ from that of the food (Gere, 1956; Hubbell *et al.*, 1965) and the difference in energy content between ingestion and egestion may be more striking than the actual weight differences. The collection in the field of the total amount of faeces produced by a population is impossible (p. 229), but a measure could be obtained for a small number of arboreal larvae under semi-experimental conditions.

E M—N

Hubbell *et al.* (1965) have compared the results of gravimetric and radio-tracer methods using strontium-85 for determining the feeding and assimilation rates of the woodlouse, *Armadillidium*, and have found close agreement.

The only other weight that can be conveniently measured is the increase in weight of the animal (Fewkes, 1960; Johnson, 1960; Evans, 1962); this is a measure of the amount of growth. When converted to dry weights two equations hold:

Production = Growth + Exuviae and other Products

Assimilation = Production + Respiration

Clearly, then, if respiration can be measured; growth + the weight of the products may be used to give an estimate of assimilation. If wet weights are used allowance must also be made for the loss of weight due to the evaporation of water from the insect (Strong & Landes, 1965).

Just as the rate of assimilation of radio-isotopes has been found to vary under different conditions (p. 362), so does the nutritional assimilation rate and the relation between assimilation and production. For example, Sush-chenya (1962) found with the brine shrimp (*Artemia salina*) that the greater the intake of food the smaller the percentage of it that is assimilated, but a slightly higher percentage of the assimilated energy was used for growth at the high levels of food intake. Thus caution needs to be exercised in the extrapolation of laboratory-determined values to field conditions.

c. Indicator methods

Assimilation can also be measured if the food can be marked with an indicator which is easily measured quantitatively, is non-toxic at the concentrations used and is not absorbed by the gut. The percentage assimilation of the food is given by:

$$\% A = \left(1 - \frac{\text{conc. indicator in food/unit dry wt}}{\text{conc. indicator in faeces/unit dry wt}}\right) \times 100$$

Chromic oxide has been widely used as an indicator in studies on vertebrate nutrition (Corbett *et al.*, 1960) and McGinnis & Kasting (1964a and b) have shown how the chemical or, more conveniently, chromic oxide paper, may be used with insects as an indicator to measure assimilation from finely divided food. As the indicator must be mixed homogeneously throughout the food, this method will be inappropriate in many instances, especially with natural diets.

The measurement of the energy loss
due to respiration and metabolic processes

1. Calorimetric

The amount of energy lost through respiration may be determined directly by the measurement of the heat given out by the animal, but as some energy will have been used to vaporize water from the animal this will be less than the total energy loss and a correction must be applied. Furthermore, it is difficult to work with small animals; one of the few studies with insects using this approach is that of Pratt (1954).

2. The exchange of repiratory gases

a. The energy equivalents of oxygen and carbon dioxide
During metabolic processes, in which energy is liberated, oxygen is utilized and carbon dioxide produced; the proportion of carbon dioxide evolved, to oxygen used, depends on the actual metabolic process and is referred to as the respiratory quotient expressed:

$$RQ = \frac{\text{Carbon dioxide produced}}{\text{Oxygen utilized}}$$

Thus if two of the three values are known the third may be found; the gases may be measured by a number of different techniques and the respiratory quotient by noting the change in volume at constant pressure and temperature when the animal respires in an enclosed space.

The amount of energy liberated in the process can be determined from the quantity of oxygen (or carbon dioxide) involved, if the respiratory quotient is known and the certain assumptions are made as to the actual metabolic processes.

If carbohydrates alone are being utilized for energy $RQ = 1$ and 0.198 c.c. (at S.T.P.) of oxygen will be consumed and the same volume of carbon dioxide produced during the liberation of one calorie of energy; with fats alone $RQ = 0.707$ and then the consumption of 0.218 c.c. of oxygen and the production of 0.154 c.c. of carbon dioxide will result from the liberation of one calorie. Tables are widely available of the calorific equivalents of unit volumes of oxygen and carbon dioxide for different RQ's assuming that carbohydrate and fat utilization are the only metabolic processes involved (Brody, 1945; White *et al.*, 1959; table 24) and ecologists have frequently approximated by using the RQ obtained from experiments as equivalent to an '*N*-free RQ', disregarding the effect of protein and other metabolisms.

If greater accuracy is to be obtained the quantity of nitrogen excreted must be measured (Shaw & Beadle, 1949) enabling the component of the gases due to protein katabolism to be established and the '*N*-free RQ' determined. The respiratory exchange involved in the production of 1 g of nitrogen from the katabolism of a protein will depend on the proportions by weight of the various elements in its molecule; the necessary calculations are explained by Kleiber (1961).

However, even this approach assumes that fat, carbohydrates and protein katabolism are the only processes contributing to the respiratory quotient, but many others may theoretically influence the RQ and as these have RQ values outside the 0.7–1.0 range small amounts may modify the composite RQ

Table 24. The calorific equivalents of oxygen and carbon dioxide for various values of *RQ*, due to the utilization of different proportions of carbohydrates and fats (modified from an extensive table in Brody, 1945; original data from Zuntz & Schumberg, 1901)

RQ	Oxygen calories/litre	Carbon dioxide calories/litre	% oxygen consumed by carbohydrate component
0·70	4·686	6·694	0·0
0·75	4·729	6·319	14·7
0·80	4·801	6·001	31·7
0·85	4·683	5·721	48·8
0·90	4·924	5·471	65·9
0·95	4·985	5·247	82·9
1·00	5·047	5·047	100·0

disproportionately; e.g. alcohol breakdown has an $RQ=0·67$, the synthesis of fat from carbohydrate an $RQ=8·0$ (Kleiber, 1961).

It is discouraging for the ecologist to note that Cahn (1956) and Kleiber (1961) report studies that show that the estimate of energy expended, obtained indirectly (from the respiratory quotient), may be found to deviate by as much as 25% from the true value calculated by direct calorimetry. As Macfadyen (1963) has pointed out, when doubt exists as to the exact katabolic processes, but assuming that these involve only fats, carbohydrates and proteins, errors will be reduced if calculations are based on the oxygen uptake rather than on the carbon dioxide produced; for the minimum volume of oxygen that is required to produce 1 calorie is 90·8% of the maximum volume, but the minimum volume of carbon dioxide that results from the production of 1 calorie is as little as 77·7% of the maximum.

b. The respiratory rate

Starved warm-blooded animals exhibit a level of respiration referred to as the basic metabolism, but there is no comparable standard available for poikilothermic animals. It is important to remember, therefore, that although respiration rate and body weight show in general a linear relationship (Brody, 1945; Berg & Ockelmann, 1959; Engelmann, 1961), with poikilotherms the rate may be varied by many factors: temperature, age, season, oxygen concentration and even the type of respirometer used for the measurement (Berg, 1953; Berg *et al.*, 1958; Allen, 1959; Berg & Ockelmann, 1959; Edwards & Learner, 1960; Keister & Buck, 1964; Golley & Gentry, 1964). When respiration rate is being related to the weight of an invertebrate it is necessary to eliminate individual variations in weight due to the contents of the gut (Allen, 1959).

c. Gas analysis

The precise analysis of the respiratory gas to determine the proportions of oxygen and carbon dioxide is described in detail in textbooks such as Swift & French (1954), Kleiber (1961) and Kay (1964), and certain of the methods are discussed in special works: Dixon (1951) and Umbreit *et al.* (1957) describe manometric techniques and Kolthoff & Lingane (1952) polarography. Therefore only a brief outline will be given here and emphasis will be placed on those most used by ecologists.

i. Isotopes. Although radioactive and stable isotopes of carbon, hydrogen and oxygen have been used by physiologists to investigate the details of respiratory metabolism (Kay, 1964), they have not been used by ecologists. McClintock & Lifson (1958) showed that the total carbon dioxide production of an animal could be determined by using 'double-labelled' water. The heavy isotope of hydrogen being eliminated only as water, but that of oxygen (O^{18}) is eliminated both as carbon dioxide and as water; McClintock & Lifson believe that the difference between the two elimination rates will give a measure of the carbon dioxide evolved. This method is of great potential value to the ecologist for the determination of respiratory rates under natural conditions; the animals could be fed with double-labelled water, released in the field, recaptured at some later time and the levels of the isotopes determined by mass spectrometry.

ii. Analysis in the gaseous phase for air-breathing animals. The animal is enclosed in a chamber and the changes caused by its respiration in the composition of the air in the chamber determined in some way. Several techniques are based on the absorption of the evolved carbon dioxide by an alkali solution (e.g. sodium hydroxide) so that the pressure or volume of the air will change proportionally to the consumed oxygen. In constant-volume respirometers, e.g. the Warburg (Dixon, 1951; Umbreit *et al.*, 1957), the reduction in pressure is measured with a manometer.

Alternatively the pressure can be kept constant and the volume allowed to change. This change can be measured, for example, by the movement of an oil droplet in a capillary tube; Smith & Douglas (1949) developed an apparatus of this type that was subsequently modified by Engelmann (1961) and Wiegert (1964). The change in volume can also be utilized in ultra-microrespirometers that operate on the principle of the Cartesian diver (Nielsen, 1961; Kay, 1964). The amount of carbon dioxide evolved may be determined by the titration of the alkali (Itô, 1964). An experiment using these types of respirometer cannot be continued for a long period, as the respiration may become abnormal as an increasing proportion of the available oxygen is utilized.

If the respiratory rate is to be recorded over a period of time the oxygen utilized by the animal must be replaced. A number of electrolytic respirometers have been developed in which the change in volume resulting from the consumption of oxygen switches on an electrolysis apparatus that generates oxygen; when the previous volume has been restored the current is switched off. The activity of the compensating oxygen generator is recorded and after suitable calibration this may be converted to give the volume of oxygen utilized (Winteringham, 1959; Macfadyen, 1961; Phillipson, 1962; Hayward *et al.*, 1963). In all these volumetric or manometric methods constant temperature must be maintained throughout the experiment; this is usually done with a water bath.

The quantities of carbon dioxide and oxygen in the air may also be assessed by methods depending on differences in the thermal conductivity, viscosity, magnetic susceptibility and other properties of the gases (Kleiber, 1961; Kay, 1964).

iii. Analysis of dissolved gases for completely aquatic species. The animal must be enclosed in a limited volume of water out of contact with the atmospheric air; Wohlschag (1957) describes a convenient 'Plexiglass' container for moderately sized animals. The gases dissolved in the water after a given time can be determined by a number of methods. Chemical methods, especially the 'Winkler', have been widely used (e.g. Teal, 1957; Richman, 1958); the procedures of the Winkler and another titration technique, the phenosafranine, are described by Dowdeswell (1959). The accuracy of these can, however, be impaired by the presence of ferrous iron, nitrites and other 'impurities' in the water (Allee & Oesting, 1934).

Polarometry or polarography in which the concentration of dissolved oxygen is measured electrolytically has also been used in many ecological studies (Berg, 1953; Mann, 1956; Heywood & Edwards, 1961) and is described by Kolthoff & Lingane (1952) and Kay (1964).

A tonometric method has been developed by Jones (1959) for use with very small volumes of fluid, and is thus more applicable to samples of fluid from within animals than from without! A small bubble of air is enclosed with the fluid and the carbon dioxide, oxygen and nitrogen in it allowed to come into diffusion equilibrium with these gases in the fluid. The composition of the bubble can then be analysed (Krogh, 1908).

Gasometric methods involve the expulsion of the gases from the fluid and their subsequent analysis. Van Slyke & Neill (1924) extracted the gases under vacuum and the quantities of both oxygen and carbon dioxide can be determined (Milburn & Beadle, 1960; Elkan & Moore, 1962; Kay, 1964). Only the oxygen and nitrogen can be measured in the method of Scholander *et al.* (1955), in which the gases are expelled from the sample by the addition of acid and a carbonate.

REFERENCES

ALLEE, W. C. and OESTING, R., 1934. A critical examination of Winkler's method for determining dissolved oxygen in respiration studies with aquatic animals. *Physiol. Zool.* **7**, 509–41.

ALLEN, M. D., 1959. Respiration rates of worker honeybees of different ages and at different temperatures. *J. exp. Biol.* **36**, 92–101.

ANDRÁSSY, I., 1956. Die Rauminhalts- und Gewichtsbestimmung der Fadenwürmer (Nematoden) *Acta Zool. Budapest* **2**, 1–15.

BERG, K., 1953. The problem of respiratory acclimatization. *Hydrobiologia* **5**, 331–50.

BERG, K., LUMBYE, J. and OCKELMANN, K. W., 1958. Seasonal and experimental variations of the oxygen consumption of the limpet *Ancylus fluviatilis* (O. F. Müller). *J. exp. Biol.* **35**, 43–73.

BERG, K. and OCKELMANN, K. W., 1959. The respiration of freshwater snails. *J. exp. Biol.* **36**, 690–708.

BRAY, J. R. and GORHAM, E., 1964. Litter production in forests of the World. *Adv. Ecol. Res.* **2**, 101–57.

BRODY, S., 1945. *Bioenergetics and growth.* New York, 1023 pp.

BROWN, D. S., 1961. The food of the larvae of *Chloëon dipterum* L. and *Baëtis rhodani* (Pictet) (Insecta, Ephemeroptera). *J. anim. Ecol.* **30**, 55–75.

CAHN, T., 1956. *La régulation des processus métaboliques dans l'organism.* Paris.

COMITA, G. W. and SCHINDLER, D. W., 1963. Calorific values of microcrustacea. *Science* **140**, 1394–6.

CONNELL, J. H. and ORIAS, E., 1964. The ecological regulation of species diversity. *Amer. Nat.* **98**, 399–414.

CORBETT, J. L., GREENHALGH, F. D., McDONALD, I. and FLORENCE, E., 1960. Excretion of chromium sesquioxide administered as a component of paper to sheep. *Brit. J. Nutr.* **14**, 289–99.

CROSSLEY, D. A., 1963a. Movement and accumulation of radiostrontium and radiocesium in insects. *In* Schultz, V. & Klement, A. W. (eds.), *Radioecology* 103–5.

CROSSLEY, D. A., 1963b. Consumption of vegetation by insects. *In* Schultz, V. & Klement, A. W. (eds.), *Radioecology* 427–30.

CROSSLEY, D. A., 1963c. Use of radioactive tracers in the study of insect–plant relationships. *Radiation and radioisotopes applied to insects of agricultural importance* (Int. Atom. Energy Ag.) STI/PUB **74**, 43–54.

CROSSLEY, D. A. and HOGLUND, M. P., 1962. A litter-bag method for the study of micro-arthropods inhabiting leaf litter. *Ecology* **43**, 571–3.

DIXON, M., 1951. *Manometric methods as applied to the measurement of cell respiration and other processes.* (3rd ed.) Cambridge.

DOTY, M. S. (ed.), 1961. *Conference on primary productivity measurement, marine and freshwater.* University of Hawaii, Honolulu, 237 pp.

DOWDESWELL, W. H., 1959. *Practical animal ecology.* London, 315 pp.

EDWARDS, R. W. and LEARNER, M. A., 1960. Some factors affecting the oxygen consumption of *Asellus. J. exp. Biol.* **37**, 706–18.

ELKAN, G. H. and MOORE, W. E. C., 1962. A rapid method for measurement of CO_2 evolution by soil microorganisms. *Ecology* **43**, 775–6.

ENGELMANN, M. D., 1961. The role of soil arthropods in the energetics of an old field community. *Ecol. Monogr.* **31**, 221–38.

EVANS, D. E., 1962. The food requirements of *Phonoctonus nigrofasciatus* Stål (Hemiptera, Reduviidae). *Ent. exp. appl.* **5**, 33–9.

FEWKES, D. W., 1960. The food requirements by weight of some British Nabidae (Heteroptera). *Ent. exp. appl.* **3**, 231–7.

FROLANDER, H. F., 1957. A plankton volume indicator. *J. Cons. perm. int. Explor. Mer.* **22**, 278–83.

GATES, D. M., 1965. Energy, plants and ecology. *Ecology* **46**, 1–13.

GERE, G., 1956. Investigations concerning the energy turnover of the *Hyphantria cunea* Drury caterpillars. *Opusc. Zool., Budapest* **1**, 29–32.

GNANAMUTHU, C. P., 1952. A simple device for measuring the volume of an aquatic animal. *Nature, Lond.* **170**, 587.

GOLLEY, F. B., 1960. Energy dynamics of a food chain of an old-field community. *Ecol. Monogr.* **30**, 187–206.

GOLLEY, F. B. and GENTRY, J. B., 1964. Bioenergetics of the southern Harvester ant, *Pogonomyrmex badius. Ecology* **45**, 217–25.

HANNA, H. M., 1957. A study of the growth and feeding habits of the larvae of four species of caddis flies. *Proc. R. ent. Soc. Lond. A* **32**, 139–46.

HAYWARD, J. S., NÖRDAN, H. C. and WOOD, A. J., 1963. A simple electrolytic respirometer for small animals. *Canad. J. Zool.* **41**, 63–8.

HEYWOOD, J. and EDWARDS, R. W., 1961. Some aspects of the ecology of *Potamopyrgus jenkinsi* Smith. *J. anim. Ecol.* **31**, 239–50.

HUBBELL, S. P., SIKORA, A. and PARIS, O. H., 1965. Radiotracer, gravimetric and calorimetric studies of ingestion and assimilation rates of an Isopod. *Health Physics* **11** (12), 1485–1501.

ITÔ, Y., 1964. Preliminary studies on the respiratory energy loss of a spider, *Lycosa pseudo-annulata. Res. Popul. Ecol.* **6**, 13–21.

IVLEV, V. S., 1934. Eine Mikromethode zur Bestimmung des Kaloriengehalts von Nähr-stoffen. *Biochem. Z.* **275**, 49–55.

IVLEV, V. S., 1939. Transformation of energy by aquatic animals. *Int. Revue ges. Hydrobiol. Hydrogr.* **38**, 449–58.

IVLEV, V. S., 1945. The biological productivity of waters. [In Russian.] *Usp. sovrem. Biol.* **19**, 98–120.

JOHNSON, C. G., 1960. The relation of weight of food ingested to increase in body-weight during growth in the bed-bug, *Cimex lectularius* L. (Hemiptera). *Ent. exp. appl.* **3**, 238–40.

JONES, J. D., 1959. A new tonometric method for the determination of dissolved oxygen and carbon dioxide in small samples. *J. Exp. Biol.* **36**, 177–90.

KAY, R. H., 1964. *Experimental biology. Measurement and analysis.* New York, 416 pp.

KEISTER, M. and BUCK, J., 1964. Respiration: some exogenous and endogenous effects on the rate of respiration. *In* Rockstein, M. (ed.), *The Physiology of Insecta* **3**, 617–58.

KLEIBER, M., 1961. *The fire of life. An introduction to animal energetics.* New York.

KOLTHOFF, J. M. and LINGANE, J. J., 1952. *Polarography.* New York.

KOMOR, J., 1940. Über die Ausnützung des Sonnenlichtes beim Wachstum der grünen Pflanzen. *Biochem. Z.* **305**, 381–95.

KROGH, A., 1908. On micro-analysis of gases. *Skand. Arch. Physiol.* **20**, 279–88.

KUENZLER, E. J., 1961. Structure and energy flow of a mussel population in a Georgia salt marsh. *Limnol. Oceanogr.* **6**, 191–204.

LINDEMAN, R. L., 1942. The trophic-dynamic aspect of ecology. *Ecology* **23**, 399–418.

LOOMIS, W. E., 1965. Absorption of radiant energy by leaves. *Ecology* **46**, 14–7.

MACFADYEN, A., 1961. A new system for continuous respirometry of small air-breathing invertebrates under near-natural conditions. *J. exp. Biol.* **38**, 323–43.

MACFADYEN, A., 1963. *Animal ecology. Aims and methods.* 2nd ed. London and New York, 344 pp.

MANN, K. H., 1956. A study of the oxygen consumption of five species of leech. *J. exp. Biol.* **33**, 615–26.

McCLINTOCK, R. and LIFSON, N., 1958. Determination of the total carbon dioxide output of rats by the D^2O^{18} method. *Amer. J. Physiol.* **192**, 76–8.

McGINNIS, A. J. and KASTING, R., 1964a. Chromic oxide indicator method for measuring food utilization in a plant-feeding insect. *Science* **144**, 1464–5.

McGINNIS, A. J. and KASTING, R., 1964b. Digestion in insects, colorimetric analysis of chromic oxide used to study food utilization by phytophagous insects. *J. agric. Fd Chem.* **12**, 259–62.

MILBURN, T. R. and BEADLE, L. C., 1960. The determination of total carbon dioxide in water. *J. exp. Biol.* **37**, 444–60.

MULKERN, G. B. and ANDERSON, J. F., 1959. A technique for studying the food habits and preferences of grasshoppers. *J. Econ. Ent.* **52**, 342.

NEESS, J. and DUGDALE, C., 1959. Computation of production for populations of aquatic midge larvae. *Ecology* **40**, 425–30.

NIELSEN, C. O., 1961. Respiratory metabolism of some populations of Enchytraeid worms and free living Nematodes. *Oikos* **12**, 17–35.

ODUM, E. P. and GOLLEY, F. B., 1963. Radioactive tracers as an aid to the measurement of energy flow at the population level in nature. *In* Schultz, V. & Klement, A. W. (eds.), *Radioecology* 403–10.

ODUM, E. P. and KUENZLER, E. J., 1963. Experimental isolation of food chains in an old-field ecosystem with the use of phosphorus-32. *In* Schultz, V. & Klement, A. W. (eds.), *Radioecology* 113–20.

ODUM, H. T., 1957. Trophic structure and productivity of Silver springs, Florida. *Ecol. Monogr.* **27**, 55–112.

ODUM, H. T. and ODUM, E. P., 1955. Trophic structure and productivity of a Windward coral reef community on Eniwetok Atoll. *Ecol. Monogr.* **25**, 291–320.

OVINGTON, J. D., 1962. Quantitative ecology and the woodland ecosystem concept. *Adv. Ecol. Res.* **1**, 103–92.

OVINGTON, J. D. and HEITKAMP, D., 1960. The accumulation of energy in forest plantations in Britain. *J. Ecol.* **48**, 639–46.

PARIS, O. H. and SIKORA, A., 1965. Radiotracer demonstration of Isopod herbivory. *Ecology* **46**, 729–34.

PEARSON, O. P., 1954. The daily energy requirements of a wild anna hummingbird. *Condor* **56**, 317–22.

PENDLETON, R. C. and GRUNDMANN, A. W., 1954. Use of phosphorus-32 in tracing some insect–plant relationships of the thistle, *Cirsium undulatum. Ecology* **35**, 187–91.

PHILLIPSON, J., 1960. The food consumption of different instars of *Mitopus morio* (F.) (Phalangiida) under natural conditions. *J. anim. Ecol.* **29**, 299–307.

PHILLIPSON, J., 1962. Respirometry and the study of energy turnover in natural systems with particular reference to harvest spiders (Phalangiida). *Oikos* **13**, 311–22.

PHILLIPSON, J., 1964. A miniature bomb calorimeter for small biological samples. *Oikos* **15**, 130–9.

PRATT, H., 1954. Analyse microcalorimetrique des variations de la thermogenèse chez divers insectes. *Canad. J. Zool.* **32**, 172–94.

RICHMAN, S., 1958. The transformation of energy by *Daphnia pulex. Ecol. Monogr.* **28**, 273–91.

SCHOLANDER, P. F., VAN DAM, L., CLAFF, C. L. and KANWISHER, J. W., 1955. Micro-gasometric determination of dissolved oxygen and nitrogen. *Biol. Bull., Woods Hole* **109**, 328–34.

SHAW, J. and BEADLE, L. C., 1949. A simplified ultra-micro Kjeldahl method for the estimation of protein and total nitrogen in fluid samples of less than 1·0 μl. *J. exp. Biol.* **26**, 15–23.

SLOBODKIN, L. B., 1962. Energy in animal ecology. *Adv. Ecol. Res.* **1**, 69–101.

SLOBODKIN, L. B. and RICHMAN, S., 1960. The availability of a miniature bomb calorimeter for ecology. *Ecology* **41**, 784.

SLOBODKIN, L. B. and RICHMAN, S., 1961. Calories/gm in species of animals. *Nature, Lond.* **191**, 299.

SLYKE, D. D. VAN and NEILL, J. M., 1924. The determination of gases in blood and other solutions by extraction and manometric measurement. *J. Biol. Chem.* **61**, 523–73.

SMALLEY, A. E., 1960. Energy flow of a salt marsh grasshopper population. *Ecology* **41**, 672–7.

SMITH, A. H. and DOUGLAS, J. R., 1949. An insect respirometer. *Ann. ent. Soc. Amer.* **42,** 14–18.

SMITH, D. S., 1959. Utilization of food plants by the migratory grasshopper, *Melanoplus bilituratus* (Walker) (Orthoptera: Acrididae) with some observations on the nutritional value of the plants. *Ann. ent. Soc. Amer.* **52,** 674–80.

STIVEN, A. E., 1961. Food energy available for and required by the blue grouse chick. *Ecology* **42,** 547–53.

STRONG, F. E. and LANDES, D. A., 1965. Feeding and nutrition of *Lygus hesperus* (Hemiptera: Miridae). II. An estimation of normal feeding rates. *Ann. ent. Soc. Amer.* **58,** 309–14.

SUSHCHENYA, L. M., 1962. [Quantitative data on nutrition and energy balance in *Artemia salina* (L.)] [In Russian.] *Doklady Akad. Nauk S.S.S.R.* **143** (5), 1205–7.

SWIFT, R. W. and FRENCH, C. E., 1954. *Energy metabolism and nutrition.* Washington.

SZALAY-MARZSÓ, L., 1958. Populationsdynamische Untersuchungen an Beständen der Rübenblattlaus (*Aphis* (*Dorsalis*) *fabae* Scop.) in Ungarn, in den Jahren 1955 und 56. *Acta agron.* **8,** 187–211.

TEAL, J. M., 1957. Community metabolism in a temperate cold spring. *Ecol. Monogr.* **27,** 283–302.

UMBREIT, W. W., BURRIS, R. H. and STAUFFER, J. F., 1957. *Manometric techniques.* (3rd ed.) Minneapolis.

WESTLAKE, D. F., 1963. Comparisons of plant productivity. *Biol. Rev.* **38,** 385–425.

WHITE, A., HANDLER, P. and SMITH, E. L., 1959. *Principles of biochemistry.* New York.

WIEGERT, R. G., 1964. Population energetics of meadow spittlebugs (*Philaenus spumarius* L.) as affected by migration and habitat. *Ecol. Monogr.* **34** (2), 225–41.

WIEGERT, R. G. and EVANS, F. C., 1964. Primary production and the disappearance of dead vegetation on an old field in southeastern Michigan. *Ecology* **45,** 49–62.

WINTERINGHAM, F. P. W., 1959. An electrolytic respirometer for insects. *Lab. Practice* **8,** 372–5.

WOHLSCHAG, D. E., 1957. Differences in metabolic rates of migratory and resident freshwater forms of an arctic whitefish. *Ecology* **38,** 502–10.

YENTSCH, C. S. and HEBARD, J. F., 1957. A gauge for determining plankton volume by the mercury immersion method. *J. Cons. perm. int. Explor. Mer.* **22,** 184–90.

Author Index

382   *Author Index*

General Index

The first page only is cited when a topic extends continuously for several pages. References in the text to species are also entered under their major taxa, generally the order (for Insecta), class (other Arthropods and Vertebrates) or phylum, e.g. Diptera, Mammals, Mollusca. Entries are also made for certain groups e.g. ants, leaf-miners, but not usually for families. The titles of papers cited in the bibliographies are not indexed.